I'm no potter - why do
I have to write in a pottery book?
Oh well. Kathie Reilly Remington
187 Mt. Vernon Ave
Rochester

CLAY and GLAZES
for the POTTER

CLAY and GLAZES for the POTTER

by DANIEL RHODES

All photographs by the author

CHILTON BOOK COMPANY

Philadelphia New York London

Published in Philadelphia by Chilton Book Company
and simultaneously in Ontario, Canada,
by Thomas Nelson & Sons Ltd.

Second printing, April 1958

Third printing, January 1959

Fourth printing, April 1962

Fifth printing, December 1963

Sixth printing, December 1964

Seventh printing, January 1966

Eighth printing, December 1966

Ninth printing, December 1967

Tenth printing, September 1968

Library of Congress Catalog Card Number: 57–11905

Manufactured in the United States of America

To LILLYAN

Author's Preface

My purpose in writing this book has been to present in as clear and understandable form as possible the important facts about ceramic materials and their use in pottery.

The ceramic medium has a rich potential. It is so various and adaptable that each culture and each succeeding generation finds in it a new means of expression. As a medium, it is capable of great beauty of form, color, and texture, and its expressions are unique not only for variety but for permanence and utility as well. To make full use of the medium, the ceramist or potter not only needs skill, imagination, and artistic vision, but he also needs to have a sound knowledge of the technical side of the craft. This knowledge has not been easy to come by, and many of those seriously engaged in pottery have learned through endless experimentation and discouraging failures. It is hoped that the present work will enable the creative worker to go more directly to his goal in pottery, and that it will enable him to experiment intelligently and with a minimum of lost effort. While technical information must not be considered as an end in itself, it is a necessary prerequisite to a free and creative choice of means in ceramics.

None of the subjects included are dealt with exhaustively, and I have tried not to overwhelm the reader with details. The information given is presented in as practical form as possible, and no more technical data or chemical theory is given than has been thought necessary to clarify the subject.

I wish to acknowledge here my debt to my colleagues at the State University of New York College of Ceramics at Alfred University, and particularly to Dr. S. R. Scholes, Sr., for his thoughtful editing of the manuscript.

I am also indebted to the Smithsonian Institution's Freer Gallery of Art in Washington, D. C., for the opportunity of photographing pieces from its magnificent collection. I have attempted to take the photographs from a potter's point of view and to bring out the quality and the texture of the clays and glazes in these masterpieces from the past.

Daniel Rhodes
Alfred, N. Y.

Preface

Daniel Rhodes
Alfred, N.Y.

Contents

CLAY and GLAZES
for the POTTER

Part One—CLAY

Clay is a simple material. It is abundant, cheap, easily acquired and prepared, and it does not require extensive processing, as do most of the raw materials which we use for making things. If this were not so, it would have been impossible for primitive people to make pottery. Pottery can still be made without resort to science.

Clay is also a temperamental material. Its plasticity or workability varies widely, so that some clays which serve quite well for one thing are useless for another. Clay shrinks when it dries and shrinks more when fired, and this creates all sorts of problems in making pottery. The reactions of clay to the fire may seem unpredictable, and even under the most carefully controlled conditions a certain amount of uncertainty attends the firing process. The practical answers to all of these problems connected with making things out of clay lie with craft rather than science. Potters, over the centuries, have successfully worked out techniques for handling their material. In recent times, of course, science has contributed enormously to the knowledge of ceramics, and what was formerly understood only vaguely, or through rule-of-thumb methods, has been clarified by modern research. It is only recently, for example, through the use of the electron-microscope, that any understanding of the exact size and shape of clay particles has been gained.

In most cases, the difficulties which arise in pottery making are due to the large number of variables involved. Even when all the materials are bought in prepared form, the variables of forming techniques, drying, firing, and glaze application remain. What the potter needs, in order to get the ceramic process under some measure of control, is an understanding of the principles which govern the behavior of his raw materials. He needs to know, among other things, why clay shrinks, why some clays shrink more than others, why pots sometimes crack during the cooling of the kiln, and how to blend and fire his materials for the desired effects. Through the applications of comparatively few principles, the variables of raw materials, composition, and fire treatment can be mastered.

Clay is one of the few materials which has no value of its own, yet which can be made into valuable objects. The value is put there by the potter. Clay itself is relatively formless, and the forms the potter makes are entirely of his invention and draw little from the inherent form of clay. Of course, clay imposes certain limitations of shape. For example, forms which are too attenuated are not suitable to clay because of the brittle nature of the fired material, and forms which are too extreme may collapse in the wet state before they can be finished. But within these limitations, the potter is free to express his preference in form, and the forms of objects made from clay have been characterized by tremendous freedom and variety.

Pottery, at least to those who make it, seems to have a value which is something quite beyond the sum of its usefulness and beauty. There is in pottery a connection with the earliest traditions of civilization and culture, and pottery forms symbolize in a particularly direct way some of the most fundamental of human activities. Any piece of pottery, no matter how crude it is, seems to share in the glory of a craft which, at its best, has succeeded in filling profound human needs, both practical and spiritual.

Ceramics may be defined as the art of making permanent objects of usefulness and/or beauty by the heat treatment of earthy raw materials. Ceramics includes not only pottery, but also glass, brick and tile and other structural clay products, refractories and fire brick, laboratory porcelain, sanitary wares of all sorts, dielectric porcelains, cements, plaster, lime, and vitreous enamels on metal. These industries as a whole form an important and indispensable part of our industrial life. They all rely on simple, abundant, and cheap earthy raw materials. Ceramics, which was one of the first useful arts to be invented by man, continues to be one of his most essential activities.

Chapter 1

Geologic Origins of Clay

1. The Nature of the Earth's Crust

In order to understand clay as a raw material it is necessary to consider its geologic origins. Clay is the product of the geologic weathering of the surface of the earth, and since this weathering process is continuous and goes on everywhere, clay is an extremely common and abundant material in nature. It is, in fact, a nuisance to the farmer, miner, and roadbuilder. Clay should not be thought of as something which is rare, unusual, or valuable in itself, but rather as an important part of the earthy material which makes up the surface of the planet.

Clay is still being produced by nature, and no doubt more clay is being formed daily than man is able to use up in ceramics. We think of the surface of the earth as being permanent and unchanging, but this is only because we have the opportunity of observing it over such a relatively limited period of time. Actually, the earth has undergone continuous change, and vast areas of the continents have been alternately mountainous or covered by inland seas. The climate of various localities has varied from arctic to tropical. The familiar surface features of the earth as we know it—such as mountains, plains, rivers, valleys, lakes, deserts, and oceans—represent the cumulative effect of geologic forces over millions of years.

In remote geologic time, the earth was a mass of molten material, and the crust of the earth, as we know it, is a relatively thin, frozen layer covering a still very hot interior. When the surface of the earth was still molten, the heavier material, such as the metals, tended to sink to deeper levels. This settling process tended to make the surface layers of molten material fairly uniform in composition. Gradually, as the earth cooled off, the upper layer, or crust, solidified. Rocks which are formed by the cooling of molten matter are called igneous rocks.

The composition of the original blanket or crust of igneous rock which covered the earth must have been quite uniform all over the surface of the globe. The variety which characterizes the surface now is largely the result of later changes. Below a depth of a few thousand feet, the earth is composed largely of a basalt layer which is more than one hundred miles thick. Below that, we are uncertain as to the exact nature of the earth, except that it is known to be heavier than the crust, extremely hot, and dense, due to the pressure of overlying material. Probably iron and nickel predominate in the earth's core.

The average composition of all the igneous rocks of the earth, down to a depth of about ten miles, is approximately as follows:

SiO	59.14
Al_2O_3	15.34
$Fe_2O_3 + FeO$	6.88
CaO	5.08
Na_2O	3.84
MgO	3.49
K_2O	3.13
H_2O	1.15
TiO_2	1.05
	99.10
All others	.90
	100.00

An interesting feature of this analysis is that a very few oxides make up the great bulk of the material at the surface of the earth. Silica and alumina make up about 75 percent of the crust of the earth, and, as we shall see, these two oxides are the essential elements of clay.

As the surface of the earth cooled into a solid, various minerals were formed. A mineral may be defined as a natural earthy substance having a definite chemical composition. During the cooling, which caused the crystallizing out of minerals from the molten mass, various conditions caused different minerals to form. Local variations in the composition of the molten material, different conditions of pressure, and different rates of cooling gave rise to numerous different minerals. As would be expected from the great preponderance of certain oxides in the molten mass, the mineral composition of the crust of the earth is quite simple. The following list gives the approximate percentage of the various minerals which make up the crust of the earth:

Feldspar	59.5
Ferro-magnesian group	16.8
Quartz	12.0
Biotite	3.8
Titanium minerals	1.5
All others	6.4
	100.0

Feldspar is by far the most common mineral, and it is the weathering of this material which largely accounts for clay. It is remarkable that only five minerals account for over 90 percent of the bulk of the earth's surface. Hundreds of different minerals have been identified in nature, but most of these are relatively rare, and many might almost be considered freaks of nature.

2. Forces of Geologic Change

About two billion years ago the forces of geologic change began to act upon the recently cooled, igneous rocks. An interaction began between the gaseous atmosphere surrounding the earth, and the surface of the earth, which affected both. As the earth cooled, the moisture in the atmosphere, which had until then existed only as vapor, began to condense, and a torrential rain began which must have lasted millions of years. This rain filled in the basins of the oceans and had a profound effect upon the surface of the earth which was at relatively higher elevations.

Water has been by far the most important agent of geologic change. It has, first of all, literally dissolved incalculable quantities of rock. One thinks of rock as insoluble, unaffected by water, but over a period of millions of years, water has washed away mountains. The presence of salt in the sea—and there are an estimated fifteen hundred billion tons of it—gives evidence of the dissolving action of rain water on the earth, which has gradually leached out soluble matter from the rocks and carried it off to the sea, where it remains in a solution of ever-increasing concentration.

In addition to its chemical action as a solvent, water which carries mineral particles has a mechanical effect of abrasion upon rocks. The abrasive effect of rainfall and the grinding of rocks in streams and glaciers readies the rocks for chemical disintegration by breaking them into smaller and smaller pieces. This attrition, so unnoticeable in any particular instance, in the aggregate is a mighty force.

Water also splits rocks by seeping into cracks and expanding when it freezes. The effect of water upon rock is to break it into ever smaller pieces and at the same time to dissolve from it all that is soluble.

Plants contribute also to this process by the action of their roots, which gain foothold in cracks and, in growing, tend to split the rocks into smaller units. Other significant forces of geologic change, which are of lesser importance, however, than water, are the abrasive effects of glaciers, and of windborne particles.

The original rocks of the earth, then, though seemingly hard and eternal, have in fact been profoundly altered over the whole surface of the earth. This process, called weathering and erosion, accounts for the varied and fascinating character of the landscape. Mountains, formed by the upward thrust of rock as the surface of the earth cooled, contracted, and heaved up, have been torn down by erosion and deposited as silt in oceans and lakes. There, these stratified layers of material have been altered by heat and pressure into new or metamorphic rock, then again thrust upward into new ridges and mountains, only to be again worn down and re-deposited.

A characteristic product of this grinding maw of geology is clay. It is an end product of the weathering of rocks. As mountains and hills are worn away by water, the resulting debris, ground ever finer by the action of water, is finally laid quietly down in still estuaries or deltas, sorted out as it settles in the water to various particle sizes. Later, these beds of disintegrated rock, from which most soluble matter has been removed, may, by gradual geologic upheaval, be elevated to dry land where they await the potter's spade.

Chapter 2

The Chemical Composition of Clay

1. Typical Composition of Clays

As one might expect, the usual chemical composition of clay is quite similar to the average composition of the surface of the earth as a whole. Compare, for example, an analysis of a common, red clay with the approximate percentages of oxides on the surface of the earth as a whole:

	Earth as a whole	*Common red clay*
SiO_2	59.14	57.02
Al_2O_3	15.34	19.15
Fe_2O_3	6.88	6.70
MgO	3.49	3.08
CaO	5.08	4.26
Na_2O	3.84	2.38
K_2O	3.13	2.03
H_2O	1.15	3.45
TiO_2	1.05	.91

Note particularly in these two analyses that the silica and alumina contents are very similar and account for the bulk of the material, and that iron is present in almost the same amount.

Clays which are more pure in composition than the specimen listed above are apt to contain a great deal less iron and relatively more alumina, as shown by analysis in following table of a North Carolina kaolin, but nevertheless the similarity of even this relatively pure clay to the typical composition of the earth's crust as a whole is noteworthy.

	North Carolina Kaolin
SiO_2	46.18
Al_2O_3	38.38
Fe_2O_3	.57
MgO	.42
K_2O	
Na_2O	1.22
H_2O	13.28

One might think of clay, then, as being almost a representative sample of the crust of the earth after it has been disintegrated and pulverized to very fine particle size by the action of erosion. Clay differs from the average of all rocks more in its physical state than in its chemical make-up. Actually, clays vary rather widely in chemical composition. The more pure, light-burning clays, such as kaolin and ball clay, have a relatively high percentage of alumina and a low percentage of iron and other impurities. Since clay is made up predominantly of alumina and silica, all other oxides present are considered impurities.

The composition of clay varies, depending on the source of the parent rock. In different localities the igneous rock which gives rise eventually to clay may differ widely, some of it being more or less free of iron, some containing much quartz, and some being loaded with iron oxide. Sometimes the debris from the erosion of a very wide area will be brought together by some river system and deposited as clay in a delta or estuary. Such clay will be a representative sample of the disintegration of the rocks of many localities.

Chemical analyses of clay indicate

considerable water. This is chemically combined water which is the result of the hydrating process, or hydrolysis, by which clay was formed.

2. The Molecular Composition of Clay

As a mineral, clay is said to have the following formula:

$$Al_2O_3 \cdot 2SiO_2 \cdot 2H_2O$$

In this formula, the relative amounts of the oxides present are stated as a molecular ratio rather than by percentage weight. In clay, one molecule of Al_2O_3 is associated with two molecules of SiO_2, and two molecules of H_2O. This formula, which is typical, overlooks the complex array of "impurities" always present in actual samplings. Kaolinite is the mineralogical name which has been given to this pure clay substance.

3. The Origin of Clay from Feldspar

In tracing the chemical parentage of clay, we must look more closely at the feldspar family of minerals, which are, as we have seen, our most abundant minerals, and which, therefore, enter importantly into the formation of any clay. Feldspars contain alumina (Al_2O_3) and silica (SiO_2) combined with one or more other oxides of an alkaline nature. Commonly occurring feldspars are illustrated in the following formulas:

Orthoclase	$K_2O \cdot Al_2O_3 \cdot 6SiO_2$
Albite	$Na_2O \cdot Al_2O_3 \cdot 6SiO_2$
Anorthite	$CaO \cdot Al_2O_3 \cdot 2SiO_2$

These are typical formulas. In the case of actual specimens of rock, it would be probable that two or more alkalies would be present in any feldspar and that there would be some impurities such as iron. Furthermore, the ratio of the molecules would seldom be exactly one, to one, to six, as indicated above. More likely, the ratio would vary somewhat from this general proportion.

When feldspar is disintegrated by geologic weathering, the alkali part, namely the soda potash, or lime, being relatively soluble, is carried off by water. This leaves the alumina and silica. Part of the silica also is split off by chemical combinations. The remaining alumina and silica, after long exposure to moisture, then become hydrated, or chemically combined with water. Stated as a chemical equation, the whole process, which may take millions of years to effect and which cannot be duplicated in the laboratory, is as follows:

$$\underset{\text{Feldspar}}{K_2O\ Al_2O_3\ 6SiO_2} + xH_2O \rightarrow \underset{\text{a clay mineral}}{Al_2O_3\ 2SiO_2\ 2H_2O} + \underset{\text{in solution}}{K_2O(SiO_2)} + \underset{\text{in solution or in the clay}}{SiO_2}$$

This sketch of the kaolinization of feldspar tells nothing of the physical properties of clay but accounts only for its chemical composition. It is obvious that clay, a material which is the end product of a long process of erosion and change, is an extremely inert material chemically. All the natural changes that can take place in clay have done so, with the possible exception of the formation from it of shale or slate by heat and pressure, but the formation of these metamorphic rocks requires rather special conditions. The melting point, or temperature, at which clay fuses tends to be high. Even common surface clays fuse at temperatures above 1000° C. (Hereafter in the text, all temperatures are given in degrees centigrade.) The reason for this, which will be explained in more detail later, is that all the more fusible alkali compounds have been removed, leaving only the very refractory oxides of alumina and silica, together with smaller amounts of iron or other minerals.

Chapter 3

The Physical Nature of Clay

1. Particle Size and Shape

The physical nature of clay is more obscure, and our knowledge of it less exact, than its chemical composition. The chemical composition of a clay can be readily determined by routine analysis. The size and shape of the particles in clay and the forces which account for its plasticity can be known only through microscopic study and other types of analysis.

Clay was formerly thought to be more or less colloidal in its physical make-up, but later studies seem to indicate that the extremely small size of the grains of clay account for most of its physical properties. Many clays have been found to have a substantial percentage of particles below one micron in diameter. (A micron is a unit of length which is one-thousandth part of a millimeter.) These small particles may be thought of as single crystals of clay. Examination under the electron microscope has revealed that these clay particles are plate-shaped, elongated in two dimensions, and thin in the other dimension.

It has been estimated that the particles in one cubic millimeter of kaolin number more than three and one-half million. This is for a relatively coarse-grained clay. A finer-grained clay such as a ball clay would have a great many more individual particles per unit of volume.

The extremely fine particle size of clay can be accounted for by the processes of weathering, chemical change and disintegration, grinding during water transportation, and the sorting out which occurs during sedimentation in quiet water. In any clay, however, in addition to the very fine particle size of the bulk of the material, there will be some fragments of larger size. These may be bits of unaltered feldspar or quartz, or other minerals which have become associated with the clay during transportation or sedimentation. In some clays, such as most kaolins, there is so much coarse material of this sort that the clay must be removed from it by washing. In other clays, there is relatively little coarse material.

Clay usually contains some organic matter in addition to the inorganic minerals present. Although the organic matter burns out and disappears in firing, its presence has an important effect on the physical behavior of the material before firing. Clay is frequently formed in situations where organic matter becomes associated with it. For example, clay may be formed in quiet estuaries where vegetation may be prevalent. This organic matter leaves a residue of carbon in the clay. Sedimentary layers of clay and coal are, in fact, frequently found one on top of the other. Carbonaceous matter in clay may also be caused by bacterial action in the damp clay itself.

As found in nature, clay may be very densely compacted and may look like a rocky material. If such clay is exposed to the weather, however, it quickly slakes into a soft crumbly mass.

2. Plasticity

Clay, when wet with the proper amount of water, will tend to hold any shape which is given to it. This property is known as plasticity. Among natural materials clay is unique in the degree of its plasticity, and it is this property which has made possible the fabrication of the endlessly varied shapes of ceramic objects. Even a small child will recognize at once the possibilities in clay and will begin to model it into shapes of various sorts. No synthetic material approaches clay in the ease with which it can be shaped.

Fineness of grain size and the shapes of the individual particles probably account largely for the plasticity of clay. When clay is wet, water penetrates and wets each individual particle and also, if enough is used, forms a film of moisture around each particle. Since a majority of the particles are thin and plate-like in shape, they tend to cling to each other and, when a force is applied, to slip upon one another and to hold their new position. The very fineness of the particles and the film of water surrounding them alone would account for some plasticity. The fact that one can model with wet sand, which when dry has no plasticity at all, illustrates this principle. Chemical attraction between particles no doubt also has an influence on plasticity.

The carbonaceous matter in clay also contributes to its plasticity. Most common clays, which have a relatively large percentage of carbonaceous matter in them, are rather plastic. The organic matter seems to act almost as a gum or glue in the behavior of clay. Bacterial action, which releases colloidal gels, may also contribute to plasticity. It is a well-known fact that clay which has been allowed to age for a while becomes more plastic and workable. It is said that in China a potter mixed up clay for his grandchildren, and that he in turn used the clay which his grandfather had prepared. But even a few days will be found to be helpful in improving the working properties of a clay, and the aging will be hastened by adding a small quantity of previously aged clay. The more thorough wetting of the clay and the accumulation of products of bacterial action probably largely account for the effect of aging. Subtle differences in plasticity are hard to evaluate in any exact way, but an experienced potter may detect such differences at once, simply by working with the material.

Different clays vary a great deal in plasticity, depending on their geologic history. Some very coarse clays are useful for making bricks and other heavy clay products such as tile and drainage pipes. Other clays are too plastic and sticky to be used by themselves and must be blended with other less plastic clays to be useful. Many clays, however, are useful just as they come from the ground and may be modeled or thrown on the potter's wheel without any adjustments in composition.

3. Primary Clay

Clays may be classified in various ways, depending on what properties are of interest to the classifier. One might classify clays according to their color as they exist in nature. Or the classification might center around the idea of use, or of geologic origin. The potter is interested in what the clay will do for him in the making and firing of pots, and he will look at clay from that standpoint. He is interested in the plasticity or workability of the clay and in its reactions during drying and firing. The division of clays into two broad groups, primary clays and secondary clays, helps to classify clays for the potter and helps him to understand and make use of the peculiar working and firing properties of various clays.

Primary clays—or residual clays, as they are sometimes called—are those clays which have been formed on the site of their parent rocks and have not been transported, either by water, wind, or glacier. Primary clays are unusual, since normally the products of weathering are carried off down slopes by water into creeks and rivers, and eventually to lakes or to seas. But in some instances, clays are left on the spot where they were formed by the disintegration of feldspathic rock.

Rock beds are broken down into clay largely by the action of ground water seeping through the rock and thus gradually leaching out the more soluble components. In some cases the percolation of steam or of gases from below may have contributed to the formation of clay. In typical deposits of primary clay, much unaltered rock remains, and the clay is found in irregular pockets. Since the clay has not been water-borne, there has been no opportunity for the selective sorting out of the various particle sizes, and large and small grains of clay are found mixed together. Deposits of primary clay are apt to be coarse-grained and relatively non-plastic. There has been little opportunity for fine grinding and sorting.

Primary clays, when they have been cleared of rock fragments, tend to be relatively pure and free from contamination with non-clay minerals. The reason for this is that most primary clays originate from beds of more or less pure feldspar, a rock which is relatively easily broken down in geologic time by the action of water alone. Another obvious reason is that since the clay is not carried by streams, there is much less chance for admixtures from other localities to alter its composition. We value primary clays, then, for their purity, their whiteness, and their freedom from objectionable mineral or organic contamination. Most kaolins are primary clays.

4. Secondary Clays

Secondary clay is clay which has been transported from the site of the original parent rock. Although water is the most common agent of transportation, wind and glaciers may also carry clay. Secondary, or transported, clays are much more common than primary clays. In nature, it is almost certain that eroded material will be carried to a new site.

Transportation by water has an important effect on clay. For one thing, the action of the water in streams tends to grind up the clay into smaller and smaller particle size. Then, when the water of the stream begins to slow down, some of the material which it carries will settle out. The coarse particles naturally settle first, leaving the fine particles still suspended in the water. When quiet water is reached, as in a lake or sea, the remaining very fine particles of clay sink to the bottom. This process of sedimentation tends to separate the coarse from the fine.

Transported clays are ordinarily made up of clay from a variety of sources. In any one stream, sediments from numerous sites are apt to be mixed together. This fact makes for the more complex make-up of most transported clays and for the presence of numerous minerals, such as iron oxide, which from the standpoint of clay must be considered impurities. Also, secondary clay is apt to contain considerable carbonaceous matter, which becomes associated with it during sedimentation.

Secondary or transported clays, then, are fine-grained and plastic, and are usually contaminated with considerable amounts of impurities in the form of other minerals, such as iron, which color the clay and make it fire to a red or brown color. Some secondary clays, such as ball clays and some secondary kaolins, contain little iron, but these are rather exceptional.

Glacial clays and aeolian or wind-deposited clays are also considered secondary clays. Clays which have been transported and deposited by glaciers are ordinarily rather impure and tend to be very uneven in particle size, since no sedimentation has occurred. Aeolian clays are more rare, but in some localities occur in rather surprisingly extensive deposits. They, too, tend to be quite impure.

Clay may be defined as an earthy mineral substance, composed largely of a hydrous silicate of alumina, which becomes plastic when wet and hard and rock-like when fired.

Chapter 4

Drying and Firing Clay

1. The Process of Drying

Clay, until it is fired and made durable, is a material of little or no practical value. The adobe, or sun-dried brick, is an exception, but no one would maintain that an adobe brick as such was superior to a fired brick. We are interested in clay not so much for what it is in the natural state, as for what it may become. By a happy coincidence, clay, which is so plastic and easily shaped, becomes, when fired to red heat or more, a hard and permanent substance.

The discovery that clay will become hard and durable when fired ranks as one of man's most important early inventions. The domestic life of primitive man was immeasurably enriched by the possession of fired clay vessels for storing grain, carrying water, cooking, washing, holding food—to say nothing of the ceremonial and purely esthetic uses to which clay objects were put. Any ancient civilization can be gaged by the quantity and the quality of the pottery which it produced. Clay was no doubt first fired accidentally in a camp fire, perhaps in the form of a mud-lined basket. Much early pottery was made in the shape and texture of baskets—a fact which strongly suggests the probability that pottery began as mud smeared on the inside of baskets to make them more water- or rodent-proof.

When plastic clay dries, it shrinks about 5 percent. Some very plastic clays may shrink as much as 8 percent. Although this shrinkage takes place rather slowly, it creates a problem in completing any object made of plastic clay. When dry clay is moistened, it takes up a surprising quantity of water. Each individual particle of clay holds water like an absorbent pebble, and in between the particles water creates a film. An average clay, to become plastic enough to model, will require about 35 parts of water, by weight, to each 100 parts of clay. Any mass of plastic clay, therefore, is about one-fourth water.

The drying of clay proceeds at a rate controlled by the humidity of the surrounding atmosphere. When the humidity is 100%, nothing dries. But if the humidity of the surrounding air is less than 100%, water leaves the clay as a vapor. When the surface of the mass of clay is dried slightly, more water is drawn out from the interior of the mass by capillary attraction. Unless the mass of clay is very thick, drying will proceed quite evenly throughout. If this were not the case, it would be impossible to make objects from plastic clay, because cracks would develop on the dried surface.

The drying of clay is always accompanied by shrinkage. As the film of water between the particles of clay is drawn off by evaporation, the particles draw closer and closer together, thus taking up the space which had been occupied by the water. The cumulative effect of each particle drawing closer to its neighboring particle is the shrinkage of the entire mass. The amount of this drying shrinkage will depend upon the size of the clay particles and on the amount of water which separates them. Those clays having a very fine particle size will shrink more because of the presence of more water-filled interstices which close up. Conversely, more open clays, that is clays with larger particle size, will shrink less. Drying shrinkage is always related to the grain structure of a clay and, therefore, also to plasticity.

When the water has evaporated from between the clay particles and all the particles are in contact, drying shrinkage is complete. At this stage, which is called the leather-hard state, the clay particles themselves may still be damp and drying will not be complete until this moisture also leaves by evaporation. The drying of the clay particles themselves does not cause any further shrinkage.

If warping, cracking, or deformation is to be avoided, objects made of plastic clay must be dried slowly and evenly. If one part of a clay object dries more rapidly than another, the unequal shrinkage between the two portions may cause warping or cracking. This may happen, for example, when a clay pot is dried in the sun or in a place where a draught strikes one side. Another familiar example is the tile which curls upward when it dries; the face of the tile, which is exposed to the air, shrinks more rapidly than the back. In the case of objects made from very plastic clays, drying may be a serious problem, not only because of the excessive shrinkage, but because of the tendency of the clay to warp and crack. Handles, spouts, and other appendages may be difficult to attach without subsequent cracking.

Drying is greatly facilitated by the presence in the clay of any sort of non-plastic particles. Such particles tend to take up much less water than clay and are, therefore, more easily dried out. Non-plastic particles also furnish open pores or channels through which moisture can escape toward the surface. Clays which contain a large percentage of non-clay particles, especially if these particles are relatively large, are called "open" bodies. When objects are to be made having thick walls or sections, as in some sculptures or terra cottas, open clay bodies are necessarily used. Grog is ordinarily used for this purpose. Grog is clay which has already been fired and then ground to more or less fine particle size. Such a material, of course, having already been dried and fired, undergoes no further shrinkage, and the addition of grog to a clay body will decrease the total shrinkage. Other materials which may also decrease shrinkage and promote rapid drying are flint and feldspar. When a very plastic clay is necessary, as in a clay designed for throwing, the non-plastics must be held to a minimum.

A piece of dried clay will contain more or less free water, as the surrounding atmosphere is, respectively, more or less humid. For this reason, drying is actually completed in the kiln. When the temperature of the kiln reaches the boiling point of water, 100°, all the uncombined water in the clay will have evaporated, and at that point the clay will be completely dry.

2. Early Stages of Firing—Drying and Water-Smoking

Profound changes occur in clay during firing. A piece of fired clay is quite different both chemically and physically from raw clay. Our material, which was once soft, easily disintegrated, plastic when wet, and without cohesion or strength, becomes when fired, hard, rock-like, and impervious to water. Clay is actually a relatively indestructible material when fired. Although a piece of pottery will break, its fragments will remain unchanged for thousands of years even when buried in damp soil or when immersed in water.

The first change which firing brings about in clay is a completion of drying. This final drying must be brought about slowly; otherwise the formation of steam within the body of the clay may cause it to burst. This is the familiar explosion in the amateur's kiln which is usually caused by a too rapid advance of heat in the early stages of firing or by pockets of air in the clay. No matter how dry a clay object may seem to be when it is put in the kiln, a considerable amount of water must still be driven off. In the case of large kilns, filled with heavy clay products such as brick or tile, large quantities of water escape from the kiln, and sometimes blow-holes are provided in the top of the kiln to let off the water vapor. In smaller kilns the escaping moisture, though present, may not be noticeable. The danger of explosions resulting from steam forming in the object is greatly increased by heavy cross-sections or thick-walled objects, and such objects must be fired with great care.

The next change which occurs in the firing of clay occurs at about 350°, at which point the chemically combined water of the clay begins to be driven off. This chemically combined water is not to be confused with pore water and water of plasticity, which escapes from the clay during drying. Chemically combined water is a part of the molecular structure of the clay and is unaffected by temperatures below about 350°. It will be noted from the chemical formula of clay that there are two molecules of water to each two molecules of silica and each single molecule of alumina. Expressed as a percentage, this means that clay contains by weight about 14 percent of water. When this chemically combined water leaves the clay, enough time must be allowed in firing to prevent the sudden evolution of steam and the possible breaking of the object.

Once a piece of clay has been fired to about 500°, it will be dehydrated, and it will no longer slake or disintegrate in water. It will also have lost its plasticity. Although such a clay may be very friable, it may not be reclaimed and used again. An irreversible chemical change has taken place. This change, known as dehydration, is not accompanied by any shrinkage. If one were to open a kiln after it had been fired to about 500°, it would be noted that the ware was even more fragile than when it was put in the kiln, and that no shrinkage had taken place.

3. Oxidation

Another important change which occurs in the clay during the early stages of firing is the oxidation or decomposition of all those components of the clay which are not already in oxide form. These would include such organic matter as carbon, and the inorganic carbonates or sulphates. The oxidation of all these compounds is usually not complete until the temperature has advanced to about 900°.

All clays contain an appreciable amount of carbon, and firing has the effect of oxidizing or burning up this carbon. This process of oxidation requires that oxygen in the form of air be present in sufficient quantities in the kiln. Ordinarily oxidation proceeds without difficulty. However, if the firing is carried on too rapidly, or if insufficient air is present in the kiln because of improper adjustment of burners, some carbon may remain in the ware. This may cause blackening or, in the case of heavy clay products, blackening and bloating. Sometimes when ware is tightly stacked together in the kiln, oxidation may be incomplete and a blackening or discoloration will be noticed. This is due to carbon still remaining in the fired piece.

Clay may contain small percentages of calcium carbonate or other impurities such as sulfates. As the firing advances, the dissociation point of these compounds is reached and the carbon or sulphur is driven off. These impurities are ordinarily present in such small quantities that no problem attends their oxidation.

4. Quartz Inversions

All clays contain an appreciable amount of quartz. This quartz may be associated with the clay in nature as an accessory mineral, or it may be quartz which has been added to the clay as flint. Crystalline quartz has a number of different forms, depending upon the temperature. When the temperature advances, the crystals of quartz rearrange themselves into a slightly different order, and these rearrangements may be accompanied by slight changes in volume. Thus when 573° is reached, quartz crystals undergo a change known as the change from alpha to beta quartz. This adjustment is marked by a slight ($\pm 2\%$) increase in volume, which is reversible; that is, upon cooling the quartz changes from beta to alpha quartz and resumes its original crystalline form and size. This change of volume in the quartz portion of a clay body, although rather slight, must be accomplished slowly to avoid damage to the ware. If one part of an object in the kiln is heated up faster than another, the unequal expansion in the piece may cause it to crack. Care must likewise be taken in cooling so that the contraction which occurs at 573° may be safely passed. A large percentage of ware which comes from the kiln cracked is damaged by either too rapid heating or too rapid cooling at this critical temperature. Large objects particularly must be carefully fired at this temperature especially if the kiln does not fire very evenly. Cracking which occurs during cooling is called dunting.

5. Vitrification

As the temperature of firing increases beyond red heat, another series of changes occur in the clay which are called vitrification. Vitrification is the hardening, tightening, and finally the glassification of clay. Vitrification gives to fired clay its characteristic hard, durable, dense, and rock-like properties. It is accompanied by shrinkage in the clay. Vitrification proceeds gradually, at first causing the clay to be rather loosely compacted and then, with the advance of temperature, causing it to become increasingly hard, up to the point of melting and deformation. The same clay may be either very soft and chalk-like or very dense, hard, and impervious, depending upon the temperature at which it was fired.

In part, this hardening results from fusions or melting of some of the components of the clay, more particularly those minerals, such as iron oxide, which are considered impurities. All substances melt at some degree of temperature and clay, being usually a rather complex aggregate of numerous oxides, tends to fuse gradually. As the heat of the kiln advances, the more fusible impurities of the clay may melt into small beads of glass. These liquid beads of melted material soak into the surrounding area, binding the particles together like a glue, and act like a solvent in promoting further fusion. If the firing is carried on to a sufficient degree of heat, clay fuses completely into a liquid, which, upon cooling, is a glass. In practice, of course, we stop far short of this, but in the case of porcelain manufacture, such a complete fusion is approached, and the similarity between porcelain and glass is apparent. Some common red clays which contain a high percentage of iron and other impurities have a relatively low melting point. The tendency of these clays to melt at temperatures of cone 8 to 11 has been utilized in making slip glazes, or glazes which are made up largely of fusible clay.

The strength of fired clay is due not only to glassification but also to the formation of new crystalline growths within the clay body, particularly the growth of mullite crystals. Mullite, which is an aluminum silicate, is characterized by a long needle-like crystal. These mullite crystals tend to grow at higher temperatures and extend themselves into the glassy matrixes within the clay. Mullite laces the structure together, giving it cohesion and strength.

Clays vitrify at various temperatures, depending upon their composition. A common red clay, for example, which is high in iron and other mineral impurities, may fire to hardness and density at about 1000° and may melt to a liquid at about 1250°. A pure kaolin body, on the other hand, may still be quite open and porous after having been fired to 1250° and may not melt until temperatures in excess of 1800° have been reached.

Further shrinkage occurs during vitrification. This shrinkage may be due to the diminished size of the particles as they approach fusion and to the closer arrangement of particles in their glassy matrix. Total shrinkage of a fired piece of clay may be as high as 10 percent, and this shrinkage will vary according to the degree of vitrification. However, when a clay actually begins to melt, it usually goes through a boiling or bloating stage and, at that point, may swell or grow in size, much as a cake rises from the distension of entrapped bubbles of gas.

The art of firing clay consists in bringing about just enough fusion and hardness in the material to serve the purposes at hand, but in not overfiring to the point of melting or the deformation of the shape of the ware. The desired extent of heat treatment, involving both time and temperature, is called maturing.

The well-fired piece of clay, then, is characterized by hardness, great compressive strength, denseness and impermeability to liquids, resistance to abrasion, chemical inertness and insolubility, and a very large and easily controlled variety of color and texture which is reminiscent of the variety in the earthy materials of the landscape. The one fault of clay wares, brittleness, may be, from the potter's point of view, an advantage, since the fragile nature of his product has ensured a steady demand for it.

Chapter 5

Kinds of Clay

1. Kaolin

There are a great many different kinds of clay. The differing geologic conditions which have resulted in clay formation have produced clays of various chemical composition and physical make-up. These differing clays may merge into one another from strata to strata and from locality to locality. From this wide variety of clays the ceramist distinguishes certain types which are similar in origin, composition, and usefulness.

One such kind of clay, kaolin or china clay, though relatively scarce in nature, is of peculiar interest to the potter. It is indispensable in the making of pure white porcelain or china. Its scarcity is indicated by the fact that the presence of deposits of kaolin in Europe was largely unnoticed until early in the eighteenth century. Deposits of kaolin occur in Europe, England, and North America, as well as in Asia, but they are by no means as common as other types of clay.

In China, wares made from white clays were fashioned at least from the beginning of the Han Dynasty, 200 B.C., or earlier. The management of kiln temperatures up to about 1200°, and the manufacture of vitrified white ware, using kaolin as the chief clay, dates, in China, to at least as far back as A.D. 600. This antedates the manufacture of porcelain in Europe by 1200 years. In China, China clay or white burning kaolins are more commonly found than elsewhere, and furthermore they are more plastic and workable than the white clays of other regions. Early Chinese potters at first made a soft white earthenware from kaolin. Gradually, over a period of development lasting several hundred years, they learned to reach higher temperatures in their kilns and to make the proper additions to their clays to achieve the hardness, whiteness, and translucency of true porcelain. This discovery of porcelain was a technical triumph in the development of ceramics.

Kaolins are primary clays and are formed by the weathering, on the site, of feldspar. They are coarse in particle size and are therefore non-plastic compared to most sedimentary clays. Kaolins are relatively free from mineral impurities such as iron.

As found in natural deposits, kaolins are usually located in pockets rather than in extensive stratified beds. The clay substance is usually mingled with rock fragments of feldspar and quartz. Before the clay can be used, these mineral fragments must be removed by some method of purification. Sometimes the clay is floated in a series of ponds or pools where the finer fractions of clay are separated from the coarser material. Hydraulic mining is sometimes used to recover kaolin. Powerful streams of water are played against the clay-beds and the resultant mixture of clay and water is led by sluices to settling ponds. The smaller particle-sized fractions of clay recovered in this manner will have a maximum of plasticity and purity.

In chemical composition, kaolins approach the formula of the mineral, kaolinite. Kaolin is a highly refractory clay and has a melting point above 1800°. Used by itself, kaolin is difficut to shape into objects because of its poor plasticity, and also, because of its refractoriness, it is difficut to mature by firing into a hard, dense object. In practice, therefore, kaolin is seldom used by itself; other materials are added to it to increase its workability and to lower the kiln temperature necessary to produce a hard, dense product. As would be expected, the shrinkage of kaolin is low because of its relatively coarse grain structure.

Kaolins will vary rather widely in their whiteness and in their plasticity. There are some secondary or sedimentary kaolins, but these tend to be darker burning, although they may have good working properties. Some of the primary kaolins are much more plastic than others, as for example some of those found in Florida which are widely used to lend plasticity to whiteware bodies. English china clay is a kaolin of unusual purity and is used where extreme whiteness in the finished ware is desired.

2. Ball Clays

Ball clays are somewhat the opposite of kaolin in their properties. They are higher in iron content, more fusible, much more plastic, and fine in particle size. Ball clays and kaolin are really complementary in character and are often combined in clay bodies to adjust the mixture towards a practical, workable clay. Ball clays are said to have been so named because of the practice in England of forming the damp clay in the mines into large balls which could be rolled up onto wagons for transport.

Ball clay is a secondary or transported type of clay which is found in stratified layers, often alternating with layers of coal and with other types of clay. It is highly plastic. Although not as pure as kaolin, ball clay is relatively free from iron and other mineral impurities and burns to a light grey or light buff color. It tightens into a dense structure when fired to about 1300°.

Ball clays are impossible to use by themselves in pottery making because of their excessive shrinkage, which may be as high as 20 percent when fired to maturity. Ball clays are usually used as an admixture to other clays to secure increased plasticity and workability. In manufacturing whitewares, ball clay is indispensable as an addition to the body to overcome the non-plastic properties of kaolin. However, if whiteness is desired, not more than about 15 percent of ball clay can be added to a clay body; more than this amount in a whiteware body results in a grey, off-white, or buff color.

In the raw, ball clays are usually dark grey because of the presence of carbonaceous material. This carbon burns off in the firing and does not affect the final fired color of the clay. The more carbon a ball clay contains, the more plastic it is apt to be. Some ball clays, however, such as those from certain districts of Tennessee, contain little carbon and are quite white in their raw state. Ball clays from England, which are valued for their high plasticity and freedom from iron, often have a great deal of carbon in them, which gives to the raw clay its dark brown or almost black color. Ball clays which contain a large amount of carbon, particularly if this carbon is in the form of bits of lignite or coal, must be carefully screened before using.

Ball clays are useful in a great variety of ceramic products and are mined in large quantities from extensive deposits in Kentucky and Tennessee. Various producers market their ball clays under different trade names, but the name "ball clay" always indicates a light-burning clay of high plasticity.

3. Fire Clays

Fire clay is not as well defined a type of clay as either ball clay or kaolin. The term "fire clay" refers to refractoriness or resistance to heat, and clays which vary widely in other properties may be called "fire clays" if they are refractory. Some fire clays are very plastic and some lack plasticity, and the fired color may vary. Any clay which resists fusion or deformation up to about 1500° may be called "fire clay." Such refractoriness or resistance to heat means that the clay is relatively pure and free from iron, although most fire clays burn to a buff or brownish color, sometimes with darker splotches which are due to concentrations of iron-bearing minerals.

Fire clays are useful in a great variety of products, principally in the manufacture of fire brick and other refractory parts for kilns, furnaces, boilers, and melting pots. Industries such as steel, copper, and other metallurgical industries could not operate without fire brick furnaces in which high temperature smelting is done.

Fire clays are also used as additions to stoneware bodies or to bodies for saggers and other kiln furniture where an increase in refractoriness is desired. In stoneware bodies, fire clay may furnish a desirable roughness or "tooth" to the body. Fire clay is also useful in mudding-in kiln doors, making clay pats for pyrometric cones, and for wadding under kiln shelves and sagger lids.

In bodies for large terra cotta pieces or sculptures, the open, coarse texture of some fire clays makes them an ideal addition.

4. Sagger Clay

Saggers are clay boxes in which ware is fired to protect it from direct heat and flame in the kiln. Sagger clay is a kind of clay which has been found suitable for the manufacture of such products. A sagger clay must be quite refractory and plastic enough to be shaped by modeling, and, when fired, it must form a dense, tough body, which is resistant to thermal shock and the "fatigue" caused by repeated firing. Sagger clays vary quite widely from medium to high plasticity, and they ordinarily fire to a light grey buff color. Sagger clays are frequently used as additions to stoneware, terra cotta, or earthenware bodies.

5. Stoneware Clay

Stoneware clays are plastic clays which mature or become vitreous at 1200° to 1300°. Their fired color ranges from a very light grey or buff to a darker grey or brown. Stoneware clays are secondary, or sedimentary, clays. They vary widely in plasticity and firing range, and there is no sharp distinction between what might be called a fire clay, a sagger clay, or a stoneware clay. The classification really hinges upon the possible use of the clay in ceramics, rather than upon the actual chemical or physical nature of the clay or its geologic origin. One clay, for instance, might be successfully used both as a fire clay in the making of bricks and refractories and as a stoneware clay in the making of high-fired stoneware. Many clays are quite suitable for making stoneware without any additions. Such clays may have just the right plasticity for wheel work and may have desirable drying and firing characteristics. The small country potteries of the last century, which produced utilitarian wares such as crocks, jugs, and churns, usually employed a single stoneware clay which was dug in the neighborhood and pugged ready for use without the addition of any other clay. Such a natural clay body may burn to very pleasing colors and textures and may take salt glazes, slip glazes, or high-fired stoneware glazes.

6. Earthenware Clays

Most of the usable clay found in nature might be called "earthenware" clay or common clay. These clays contain iron and other mineral impurities in sufficient quantity to cause the clay to become tight and hard-fired at about 950° to 1100°. In the raw, such clay is red, brown, greenish, or grey, as a result of the presence of iron oxide. Fired, the color may vary from pink to buff to tan, red, brown, or black, depending on the clay and the condition of the firing. Most of the pottery the world over has been made of earthenware clay, and it is also the common raw material for brick, tile, drain tile, roof tile, and other heavy clay products.

Common red clay may be highly plastic—in fact, too plastic and too sticky to be used by itself; or, on the other hand, it may be quite non-plastic because of the presence of sand or other rocky fragments. The potter will look for a smooth plastic earthenware clay which he may modify by the addition of some sand or some non-plastic clay. The brick maker will look for an earthenware clay which is naturally coarse and contains considerable sand or other non-plastic fragments, and with such a clay he will be able to press, dry, and fire his bricks without having them warp, crack, or shrink excessively.

Vast quantities of common red clay outcrop on the earth's surface. Much of it is unusable because it contains either fragments of calcite or soluble alkaline salts. There are, however, immense reserves of usable clay.

7. Other Kinds of Clay

Adobe is a surface clay which is suitable for making adobe or sun-dried bricks. It is rather non-plastic and contains a high percentage of sand.

Flint clay is a refractory clay which has been compacted into a relatively hard, dense, rock-like mass.

Shale is a metamorphic rock formed by nature from sedimentary clay. It has very little plasticity unless it is finely pulverized and allowed to temper for a long while. Shale may be used as an addition to, or as the principal ingredient of, bricks and other heavy clay products.

Bentonite is a clay of volcanic origin. Although its chemical composition is like that of clay, its physical nature is different in that it contains more colloidal matter. Bentonite is used to lend plasticity to clay bodies. A small percentage of bentonite added to a clay body may bring about a marked increase in plasticity. Bentonite cannot be used by itself because of its tendency to swell when wet and because of its stickiness and extremely high shrinkage.

Terra cotta clay is a low-grade fire clay which may be used in the manufacture of large terra cotta pieces. It has an open, coarse grain structure which permits rapid and even drying.

High-alumina clays, such as bauxite or diaspore, are clays which contain a high percentage of alumina. These clays may be highly refractory and may be used as the raw material for the production of the metal aluminum.

Gumbo is a surface or soil clay which is very plastic and sticky and which contains a considerable quantity of organic matter.

Chapter 6

Clay Bodies

1. Definition of a Clay Body

A clay body may be defined as a mixture of clays or clays and other earthy mineral substances which are blended to achieve a specific ceramic purpose. Many clays found in nature serve very well just as they are. In brick making, for example, it would be uneconomical to have to do much mixing or blending of raw materials, and, in fact, clay which will do quite well for common brick manufacture is found in many localities. Similarly, many clays can be dug out of the ground, kneaded with the right amount of water, and made into pottery without making any additions. Such clays might be called natural clay bodies. The potter, in pre-scientific times, relied largely upon such clays for his raw material and made little or no additions to them. Sometimes, however, adjustments were made for better working properties. For example, some sand might be added to reduce the shrinkage and lessen the tendency of the clay to warp when dried and fired.

However, the demands which we make of clay, as a material, usually make it necessary to blend two or more materials in order to achieve the desired results. Such demands may be, for example, extreme plasticity to make the clay suitable for throwing, or complete density at a given firing temperature, or whiteness and translucency when fired, or the property of casting, as a fluid slip, or the development of certain desirable colors and textures. In order to arrive intelligently at suitable mixtures for a given use, one must understand the physical properties of clays and their response to firing, and also the physical and thermal properties of other materials used in clay bodies.

2. The Ways in Which Clay Bodies Need to be Altered to Make Them Useful

In practice it is usually necessary to make additions to a natural clay in order to have it serve the practical needs of forming and firing. The ways in which one might wish to change a clay for practical purposes may be listed as follows:

(1) Changes of color or texture. It may be desired to alter the fired color of the clay to make it either a lighter or a darker shade, or to increase or decrease its granular roughness or texture.

(2) Changes in plasticity. It may be desired to make a clay more plastic or less plastic.

(3) Changes to decrease shrinkage or to improve drying and firing with a minimum of warpage or cracking.

(4) Changes to lower the maturing temperature or to raise the maturing temperature. Or, stated another way, changes which will increase or decrease density at a given temperature.

(5) Changes to improve the fit of glazes.

Leaving aside for the moment changes in color and texture, it will be seen that all adjustments in clays involve either: (a) Adjustment of its physical properties to give the desired plasticity, workability, and shrinkage; or (b) adjustment of its reaction to firing, either raising or lowering the degree of heat necessary to bring about the desired degree of density.

Changes of the first type are made by adding clays or other materials of more or less plasticity and of varying particle size. Changes of the second type are made by adding clays or other materials of more or less fusibility.

3. Porcelain as an Example of a Clay Body

An example of a clay body would be the type of mixture or blend of materials used in making white, translucent porcelain, fired at about 1300°. The proportion of materials which has been found satisfactory for such a body is approximately as follows:

China Clay or Kaolin	5 parts
Feldspar	3 parts
Flint	2 parts

China clay by itself would not be practical for porcelain because its high melting point, 1500° or more, would require an impractical degree of heat to bring about fusion and translucency or glassiness. We add, therefore, feldspar, which, by itself, melts to glass at a temperature of about 1300°. This material acts upon the clay, bringing the whole mass to the point of fusion. We find it further necessary to add flint or powdered quartz for the double purpose of improving the resistance of the body to warping and of giving hardness and stability to the semi-glassified final body. As we shall see later, the flint also enables us more easily to fit a glaze to the body.

While the above composition may fire to a pure white, translucent body, it will be difficult to use in making pottery because of the non-plastic character of the mixture. The clay is apt to be too mealy and crumbly to model or throw, and is likely to cast too rapidly in molds and be difficult to smooth and finish. To correct these troubles, a more plastic clay must be added, such as a ball clay. While such an addition may correct the working properties of the body, it would also decrease the whiteness of the fired clay, because of the higher iron content of the ball clay. Some compromise must then be made, either with whiteness or with workability. A practical porcelain body, then, might have approximately the following composition:

China Clay	4 parts
Ball Clay	1 part
Feldspar	3 parts
Flint	2 parts

Final adjustment of such a body would depend on the exact temperature to be used, the kinds of clays available, and the fusibility of the feldspar. The combination of china clay and feldspar and its firing at elevated temperatures was essentially the closely guarded secret of the Chinese potters in their manufacture of white, translucent porcelain. The plasticity of the kaolins in China made it necessary for them to use little, if any, plastic materials of the ball clay type; and their clay bodies, of marvelous purity of color and translucency, were rightly the envy of European potters. The method of compounding and firing porcelain bodies was first discovered in Europe in 1710 by Boettger, in Meissen, Germany.

4. The Method of Arriving at a Suitable Blend of Materials

The logic involved in formulating a porcelain body is obvious, given the desired end product and the nature of the ingredients. However, the question arises as to how the relative amounts of the various ingredients are arrived at. In practice this is done empirically, or by experimentation and testing. The primitive potter who added more sand to his clay until it would dry without cracking, and fire without breaking, was making a clay body. He proceeded by cut-and-try methods, and, although he may not have known the logic of his procedure, he arrived at workable compositions.

Actually, we proceed today in much the same fashion. If a clay does not work properly by itself, we correct its bad habits by making additions of other clays, or other materials, to it. Theoretically, in the light of our relatively complete knowledge of the chemistry and physics involved in physical and thermal reactions, it might be possible to predict with some accuracy what any combination of clays might do in a body fired to a given temperature. But such a prediction would still need to be tested to be verified. The ceramist thus proceeds by making predictions or guesses, and then, through trial and error, arrives at a mixture which works well in practice. The actual chemical composition of clay bodies is seldom of much interest in the process of formulating mixtures. What is of most interest is the physical character of the ingredients, such as plasticity and grain structure, and their thermal behavior, such as shrinkage and fusibility.

For convenience, all the materials which go into clay bodies may be thought of as being plastics, i.e. clay; or as fillers, which are non-plastic materials like flint, grog, or calcined clay; or as fluxes, such as feldspar or frit. Plastics lend the necessary workability and plasticity to a clay body, and even a clay body which is to be used in casting or pressing needs to have a certain degree of plasticity. The fillers enable the clay to dry out safely without undue warping or cracking, and they decrease the amount of shrinkage. The fluxes control the fusion or hardening point of the clay and make it fire to a satisfactory degree of density at whatever temperature is being used.

5. Formulating a Stoneware Body

As an example of the kind of thinking which goes into the formulation of a clay body, and of the way testing such a body might proceed, the following example is given.

Suppose we wish to formulate a stoneware body for use in general pottery making, and particularly for working on the potter's wheel. We might want the clay to mature to a nearly vitreous body at 1250°, and we might also want it to shrink no more than 13 percent, and to be relatively free from warping, deformation, and cracking. This is an easier problem than making a porcelain body because it is much more likely that some naturally occurring clay will serve as a complete body with little or perhaps no adjustment. The first step in formulating such a stoneware body will be to find a clay which will be, as nearly as possible, serviceable without any alteration. Suppose that the best natural, unadulterated clay available has the following characteristics:

Plasticity—good, but not quite good enough for the intended use
Shrinkage—a total drying and firing shrinkage of 10 percent at cone 9
Water absorption of fired clay—6 percent
Warping or cracking—none

From these data, which can be obtained by a few simple tests for plasticity, shrinkage, and absorption (see appendix), it will be seen that, in this instance, a further increase of plasticity is needed, and that, moreover, the fusibility of the clay needs to be increased in order to make it mature into a denser, less absorbent fired structure at this particular working temperature. Since the shrinkage of the clay is only 10 percent, somewhat more plastic clay can be added without the danger of increasing the shrinkage unduly or causing excessive warping. The stoneware clay, in other words, is not quite plastic enough and does not mature at the temperature at which we wish to work, and it must be changed to make it satisfactory for use.

The next step might be to make a chart, indicating a series of predictions or guesses, as to the best combinations of materials for the purpose. Only a few, or a great many, tests might be made. Usually, it is better to start with a few trials, since the results of these preliminary trials may give a more precise indication of what further work needs to be done. The first tests might be made as indicated in the chart below, which shows four different bodies, all made by adding materials to the original stoneware clay.

	#1	*#2*	*#3*	*#4*
Stoneware clay	55	45	60	50
Ball clay	20	20	15	15
Flint	15	15	15	15
Feldspar	10	20	10	20

Test Number One represents an estimate of exactly what materials need to be added to solve the problem and make a workable body. The 20 parts of ball clay are added to increase the plasticity of the mixture. The 10 parts of feldspar are added to lower the fusion point of the clay and to make it more dense at the intended temperature. The 15 parts of flint are added to insure good drying, give a harder fired body, and to improve the chances of glaze fit.

The question is: how does one arrive at these figures? Actually, they depend upon knowledge of the materials being added and are based largely upon previous experience with similar problems. In other words, there are really no fixed rules for formulating clay bodies. The ceramist proceeds empirically rather than on the basis of exact theory.

Since it is uncertain exactly how Body Number One will actually perform or fire and since it represents merely the best guess out of many possibilities, other combinations may also be made. In Body Number Two, flint and ball clay are held constant, and an additional 10 parts of feldspar are added at the expense of the stoneware clay. This mixture covers the possibility that the 10 parts of feldspar in Body Number One might not be enough. Bodies Number Three and Four are the same as Numbers One and Two, except that the ball clay content is lowered by five parts and the stoneware clay is increased by five parts. This covers the possibility that the original 20 parts of ball clay in Numbers One and Two might be too high and cause excessive shrinkage.

In such a group of tests the number of variables in the series is held to a minimum. If new variables are introduced in each test, interpretation of the results becomes difficult. If several ingredients are changed in one test, it may be impossible to know exactly what material or combinations of material caused the fired result.

As the next step, the four bodies indicated on our chart would be mixed up, made into plastic samples, and tested. Tests for plasticity are inexact, but in practice, if ware is made from the test bodies by throwing or jiggering, a fairly good idea can be obtained of their workability. Other properties may be determined from fired samples. Suppose that after firing to cone 9, the four body tests were evaluated somewhat as follows:

	Body 1	*Body 2*	*Body 3*	*Body 4*
Dry shrinkage	5%	4.5%	4%	4%
Plasticity	good	good	good	good
Total shrinkage	13%	12%	11%	11.5%
Absorption Fired to cone 9	5%	2%	5%	2%
Warping	none	none	none	none

From these results we have learned that the addition of ball clay in Number One has corrected the plasticity towards a point near our objective. Numbers Two and Four are too dense, indicating the presence of too much feldspar. Numbers One and Three are not quite dense enough, indicating that the proper amount of feldspar would probably be somewhere between 10 and 20 percent.

The next set of tests would aim at further adjustments of the body towards the desired objective, and the final choice of a body composition might be as follows:

Stoneware clay	52
Ball clay	20
Flint	10
Feldspar	18

This process of formulating body compositions is somewhat like cooking, in that the proof of the pudding is in the eating. The recipe is improved over a series of variations until it performs for us, in practice, as we want it to. The number of ingredients is usually not great, and the individual behavior of each ingredient may be well known. For this reason, formulating clay bodies is not particularly difficult and may usually be accomplished with fewer tests than are required in the case of originating glazes. The tolerance of minor variations in a clay body is great. Any one of the ingredients may be changed by 5 or 10 percent without making an easily detectable difference. In studio work or small-scale production, the exact control of body composition is less necessary than in large-scale industry where complete uniformity of results is essential. Sometimes, however, after a clay body has been used for considerable time, difficulties in production and firing may appear which were unnoticed at first, and minor adjustments may be needed to correct the body. In such a situation a rational attack on the problem, based on the known properties of the material, may save a great deal of time.

6. Clay Bodies Designed for Particular Methods of Making

Not only must clay bodies be designed for a particular firing temperature so as to give, at that temperature, the desired color, texture, and degree of hardness and density required; but they must also be designed for particular methods of making. Clay may be shaped into objects either by modeling, throwing, jiggering, pressing, dry pressing, or slip casting in molds. Each of these methods of shaping demands certain physical properties in the clay. For example, a clay for throwing on the wheel must be very plastic; while for modeling or pressing, much less plasticity is required and may, in fact, be a hazard because of the excessive shrinkage of highly plastic clay. Some clays which are quite adequate for some processes will not work at all for others. It is unlikely, for example, that a clay which casts well will be good for wheel work.

7. Throwing Clays

In throwing, we make extreme demands on the plasticity of clay. A really good throwing clay should not take on water too readily while being worked, and should stand well and hold its shape even when soft and thin in section. While it is possible to throw simple forms from very granular and non-plastic clays, the complete range of possible thrown shapes demands a dense, highly plastic, and cohesive clay, with just enough rough material in it to furnish a slight "tooth" to aid the clay in standing while wet and soft at the end of the throwing operation. In throwing clays, we must be prepared to accept a high shrinkage and some tendency towards warping, and the ware must be carefully managed in drying and firing.

As a general rule, throwing bodies are made with as small a percentage as possible of non-plastic substances in them, such as flint and feldspar. A single, naturally occurring clay may be an excellent one for throwing, and such clays are not unusual, especially in earthenware types of clay. If such natural bodies are unavailable, a combination of several plastic clays of various kinds may do as well. Ball clay is almost always used to increase plasticity. When the proportion of ball clay rises to about 50 percent, however, trouble with shrinkage and drying may begin, and the body may become unpleasantly sticky.

Adding flux to a throwing body is something of a problem, because non-plastic powders—such as feldspar, talc, or frit—may seriously decrease the plasticity. If a dark-burning clay is desired, the difficulty may be overcome by adding a red clay of low fusibility and high plasticity, which acts as a flux.

Although throwing clay must be plastic and dense, every thrower discovers that a clay which is too smooth and fine-grained throughout will not stand up in large or tall forms. For making such forms, and especially for pieces which are to be more than about 12 inches high, a clay with some "tooth" to it is necessary. Grog or coarse clay in a throwing body seems to give it the necessary bones or structure to make it stand up. It has been found that grog which has been sized to pass the 30-mesh screen and to stay on the 80-mesh screen is the most suitable for throwing clay. If the grog is too fine, it decreases plasticity and makes the clay wet too rapidly, and if, on the other hand, the grog is too large in grain size, it makes the clay excessively abrasive to the hands. A rough fire clay or ground flint clay may be added to throwing bodies in place of, or in addition to, grog. In general, about 8 to 10 percent of granular material will much improve the performance of a throwing clay. If more than 10 percent of grog is present, it may be found that the clay wets too rapidly during throwing and is insufficiently plastic.

A potter can make only so large or tall a pot with any given clay. Each clay body will reach a point where it will not stand in a higher cylinder, but will slump down. No matter how skillful the thrower is, he cannot achieve a taller piece than his material will allow in structural strength. It is for this reason that the skilled thrower is very much concerned with his clay. He wants a material which will allow him to achieve the full range of form and scale which his skill permits. And once accustomed to a certain clay, the potter may find it difficult to throw well with any other. It is true that many beginning pottery students struggle along with clay mixtures which the most skilled thrower would find impossible to manage, and in ignorance they tend to blame themselves rather than the material for their failures. The right clay body for wheel-work is very important, and a large part of the creative pleasure in throwing pottery lies in the possession of a dense, fat, well-aged, and responsive clay.

Bentonite may be added to a clay to improve its workability on the wheel. Bentonite swells and forms a gel when wet, and the presence of a small amount of it in a clay body will greatly increase plasticity. If more than about 2 percent of bentonite is used, however, the clay may become excessively sticky and be difficult to wedge. Too much bentonite also may cause drying trouble.

8. Modeling Clays

Making clay mixtures which will be good for modeling is a relatively simple problem. Since modeled objects such as sculptures, tiles, architectural pieces, or large built-up pots are usually rather thick, a clay is required which will dry out rapidly and safely with little danger of cracking. The clay must also fire safely, especially during the initial stages of heating when water is being driven from the clay. A large amount of grog brings about these necessary properties in a modeling clay. Twenty to 30 percent of grog is the usual amount. The grog may be coarse or smooth, depending on the textural effect desired, or a coarse fire clay may be used instead of, or in addition to, grog. Some coarse fire clays by themselves make splendid modeling clays. Some processes, such as building intricate shapes in coils or ropes of clay, or the making of extreme shapes may call for considerable plasticity as well as for coarse texture. Mixtures of very plastic clay, such as ball clay, with coarse material, such as fire clay and grog, may give the right degree of plasticity without unduly increasing shrinkage or making drying and firing difficult. A small percentage of bentonite, up to 2 or 3 percent, has been found useful in giving added cohesiveness and "stand" to a modeling clay. Modeling clay which is too smooth and greasy can be very unpleasant to work with, and even a small amount of experience will make the modeler appreciate a good, rough-textured, plastic clay which can be finished off either smoothly by pressing or burnishing-in the grog, or roughly by scraping the surface.

9. Casting Clays

A clay body which will cast well must be designed with the physical nature of casting slips taken into account. The process of casting requires a fluid suspension of clay in water, which will flow readily but which will not settle in the molds. The clay slip must pour smoothly from the mold, leaving a surface which is free from lumps or roughness. Furthermore, pieces which are cast must not wet the mold unduly, must release themselves from the mold upon drying, and must not have an excessive shrinkage or warpage.

An ordinary mixture of clay and water will not cast well in a plaster mold. For one thing, a great deal of water is required to make clay flow as a liquid suspension. Usually it takes about as much water as clay, by weight, to make a slip. Such a slip, although it will flow, has the serious disadvantage of a tendency to settle, leaving water at the top and a heavy sludge at the bottom. Also when such a slip is drained out of the mold, it will leave a roughness and lumpiness where the excess clay has drained away. Upon drying, the piece is very apt to stick to the mold in spots and to shrink and warp excessively because of the high water content of the clay.

Casting, then, would not be a practical way of making pots unless there were some way of cutting down on the amount of water required to make a fluid slip. The process which achieves this result is known as deflocculation. When clay and water are mixed together to form a slip, they are said to be in a flocculent condition. That is, the minute grains of clay are gathered together in clumps or "flocks," and each grain of clay, instead of floating separately by itself in the water and thus flowing easily over and around its neighboring particles, is drawn into a globule of many particles. These "flocks" or clumps of clay grains require a lot of water, relatively, to make them flow.

The tendency of clay particles to draw together into groups when suspended in water can be explained by electric attraction.

In order to decrease the amount of water needed in the clay slip, it is necessary to disperse the clay particles, to break up the flocks, so that each particle of clay is floating by itself. This is accomplished by adding to the clay some substance—usually an alkali such as sodium silicate or soda ash—which is known as an electrolyte. An electrolyte has the effect of changing the electrical charge on some of the particles of clay and thus causing them to repel each other and to float individually in the water rather than clinging together in groups.

In practice a very small amount of electrolyte, or deflocculant, is necessary to prepare a casting slip. About one-third to one-half of one percent of the weight of the clay will usually be sufficient. The most commonly used deflocculants are sodium silicate and soda ash. Sodium silicate is the familiar "Water glass." It is a compound of soda and silica which is made by fusing the two into a glass, which is then dissolved in water by heat and pressure. The relative amounts of silica and soda and the amount of water present in sodium silicate vary, and various brands will have different formulas. It is well always to use the same type of sodium silicate to be sure of consistent results in deflocculation. The sodium silicate is weighed out in a beaker, rather than measured, even though it is a liquid. Soda ash, which is also commonly used as a deflocculant, is a crystalline powder, readily soluble in water. It may be weighed out and then dissolved in the water with which the slip is to be made. It is common to use a combination of both soda ash and sodium silicate, in about equal parts, for deflocculating slips.

When a deflocculant is used in making a slip, very much less water is necessary to make a smooth-flowing liquid suspension. Whereas in a mixture of clay and water, about equal parts of each by weight are required to make a slip, in a deflocculated slip, something less than half this amount of water will be needed. Most casting slips contain from 35 to 50 percent of water to the weight of the clay, by weight. This amount of water, if no deflocculant is used, is barely enough to make a clay plastic enough to model. It is quite surprising what a potent effect a small amount of deflocculant has upon the physical nature of a mixture of clay and water.

The usual casting slip, then, has about 35 to 50 parts of water to the dry ingredients by weight, and about one-third of one percent of deflocculant by weight of the dry ingredients. In other terms, 100 parts of clay would require 35 to 50 parts of water and one-third of a part of deflocculant. In mixing a casting slip, the best procedure is to weigh out the water and the dry ingredients first. Then the deflocculant is carefully weighed out and added to the water and stirred until it is thoroughly dissolved. Then the dry ingredients are gradually added, mixing continuously. Unless the deflocculant is first dissolved in the water, the mass of clay may remain so heavy as to make mixing impossible, even when all the water is added.

Although sodium silicate and soda ash are the most commonly used deflocculants, others are sometimes used. Sodium hydroxide is a strong deflocculant, but it has the disadvantage of being caustic and must be carefully handled. Sodium pyrophosphate, which is usually sold as a wetting agent or cleaning aid, may be used. Tetra-sodium pyrophosphate, another soda compound, has been found to be effective in deflocculating some clays which do not seem to respond to other deflocculants. Sodium tannate, an organic compound, is also sometimes used.

Some clays do not deflocculate at all and cannot be used in casting slips. Common surface clays containing considerable iron or free alkali are usually difficult, if not impossible, to make into practical casting slips. The more pure clays, such as kaolin and ball clay, usually can be readily deflocculated and make good casting slips. Many buff-burning stoneware clays and fire clays also deflocculate and cast well.

To determine the amount of deflocculant and water needed for a clay body to make it into a serviceable slip, the following procedure may be employed. The problem is, of course, to determine the minimum amount of water and the proper amount of deflocculant which will be required. First, the clay body is thoroughly mixed with an excess of water. This serves to thoroughly intermix all the ingredients of the body, such as clay, flint, and feldspar. After mixing, the slip is partially dried out in a plaster vessel and then allowed to become bone-dry. Drying in a dryer or oven at slightly more than 100° will insure complete drying. The dried clay is then pulverized in a mortar to a powder which will pass through the 20-mesh screen. It is next weighed out in 50-gram packets. The test is usually made on a total amount of 500 grams of clay. Water is next measured into a clean bowl. Since we are trying to deflocculate 500 grams of clay, it can be assumed that at least 300 grams of water will be needed, since slips seldom if ever contain a smaller percentage of water than this. The clay is added to the water 50 grams at a time, and each addition is stirred so that it is completely mixed into the water without lumps. After about 250 grams of clay have been stirred in, it will be noted that the mixture is becoming pasty and is no longer fluid. At this point some deflocculant is added. This is accomplished by slowly adding sodium silicate, drop by drop, from a burette. To facilitate the flow of drops of fluid from the burette, the sodium silicate may be reduced in viscosity by mixing it with an equal part of water, thus making a 50-percent solution. After a few drops of the deflocculant have been added, the slip will again become very fluid and more clay can be added until the slip is again too stiff to flow. Then another drop or two of the deflocculant is added. Clay, sodium silicate, and more water are thus added until all the clay has been put into the mixture. Then it can be noted how much sodium silicate is missing from the burette, which is the amount required to deflocculate the given amount of clay. If the amount of water required goes higher than 50 parts of water for each 100 parts of clay, it is not likely that the casting slip will be satisfactory, since the large amount of water causes excessive warping and shrinking, and may make the pieces stick to the molds. If the slip does not deflocculate at all on the first test, but remains thick and non-fluid, some other deflocculant or combinations of deflocculants may be tried. If these do not work, it may be that no matter what deflocculants are used, the particular clay being tested will not make a satisfactory casting slip.

After making a test for deflocculation, it is well to let the slip stand for an hour or more to determine whether or not it has a tendency to gel. If it does, too much or too little deflocculant may have been used. It is important that casting slips remain in a fluid state even when not being stirred. If the trial slip is cast into a small mold, its performance in actual casting may be checked. If the slip drains from the mold, leaving the piece with a smooth, regular interior, it is working well. Sometimes the slip is not fluid enough and leaves bumps, lumps, or "curtains" on the inside of the piece. In this case, its viscosity will have to be adjusted by changing the kind or amount of deflocculant, by increasing the water content, or by altering the formula of the body, substituting, perhaps, clays which are better casters for those which are causing the trouble.

It is sometimes quite difficult to get a slip to behave perfectly in practice, and in large scale manufacture, the condition of the slip is always of concern. Minor adjustments may be necessary after a slip has been thoroughly tested over a period of time by daily use in casting. Sometimes difficulties arise from the alkalinity of the water, from a change in the water, from subtle changes in the clays used, from the moisture content of the dry clays or other materials used, or from mechanical difficulties in mixing and getting the air stirred out of the slip. All these difficulties are of course curable, but it sometimes takes careful and perhaps extended testing to remove the cause of the trouble.

After pottery is cast in molds, there is usually a spare part at the top which must be trimmed away to form the finished edge. The scrap from such trimming is perfectly good clay, and the potter will want to reclaim it and use it again. The trouble is that the scrap has some deflocculant left in it. Not all the deflocculant is there, because some of it migrates into the mold along with the water which is sucked out of the slip during the casting process. It is hard to tell just how much more deflocculant should be added to scrap to make it similar to its original condition. The usual practice is to keep the scrap and add to each new batch of slip a certain amount of scrap, either dry or in the damp state. By rule-of-thumb, it can be determined just how much additional deflocculant should be added to the mix to take care of the deficiency in the scrap.

Cast pieces frequently stick in the molds, which causes warping and cracking. This trouble may be caused by too much water in the slip, or by a combination of materials in the slip which makes it too plastic and sticky. If neither of these conditions is at fault, the trouble must be sought for in the condition of the molds, which may be wet, or may have surfaces which are sealed over with soap, grease, or other foreign matter. Sometimes slips which contain free iron oxide tend to stick in the molds, and if a red slip is wanted, it is better to rely on red-burning natural clays, if possible, rather than on an addition of iron oxide.

Deflocculants have a corrosive effect on plaster molds, and for this reason the less deflocculant a slip contains, the better. The sodium silicate and soda ash penetrate the mold as a solution in the water of the casting slip, and they tend to stay in the mold, except for some of the material which forms as a delicate fuzz on the surface of the mold when it dries. The surfaces of the molds are, of course, subject to mechanical wear in addition to the chemical deterioration caused by the deflocculant, and for this reason molds cannot be expected to last beyond a certain number of casts. Some new and more permanent material for molds would be a blessing to the pottery industry, but no such material has as yet appeared to displace plaster of Paris.

Different casting slips will vary in the length of time required to make a casting of normal thickness. Slips which are quite non-plastic and contain a high percentage of flint, feldspar, or other non-clay substances, will cast rapidly. The wall of solid clay which forms on the mold in the case of such non-plastic slips offers little barrier to the flow of water toward the mold, and a thick coating is rapidly formed. On the other hand, slips which are highly plastic will be slow casters. Slips which are too non-plastic are very hard to cast because of their speed, and also because they are difficult to trim, and have so little strength in the leather-hard state that it is difficult to get the pieces out of the molds. More plastic compositions make for more leisurely casting, easy trimming and handling, and a higher percentage of good pieces. The usual casting time for a normal clay and for a vessel with normal thickness is from 10 minutes to one-half hour, depending on the condition of the mold, the type of piece, and the exact thickness desired.

In formulating bodies for slip casting, the factors of deflocculation and casting properties must be taken into account.

Chinese earthenware vase from the Han Dynasty. Many of these noble pots have been found in early Chinese tombs. Their shape suggests that they were made in imitation of bronze vessels. They are glazed with lead glazes, which in many cases have weathered and decomposed, giving a soft, grey green, iridescent surface. *Courtesy of The Smithsonian Institution, Freer Gallery of Art, Washington, D.C.*

Chinese jar from the T'ang Dynasty. This jar, which is made of soft earthenware and glazed with a lead glaze, is notable for its strong swelling form and fine proportion. The glaze is white, green, yellowish brown, and blue. The fluidity of the glaze has caused the colors to fuse together somewhat. *Courtesy of The Smithsonian Institution, Freer Gallery of Art, Washington, D.C.*

Chinese stoneware tea-bowl from the Sung Dynasty. This small bowl, made from a dense brown clay, is glazed with the familiar type of slip glaze known as "Temmoku" or Hare's Fur. Ware of this type was fired in an oxidizing atmosphere to about 1280°. The fluid glaze forms streaks of black and brown and collects in a roll at the bottom of the piece. The rim is finished with metal applied after firing. *Courtesy of The Smithsonian Institution, Freer Gallery of Art, Washington, D.C.*

Chinese stoneware bowl from the Sung Dynasty. This exquisitely shaped bowl is covered with a thick bluish grey-green glaze which has crackled in a wide pattern. The crackle lines are stained brown. The glaze is a high-fired feldspathic type, and its cool color results from the presence of a small amount of iron. *Courtesy of The Smithsonian Institution, Freer Gallery of Art, Washington, D.C.*

Chinese Chun Yao stoneware vase from the Sung Dynasty. The body of this piece is a very dense light grey clay. The glaze, which is thick and opalescent, is a lavender blue splashed with purple. Chun wares of this type were fired to about 1250° or more in a reducing atmosphere, and the colors result from small amounts of iron and copper in the glaze. *Courtesy of The Smithsonian Institution, Freer Gallery of Art, Washington, D.C.*

(below)
Chinese bowl, perhaps from the Ming Dynasty. This beautifully shaped and decorated pot is made from a hard grey stoneware clay. The fish decoration is carried out with great freedom in brush strokes of black and brown slips, covered with a simple stoneware glaze. *Courtesy of The Smithsonian Institution, Freer Gallery of Art, Washington, D.C.*

Since casting does not require any manipulation of clay in a plastic state, the plasticity of the clay can be very much less than that required for bodies which are to be thrown. Actually, too much plasticity in a casting clay can be a source of difficulty. In practice, casting bodies usually have not much more than 50 percent of clay in them, the rest being made up of non-plastic materials such as flint, feldspar, and other fluxes. Some ball clay, however, is usually necessary in a slip to ensure adequate dry strength and to make trimming and handling easy. Clays are selected which are known to cast well, and some clays which might be otherwise desirable may have to be passed up because they cannot be made to deflocculate. Other than the factors of plasticity, castability, and the balance between plastic and non-plastic ingredients, the usual principles prevail in the formulation of casting bodies. A body which casts well is usually not plastic enough for throwing; but frequently a body can be made which will cast well, and which will also press and jigger well.

10. Bodies for Jiggering and Pressing

If objects are to be made on the jigger wheel, the clay body must be of medium plasticity and must dry with minimum shrinkage and warpage. Pieces are usually left on the mold after jiggering, and the drying shape must accommodate itself to a new position on the mold as it dries and shrinks to a smaller size. This requires a clay of some toughness, yet one which does not shrink excessively. A blend between the ball clays on the one hand and the more non-plastic kaolins, stoneware clays, or earthenware clays on the other, will give the desired properties for any given process or system of drying. In arriving at a suitable jiggering clay, there is no substitute for trial-and-error testing. There is no way of predicting beforehand exactly what any given combination of clays will do when subjected to a particular process, such as jiggering.

Bodies which are to be pressed from plastic clay may be considerably less plastic than those bodies which are to be formed by jiggering. In pressing, the clay must be soft enough to flow into the cavity of the mold while under pressure, but the plasticity of the clay is not much of a factor, except inasmuch as plasticity and strength are related. Pressed ware is commonly handled immediately after pressing and must be strong enough to retain its shape.

11. Color and Texture in Clay Bodies

Fired clay may range in color from pure white or grey, through light tans, buff, red or orange-red, through brown and dark brown to black. This range of color, although it is predominantly warm and rather limited in hue, is actually sufficient to give a wide selection of color for various kinds of pottery. In texture, clay may range from the very smooth to the extremely rough. The color and texture of fired clay is very reminiscent of the rocks, sands, and outcroppings of the earth, and in fact the color of ceramic pieces is usually produced by iron oxide, just as the color of the earthy substances around us is produced by iron in one form or another. We respond sympathetically to the color of fired clay because, perhaps, it shares this earthy, or rocky color which we associate with the landscape. Almost everyone has a liking for the simple, honest texture and color of bricks, flower pots and other fired clay objects such as drain tile and red roof tiles. This earthy range of color comes about very easily and naturally in ceramics, and though it is easy, as we shall see, to alter the color of a clay body, the colors of natural clays when fired are more often than not found to be very pleasing.

Almost all clays contain enough iron to give them a slightly warm tone when fired. The pure white clay is certainly the exception, and most of the surface or common clays have enough iron in them to give a pronounced brown, tan, red, or buff when fired. Other coloring oxides are apt to be in clay besides iron, notably manganese, but these are usually in such small quantity that their coloring effect is overwhelmed by the iron. Some clays, however, are so contaminated with iron, manganese, and other metallic oxides that they will fire a very dark brown or black. Most clays fire to a buff, pink, red, or brown.

Not only does the presence of iron have an effect upon the color of the fired clay, but—perhaps as important—the temperature of firing and the atmosphere in the kiln vitally affect the color of the finished piece. For example, one clay might be a light pink color when fired to cone 08. At cone 04 it might be a brick-red color, and at cone 1 it might be a chocolate brown. At cone 6 it might be almost black, and cinder-like in texture. If fired at cone 04 in a reducing atmosphere, the same clay might be black. Any given clay, in other words, will yield a great variety of colors, depending on how it is fired. The effect of reducing or smoky atmospheres on fired clay is dealt with in detail in a later section, but in general, reduction has the effect of bringing out cool rather than warm tones. On clay which has only a small amount of iron, reduction will produce grey or grey to buff colors. Those clays which normally in oxidation burn to a red color will in reduction tend to be black. Or if the atmosphere of the kiln is uneven, the same piece may exhibit colors of black and red resulting from flashing or the partially reducing conditions prevailing near one side or part of a piece. Bricks are sometimes deliberately fired in this way to give a mottled color.

The rich brick-red color of fired clay is possible only when the clay is fired somewhat short of vitrification. When the firing for any given body proceeds to a certain point, the production of glass in the clay body will result in tones of brown, grey-brown, or black, rather than red. In fact, paving brick often show a greenish darkness, because the glassy phase is so colored by iron.

The color of clay may be altered by adding coloring oxides. If darker tones of red or brown are desired, iron oxide may be added. If a light-burning clay is given an addition of 2 to 4 percent of iron oxide, it will burn red or brown. Red iron oxide is usually used for this purpose. One disadvantage is that the iron oxide is very potent in color in the raw body, and the hands, tools, and clothing become stained a deep rust color. Iron oxide acts as a strong flux in clay, and the addition of more than a small percentage of iron may make the body too fusible for the intended temperature. Tests may easily be made to determine just how much iron should be added to get the desired effect.

Black iron oxide may also be used to color clay bodies. It is coarser in particle size than the red iron oxide and may result in a somewhat speckled color in the fired clay. Black iron oxide may not oxidize completely in firing and may result in a somewhat greyed color as compared to the red oxide. It does not have the disadvantage of staining.

If a very dark color or a mottled or speckled appearance is desired, other coloring oxides or combinations of oxides may be used. Combinations of iron oxide and manganese dioxide will give tones of grey-brown, to dark brown or black. About 2 percent of manganese dioxide is enough to darken a clay appreciably. Used alone, manganese dioxide will give grey-brown colors, with more or less prominent specks. This is due to the relatively coarse particle size of the manganese. If very prominent specks or splotches are desired, granular manganese may be used. Manganese ground to pass the 80-mesh screen will be found to be sufficiently coarse to give a very strong speckled color. If a black color is desired, combinations of iron, manganese, copper, and cobalt may be used. The latter two oxides are very strong fluxes and also, being very soluble in glass, will color any glaze which is put over them; and, for these reasons, they must be used sparingly, if at all, in clay bodies. Furthermore, they are expensive. In general, for practical reasons of expense and firing, the amount of coloring oxide added to a clay body should be held to below 3 percent, but in some cases it may rise to as much as 5 percent for special effects. Here, as in compounding most ceramic materials, the nearer one can stay to natural materials, the better the results are apt to be. It is better to use naturally occurring red clay than to doctor up a white clay by putting iron into it.

Sometimes clay bodies which burn to colors of ochre, blue, or green are desired. These colors, especially those which are cool, do not seem very characteristic of the material, but it is possible to tint white-burning clays to a variety of shades by adding coloring oxides. Blues are produced by adding stains prepared from cobalt oxide, greens from copper and chrome, and the like. Color manufacturers furnish body stains prepared for this purpose. They have been widely used in the tableware industry to produce ware which is colored all the way through, so that when a blue plate is chipped, the clay body underneath is blue, which makes the flaw less noticeable.

Texture in clay may be of two sorts: one, the texture which is actually a roughness; and the other, a visual impression of texture which results from broken color, spots, specks, or splotches. If an actual roughness is desired, grog of various sizes may be added to the clay. Grog is clay which has already been fired and then ground into granules. It may be purchased in a variety of types, such as fire clay grog, which is usually buff color, or porcelain grog, which is white. Or grog may be prepared by grinding any fired clay, such as red bricks or specially prepared mixtures. Grog is ground, then screened for size. A grog which will pass the 20-mesh screen is quite coarse and will give a very rough and earthy texture if added to a clay body in the amount of about 15 percent. Grog which will pass the 40-mesh screen could be considered to be of medium size and could be used to give tooth to throwing bodies. Sometimes very coarse grog is used—10-mesh or even bigger—for large terra cottas or for sculptures or other objects where good drying is needed and where a heavy texture is desirable. Rough fire clays, flint clays, or shales may have the same effect as grog in making a rough texture in clay bodies. The fire clays are apt to slake down over a period of time, however; and while the freshly made-up clay may be quite rough because of the presence of a rough fire clay, after the clay has tempered for a month or so, it may be found that the fire clay has softened and that the body has become considerably more smooth. Some fire clays, by themselves, are very excellent workable clays, of a rough and ready sort, for modeling and for certain kinds of pottery. Shale is very hard and slakes only very slowly, if at all. It can be used as a grog if its color and fusibility are right for the intended heat treatment and finished appearance.

Although rough and groggy bodies are obviously not suitable for tableware or for certain other ceramic products, they do have an appeal, both visual and tactile, which makes them a very suitable medium for sculpture, hand-made pottery of various sorts, and for many kinds of useful and ornamental ceramic objects. The effort of potters, historically, has of course been directed towards ever-smoother and more refined clay bodies. This development culminated with the appearance of pure white, vitrified porcelain in China. While this achievement may always remain as an ideal, modern ceramists tend to maintain an open mind about all types of ceramic effects and to use roughness where roughness is called for, either practically or aesthetically.

Texture of a visual sort which is the result of spots or specks can be induced in a clay body by adding coloring oxides in granular form which will burn to a darker color than the surrounding areas of clay. Manganese has already been mentioned in this connection. Also frequently used is ilmenite, which is an ore containing iron and titania. Ilmenite can be purchased in various grit sizes. Material passing the 80-mesh screen will give a prominent black speck to clay. Iron in granular form will also give very prominent specks and splotches. Sometimes rust scrapings, blacksmith's scale, or iron filings are used for this purpose. The size of the iron particles and the temperature of firing will determine the nature of the spots. Another source of black specks may be grog from red brick or shale which, when carried to sufficient temperature, will reach the point of fusion and will produce a strong dark speck. Materials which induce dark specks will, of course, influence the glaze also, especially high-temperature glazes, which are strongly influenced by the clay body beneath them. The amount of material which is added to a clay to bring about specks will depend on what is used and the density or strength of the specks desired. In general, about 2 percent of ilmenite will give a very noticeable effect, and in a high-fired body, about 5 percent of red brick grog will give strong speckled texture. Trials must be made to determine the most suitable composition for any given situation.

White specks may be induced in a clay body by adding a white grog. Porcelain grog is very suitable for this purpose. After the object has been made and before it has been fired, it may be necessary to sponge, sandpaper, or scrape the surface to reveal the white grog; otherwise the grog will remain covered, even at the surface, by a thin film of clay and will not be noticeable. The combination of black and white specks in a brown or grey clay may give extremely handsome textures which are akin to granite.

As in the case of colors in clay bodies, those textures which occur naturally seem the most pleasing in the finished product. Specks, for example, which are too prominent and too evenly spaced and too unrelated to the other colors of body and glaze will surely have an artificial appearance. This kind of contrived texture is often noticeably out of place on low-fired ware which is being made to simulate high-fired stoneware. The virtues of each material and of each process and firing temperature had best be allowed to speak for themselves.

12. Earthenware

Earthenware is usually fired at temperatures below cone 6, and the fired clay remains somewhat porous and open in structure. The vast majority of the world's pottery has been earthenware because of the wide prevalence of earthenware clay and the relative ease of reaching, in the kiln, the temperatures necessary to fire it.

Earthenware bodies are usually made up of common red- or buff-burning clays, with only enough other materials added to achieve good working and firing properties. In almost every part of the world there are clays readily available which serve quite well for making earthenware, and the abundance of such clays partly accounts for the fact that man has depended everywhere upon pottery for the utensils of daily life. Common red clay is usually quite plastic and suitable for modeling, hand-building, throwing, pressing, or any process which makes use of the plastic clay in forming. The presence of iron oxide in nearly all of the secondary clays found near the surface of the ground accounts for the typical buff, brown, tan, or red color of earthenware clays, and also accounts for the relatively low temperatures which are needed to make sound, serviceable ware from it.

In formulating bodies for earthenware, the best plan is to rely largely on one natural clay. Most of the common red clays fire to a fairly dense and hard state in the range from cone 06 to cone 1. The first step is to locate a good source of supply for such a clay. Many ceramic supply houses sell common red clay which is serviceable for earthenware. However, the cost of such clay, especially if it must be freighted for a long distance, may make it advisable to look into local sources. If one is willing to do the work, red clay can be located and dug in most localities. Or a local brick yard or flower-pot factory may have available an excellent earthenware clay ready for use.

Once a clay has been located, the next step is to test it to find out what its characteristics are. Tests for plasticity, shrinkage, and absorption should be made at the various temperatures. It will then be known what additions must be made to the clay to make it work well with the intended processes and firing temperature. The additions are apt to take one of the following forms:

(1) If the clay is too refractory—that is, if it does not become hard enough at the temperature at which it must be fired—some flux must be added to it. This flux might be iron oxide, talc, or a frit.

(2) If the clay is too fusible and becomes too dense at the intended firing temperature, refractory materials must be added, such as kaolin, ball clay, stoneware clay, flint, fine grog, or fire clay.

(3) If the clay is too sticky and shrinks too much, it will need the addition of more non-plastic material such as flint, kaolin, grog, or fire clay.

(4) If the clay is mealy and not sufficiently plastic, it will need the addition of some more plastic material such as ball clay or bentonite.

(5) If the color of the clay is to be changed, iron or other coloring metallic oxides may be added.

Tests must be made to determine not only the necessity for changes in the clay but also the amount of the additions which will result in the most serviceable earthenware body.

The chart below indicates some typical earthenware body compositions for firing in the range of cone 06 to cone 1. These bodies are based on the following hypothetical red clays, which represent, however, common types.

Red Clay #1. Very plastic and sticky. Fires to a dark brown, very dense mass at cone 04. Total shrinkage at cone 04 is 13%. Absorption at cone 04 is 1.5%.

Red Clay #2. Good plasticity. Fires to a terra cotta color at cone 04. Total shrinkage at cone 04 is 11%. Absorption, 6%.

Red Clay #3. Fair to poor plasticity. Fires to a light buff at 04. Total shrinkage, 8%. Absorption, 13%.

Clay Number One is too plastic and too fusible. Number Two is about right; Number Three is not plastic enough and does not mature sufficiently in the intended range of temperature.

The compositions A, B, C are adjustments designed to correct the red Clay Number One. This clay is, by itself, too plastic and too fusible. It may be adjusted by adding more refractory clays and flint. The compositions D, E, F, and G are based on Clay Number Two, which by itself is close to being satisfactory. In E, a small amount of ball clay is added to increase the plasticity. In F, fire clay is added, which might make the clay better for modeling or for large pieces. In G, both ball clay and some frit are added to make a slightly denser body.

The compositions H, I, J, and K are designed to correct Clay Number Three, which is too lean and does not mature sufficiently in the intended range of temperature. Plastic clay, bentonite, and

	A	*B*	*C*	*D*	*E*	*F*	*G*	*H*	*I*	*J*	*K*
Red clay #1	75	50	75								
Red clay #2				100	90	90	90				
Red clay #3								75	60	50	85
Kaolin	15										
Ball clay					8		5	20	25	25	
Stoneware clay		25									
Fire clay		15	25			10					
Talc										20	
Body frit							5	5	5		10
Flint	10	10									
Bentonite											3
Iron oxide					2					5	2

fluxes are added to overcome the difficulty.

If no red clay is available for making a red earthenware type of body, kaolin, ball clay, and iron oxide may be used, together with some flux to bring the clay into the lower range of temperature. A typical composition for such a clay body might be:

Kaolin	25
Ball clay	30
Body frit	17
Talc	5
Flint	10
Iron oxide	3

The difficulty with compositions of this sort is that when the necessary amount of flux is added, the percentage of plastic material is apt to be too low to make a good clay for throwing. For casting, however, such a mixture might work better than a body made largely from natural red clay. For all plastic processes it is better, simpler, and cheaper to make earthenware clay bodies as nearly as possible from common, natural, red-burning clay.

White or very light earthenware bodies may be made by combining light-burning clays such as kaolin, ball clay, or stoneware clay with suitable fluxes for the intended temperature. In bodies of this type, the problem centers around the type of flux to be employed and the development of sufficient plasticity in spite of the necessarily large amount of non-plastic material. Actually, the number of fluxes which can be used in white earthenware is severely limited. Feldspars, with the exception of nepheline syenite, are too refractory to have much influence on a clay body below about cone 1. In practice, talc, frit, nepheline syenite, or combinations of these must be relied on.

Frits sold for use in clay bodies are usually leadless and of a somewhat higher melting point than glaze frits. The use of frit in a clay is an effective way of making it mature at a low temperature; however, it has the serious disadvantage of shortening the firing range. A natural red clay body may have a comfortable firing range of four or five cones, whereas a body fluxed with a frit may have to be accurately fired to within two cones. If it goes slightly higher in firing, it may warp, slump, and begin to fuse; or, if it is slightly underfired, it may remain too soft and chalky. Another problem in using frit in clay bodies is their tendency to deflocculate slightly when the clay is stored moist over a period of time. Most frits are slightly soluble, and the frit in a clay may dissolve to the extent of releasing enough sodium to cause deflocculation. This causes the plastic clay to become limp, soft, and impossible to form. The tendency may be counteracted by the use of about one-half of one percent of aluminum sulfate or magnesium sulfate in the clay, which tends to neutralize the alkalies which are causing the trouble. But soluble salts added to the clay may bring about other difficulties, such as efflorescence or the forming of scum on the surface of the clay.

Talc has been widely used in commercial clay bodies which are sold for use by hobbyists and schools. With the use of talc, a body can be formulated which is white and which matures at a low temperature and has a long firing range. Talc has the property of forming fairly low-melting compounds with the clay and silica of the body. The only difficulty is that a great deal of talc must be used to make a clay tighten and mature at cone 01 or below, if no other flux such as iron or a frit is present. The result is that talc bodies are relatively non-plastic and are really only suitable for casting. If casting is the only forming process to be employed, however, a talc body may be satisfactory in every way.

Combinations of talc, frit, and nepheline syenite may be used to make low-fired clay bodies of extreme density, or even translucency. If the fluxing ingredients are increased sufficiently, the make white translucent wares in their kilns, which were not capable of attaining the necessary high temperatures for true porcelain. They probably employed ground alkaline frit or soda ash to bring down the fusion point of white clays. None of these attempts to simulate porcelain was very successful.

The following chart indicates typical compositions for white or light buff earthenware to be fired at cone 04.

	A	*B*	*C*	*D*	*E*	*F*	*G*	*H*	*I*
Kaolin	25		25				15	25	
Plastic Florida kaolin	15	25			20		25		40
Ball clay	30	20	25	60	50	60	10	25	10
Stoneware clay		15	10						
Frit	15	10	15			5	10		15
Talc	5	10		40	20	30	20	20	20
Nepheline syenite		10	10		10	5	20	30	15
Flint	10	10	15						

composition may approach that of glass, with, of course, an attendant sacrifice of plasticity in the clay. Low-fired simulations of porcelain may be made from combinations of white-burning clays and fluxes. While pottery made from material of this type may have the virtue of density or possibly translucency, it will not be mistaken for true porcelain because of its glassy and rather cheap appearance. It is interesting that before the discovery in Europe of the method of making true porcelain, the Italian potters attempted to make porcelain by adding ground glass to white clay and firing it at the same low temperatures which they employed for making earthenware. The Persian potters, who admired tremendously the porcelain wares from China, also attempted to

Bodies A, B, and C use combinations of frit, talc, and nepheline syenite for flux. Sufficient ball clay is added to ensure reasonable plasticity. B and C contain some stoneware clay which lends a buff tone to the body. Bodies D, E, and F are talc bodies, with talc used in amounts up to 40 percent. When this much talc is present, the entire remainder of the body is made up of ball clay. Bodies G, H, and I contain a great deal of flux and tend towards a dense glassy structure.

Another type of earthenware body is that employed in the manufacture of inexpensive white tableware. Such bodies are usually fired at cone 2 to cone 5. At this relatively higher temperature, the problem of body composition is simple, and white-burning clays, together with some feldspar, talc, and flint, result in fired ware which, although it is slightly porous and presents no difficulty in firing such as warpage or slumping, yet is reasonably hard and serviceable in use.

Earthenware which is fired in the middle range of temperature, from cone 1 to cone 5, has the virtue of hardness, strength, density, and durability of glaze. In earthenware fired at these temperatures, some of the virtues of stoneware can be achieved, while at the same time the possibility remains of the brilliant and varied color which is typical of lower firing. Since less flux is required in middle-range bodies, plasticity is easier to achieve. In general, there is much to be said for the range of cone 1 to cone 5 as a working temperature for pottery making. On the one hand the softness of glaze characteristic of the lower-fired wares is avoided, and on the other hand the difficulties of high firing, with its attendant wear and tear on kiln and kiln furniture, to say nothing of expense, are avoided. In formulating a dark-burning, middle-range body, as in the case of lower-fired earthenware bodies, it is well to start with a clay which by itself matures at about the right temperature. Middle-range clays of this sort are much rarer than clays which mature at around cone 04, but they can be located or purchased.

The following chart indicates some typical formulas for earthenware bodies in the middle range of temperature, cone 1 to cone 5.

A, B, and C are dark-burning plastic clays. In A, 30 parts of fusible, low-fired red clay are balanced by stoneware clays and ball clay to make a cone 4 body, which burns to a medium red color. In B, a middle-range red clay is used, and is altered only by the addition of some ball clay and flint. In C, a lighter color clay is made by keeping the red clay content at 25 parts and making the stoneware and ball clay total 55 parts. Ten parts of nepheline syenite are added for flux. D is a vitreous white casting body in which nepheline syenite and talc are used together as a flux. E is a commercial-type white earthenware body.

	A	*B*	*C*	*D*	*E*
Common red clay	30		25		
Stoneware clay	25		35		
Middle range red clay		75			
Ball clay	25	15	20	20	20
Kaolin				30	35
Fire clay	10	10			
Flint	10		10	10	20
Nepheline syenite			10	30	10
Talc				10	15

13. Stoneware

Vitreous, grey, buff, or brown ware, fired in the range of cone 6 to cone 14, may be considered stoneware. The name comes, of course, from the dense, hard, impervious character of the body.

In some ways, the formulation of stoneware bodies is simpler than earthenware, because the higher heat makes less flux necessary. As in the case of earthenware, the best solution is to find a good stoneware clay which, by itself, comes near to answering the needs of plasticity, fired density, and color. Many fine stoneware clays are available, particularly in the central and eastern parts of the country. They may be used straight, or altered slightly for more plasticity or for a desired change of color, texture, or glaze fit. A good natural stoneware clay should be plastic enough for throwing; fire to a tan, grey, or light brown color; and bc fairly dense at cone 6.

The relatively higher heat of stoneware firing makes possible the use of feldspar as the principal body flux. Feldspar is an ideal body flux because it has a long firing range, is cheap, and presents no difficulties or hazards.

For texture, grog and fire clays may be used. Some fire clays are actually quite similar to stoneware clay, although they may have a higher firing range and be coarser and less plastic. For rougher types of bodies, combinations of stoneware clays and fire clays are ideal.

When no natural stoneware clay is available, adequate bodies for high firing may be made up from kaolin, ball clay, feldspar, and flint, with iron oxide or red clay added for color. Such bodies, however, may lack the plastic quality of a natural stoneware body.

Fired stoneware should have an absorption of 3 percent or less. At its best, it is dense and impervious and has a rich earthy color and texture.

The following chart gives some typical cone 8-10 plastic stoneware compositions:

	A	*B*	*C*	*D*	*E*	*F*
Stoneware clay	80	75	40	30		20
Sagger clay			20			
Ball clay	10	15	20	30	30	15
Kaolin					40	25
Red clay				10	5	
Feldspar	10	10	10		15	20
Flint			10		10	20
Fire clay				30		

Body A is largely of stoneware clay, with only enough ball clay and feldspar added to improve the plasticity a little, and to make the clay fire to a denser mass. E is similar, but somewhat morc plastic because of the increased ball clay. C is a somewhat less plastic clay in which sagger clay has been used and 10 parts of flint are added to ensure glaze fit. D is a rough type of body with a large percentage of rough fire clay. E is a stoneware body which relies mainly on kaolin and ball clay instead of on stoneware clay for its plasticity, and which is colored by a small addition of red clay. F is a stoneware body designed for casting or jiggering.

14. Porcelain

Porcelain is a vitreous whiteware of more or less translucency fired to cone 9 or more. It is made by combining white-burning clays with feldspars and flint. The relatively high heat acting upon the fluxes in the clay results in a dense, impervious body which approaches glass.

Compounding porcelain bodies is actually quite simple since the ingredients are few and the best proportioning of the ingredients is well established in practice. The main difficulty is that, if only pure and white-burning clays such as the kaolins are used, the clay body is so non-plastic that it is hard to make anything out of it even by casting.

The proportion of five parts of clay, three parts of feldspar, and two parts of flint may be taken as the starting point in formulating porcelain bodies. The clay must be divided between kaolin and ball clay to make the body workable. If extreme whiteness is not desired, more ball clay may be used, and the body as a result will "pot" with less difficulty.

Usually, in the interests of uniformity in case slight changes occur in the composition of the clays, several kaolins are used. If a soft feldspar such as nepheline syenite is used, less of it will be needed to bring about translucency. The flint content may vary, but if it exceeds about 25 percent, dunting may result. The proportioning of the materials depends, of course, on the exact firing temperature, and a body designed for firing at cone 14 will have a good deal less feldspar in it than one designed for cone 9.

Some kaolins, particularly those from certain parts of Florida, are relatively plastic, and the use of these clays helps in the formulation of porcelain bodies which are white and yet reasonably workable. The exceptionally iron-free kaolins from England and from Georgia in the United States tend to be quite non-plastic. Since some ball clay is necessary, the selection of the kind is critical, since ball clays vary a great deal, both in plasticity and in iron content. English ball clay is perhaps the best for porcelain since it is both highly plastic and relatively iron-free. English ball clay contains considerable carbon, which must be screened out before the clay is used.

Some typical porcelain compositions are given below:

	A	*B*	*C*	*D*	*E*	*F*
Georgia kaolin	35	25	25	5	30	25
Florida kaolin	10	15		40	15	15
English ball clay	5	10	25		15	10
Kentucky ball clay				10		
Feldspar	30	30	25		20	
Nepheline syenite				25		30
Flint	20	20	25	20	20	20

A is a very white cone 10 to cone 11 body. Its small ball clay content makes for low plasticity. B is essentially the same body but modified by an increase in the ball clay which makes for better workability but some sacrifice of whiteness. C is composed of equal parts kaolin, ball clay, feldspar, and flint. Although somewhat grey in fired color, it casts and trims well. In D, plasticity is partly achieved by a high percentage of Florida kaolin. E is a body for cone 12 to cone 14. It has a smaller than usual percentage of feldspar. F is designed to mature at cone 9 and relies on nepheline syenite instead of feldspar for flux.

Sometimes, in addition to the materials used for the above bodies, a small amount of lime is introduced into porcelain bodies to act as an auxiliary flux or catalyst. One or 2 percent of whiting or dolomite may be used for this purpose.

In oxidation, porcelain bodies tend to be creamy white in color. When fired in reduction, the small amount of iron present in the body gives a blue-grey tinge, which, like bluing in the wash, gives the appearance of brilliant white.

Bodies which are used commercially for the production of vitreous china are essentially the same as porcelain bodies. In the manufacture of china the body of the ware is matured in a first firing, without glaze. In this bisque firing, since the ware is not glazed, it can be supported by special refractory setters, or by nesting in silica sand, and this prevents much of the warping or deformation which would otherwise occur. The ware is glazed in a second firing at about cone 4, usually with a lead boro-silicate glaze. In true porcelain, as distinguished from china, the body and the glaze are both matured in a high firing. This means that the ware must survive the high fire without support from refractory setters, and one of the difficulties of making porcelain is that the body, as it nears maturity, becomes so soft and glass-like that warping and slumping are very apt to occur. Careful design of the shapes and careful setting and firing will get around most of the difficulty, but losses in porcelain making are inevitably high. The advantage of true porcelain is that not only is the body vitreous and translucent, but the glaze is very hard, scratchproof, and lustrous, and the contact between glaze and body is so intimate and so indistinct that the glaze, instead of appearing as a glassy coating, appears as an integral part of the body.

Although porcelain can be made to cast and jigger well, it is very difficult to achieve a porcelain body which will be good for throwing. This is due to the inherently non-plastic character of white clays. If sufficient ball clay is put in the body to make a highly plastic clay such as is needed for wheel work, the fired result will be cream color or grey rather than white. Bentonite also, when it is used to increase plasticity, makes the body grey. The following body, designed for throwing, indicates the kind of compromise which must be made to obtain plasticity:

English china clay	10
Florida kaolin	20
Tennessee ball clay	26
Feldspar	24
Flint	20

If a white body is to be used for throwing, it should be made up well in advance to allow for aging, which may make a considerable difference. Since white clays, even at their best, are far from being as plastic as the darker clays, it is well to confine the thrown shapes to simple ones of modest size. If extreme thinness and translucency are desired, the pots can be trimmed down when leather-hard to the proper cross-section. To avoid warping in thrown porcelain, very careful handling and drying are necessary. And in making any kind of porcelain, great care must be taken to prevent contamination with iron or other impurities which would cause specks. All the utensils used must be clean. When dark clays are being used in the same work-rooms where porcelain is being made, it may prove impossible to keep the white clay clean.

15. Oven-proof Bodies

Pottery is serviceable for use in cooking in the oven, and casseroles, bean-jars, warming pots, and other cooking ware have the advantage of being inexpensive, durable, and of keeping food warm for a long time. Pottery cooking vessels may be not only serviceable but handsome enough in appearance to use at the table.

Pottery intended for use in the oven must be made so it will not crack from the heat shock of being placed in a hot oven, or of being taken out of the oven and suddenly cooled to room temperature. Actually, most earthenware and stoneware will serve quite well for oven use, especially if it is not subjected to any unusual heat shock such as would result from placing it directly over a flame, or cooling it suddenly by placing it in water while it is still hot.

One type of body which has proved to be very durable for cooking is an open, porous, non-vitreous, or underfired body. Soft ware of this sort is loose enough to accommodate itself to the expansion and contraction which result from heating and cooling. French provincial cooking ware and most Mexican pottery are of this type and can be safely placed over a low charcoal fire. While such ware is not apt to crack during use in cooking, it does have the disadvantage of porosity, and usually also of having a glaze which is crazed and which thus permits liquids and grease to permeate the body of the ware. It is very difficult to fit a glaze to a soft, underfired clay body.

Most stoneware which is glazed with a fitting glaze is suitable for use in the oven. If the body is overfired, however, and is extremely vitreous and dense, it may be more subject to cracking from sudden heat shock than bodies which are more open. In vitrified or semi-vitrified ware, there may be residual strains in the body resulting from the volume adjustments which occur during the cooling of the kiln. Such strains, which may cause breakage later in oven use, are more apt to be present in clay bodies which have a high flint content, because silica, as it cools, contracts as it forms a new crystalline form in cooling past about 573°. For this reason, clay bodies which are low in flint may be more resistant to thermal shock than bodies which contain considerable flint.

Sometimes pieces which are glazed on the inside only, or are more heavily glazed on the inside than the outside, will crack when used in the oven. This is caused by the expansion of the glaze which exerts a compression on the inside of the piece sufficient to break it. Such breaking is more apt to occur if the glaze is already in a state of compression, and in fact most glazes which fit a clay body without crazing are under some compression. In all ware intended for cooking, it is wise to avoid glazes which are excessively thick, unevenly applied, or applied to the inside of the piece only. The problem of glaze fit is discussed in a later section.

Pottery is ordinarily not suited for use in cooking directly over the flame. The sudden and uneven heating will crack the body of the piece. An exception to this is the type of porcelain which is made for use in laboratory work. Ware of this type is fired at cone 14 or higher and is composed of flint, feldspar, and clays in a vitrified condition. The flint becomes, in the high firing, more or less fused into vitreous silica, which does not have the adverse effect on resistance to heat shock that crystalline silica has. Another factor in such high-fired porcelains which gives them exceptional resistance to heat shock is the presence in them of considerable mullite, which forms as crystals in the body, during firing. These mullite crystals serve to knit the body together and prevent it from breaking from the sudden expansion of heating. Another example of this type of body is the porcelain used in spark plugs for gasoline engines. The ceramic part of the spark plug is subject to the sudden heat of combustion in the cylinder, yet it does not break.

Chapter 7

Mining and Preparing Clay

1. Prospecting

Although the present work is obviously not the place for an exhaustive description of clay mining and prospecting, a few words on the subject may be of interest, especially to those who wish to make use of resources which lie close at hand. One of the valuable things about ceramics, especially from the viewpoint of teaching, is that the raw materials are very common and can usually be found, processed, and used without recourse to outside suppliers or commercial processors. It would seem desirable, furthermore, that everyone who is seriously interested in ceramics should have the experience of finding, digging out, and using a native clay. Such an experience, although it may have no commercial implications, is bound to give the potter a broader viewpoint in dealing with his materials.

The occurrence of clay is so widespread that finding beds of clay is quite easy in most localities. However, one must know how to look. Clay is ordinarily covered over with loam and topsoil which conceal it. This is particularly true in areas of ample rainfall where the ground is normally completely covered with vegetation of one sort or another. In drier country, the earth may be more exposed, and clay may be found at the surface.

The most likely place to look is usually some spot where the earth has been cut through, revealing some of the underlying strata. Along creeks and rivers, or where highway or railroad grading has cut down into the earth, one can find the layers of clay that so frequently underlie the topsoil. Clay may be recognized by the irregular and rather crumbly surface produced in its exposed faces by the rain. Outcroppings of rock tend to hold their shape, whereas clay is very rapidly disintegrated and washed down by water.

If one suspects that an outcropping is clay, closer inspection and a few simple field tests will quickly determine whether it is clay or not. If a small sample is mixed with a bit of water and it produces a plastic sticky mass, it is undoubtedly clay. If, on the other hand, the resulting mixture remains sandy and non-plastic, the material may be sandy loam or some mixture of sand and clay, with the former predominating.

Beds of clay may be revealed during the excavation for buildings, or when land is being plowed or graded. Or flood conditions may deepen or widen stream channels, revealing clay beds whose presence was not suspected before. If one is searching for clay, expert advice may be sought from local well-drillers who usually have a wealth of data on what kind of strata underlies a particular region. Or a geologist may be consulted. State geologists can sometimes be of real help in locating good clay. For many regions of the country, extensive geological and mineral resource studies have been published which may indicate the presence of usable clay in various places.

When some clay has been located, the next step is to determine of what use it might be in ceramics. Many clays, if not most, are not suitable for any practical purpose. For example, a clay which is too highly contaminated with soluble alkalies is not worth the digging. The presence of these soluble impurities can usually be detected by scum or white staining on the dried clay. If a small piece of clay is wet down to the plastic state and then allowed to dry out, the presence of a noticeable scum on the surface, or of discoloration, usually indicates the presence of undesirable alkalies. Another impurity which disqualifies a clay for ceramic use is lime. Lime or bits of limestone cannot be tolerated in a clay, because when lime is fired it is altered from calcium carbonate to calcium oxide. Calcium oxide is an unstable oxide in the atmosphere, because it takes on water or hydrates. This hydration, which will go on slowly even in a small lump of limestone buried in a fired clay object, causes the lime to swell. The swelling exerts an irresistible pressure against the fired clay which surrounds the bit of lime and the piece will break, or a flake of clay will break off, revealing the troublesome impurity. Bits of plaster of Paris in fired clay cause the same difficulty. This breaking or flaking off will occur within a few days or months after firing, depending on how porous the clay body is and on the humidity to which it is exposed. It is extremely difficult to extract lime from clay, especially if the lime is in small particles; if a clay contains lime, it is better to look for another one which does not. A simple test will reveal the presence of lime in clay. A sample of clay is dropped into a beaker containing a 50-percent solution of hydrochloric acid. If lime is present, an effervescence or bubbling will be noted.

Even if a clay is not contaminated with either soluble alkalies or with lime, it may be difficult to use because of the presence of too much sand or other mineral fragments. Such granular material can be screened out of the clay, but it may be found that it is not worth the trouble, especially if another clay can be located which is freer of impurities.

The presence of too much organic matter may also disqualify a clay for use. Surface clays are sometimes so loaded with carbonaceous matter and decayed vegetation that they are unusable. If a clay is excessively sticky when wet it is probably impractical for this reason, especially if it is dark brown or black.

Clay in the natural state may be grey, tan, red, greenish, brown or brown-black, or white. Color in the raw clay indicates the presence of either iron oxide or carbonaceous matter. The great majority of clays contain considerable iron, and any clay which, in the raw state, is grey, brown, red, yellow, or greenish may be expected to fire to a red color. The variety of color in raw clay is due to the presence of iron in different forms. Iron which is present as hematite, or red iron oxide, will produce a red color. Limonite will give a yellow color; while ferrous iron will produce greys, greens, and blacks. All these forms of iron become hematite upon firing and produce the familiar red, tan, or brown color of fired clay. Most surface clays contain from 2 to 5 percent of iron oxide, and for this reason, they cannot ordinarily be fired to temperatures above about cone 1. If the iron content is below 2 percent, the clay may be usable as a stoneware or hard earthenware clay at temperatures in excess of cone 1.

If a clay in the raw state is white or very light in color, it may be assumed that it has little iron in it and that it will fire to a light color. Such white-burning clays are usually primary or residual clays and would be more apt to occur in pockets rather than in strata. White clays are almost always of a non-plastic kind and are frequently found intermingled with considerable sand or other mineral fragments.

The degree of plasticity of a clay can best be tested by using it in whatever process is intended. One simple test is to wet the clay into a plastic mass, then to make a little rope of it about the thickness of a pencil. If such a coil of clay can be bent into a ring of an inch or less in diameter without showing cracks, the clay is reasonably plastic. If a small amount of clay is put into the mouth and does not grit on the teeth excessively, it can be assumed to be very fine-grained. It is recommended that this test be used with restraint!

Clay is mined commercially either in open-strip mining or in underground mining of seams or strata below the surface of the earth. In strip mining, the clay is scraped, dug, or planed off by power machines. Terraces are maintained which give access to the clay. Kaolins are frequently mined hydraulically, streams of water under pressure being used to dislodge the clay from the deposit and to wash it into settling ponds.

If clay is to be dug for small-scale use, the bed or seam of clay must first be uncovered and all soil, sand, or rock shoveled back so it will not get into the clay. Then the clay is dug out with a small sharp spade. Even if only a relatively small amount of clay is needed, it is well to select, if possible, a source which is not likely to be soon exhausted. Also it is well to try to establish one's digging at a place where the clay is uniform in color and texture over some considerable area, so that uniform results can be expected from various batches which are dug. Sometimes beds or strata of clay are tilted vertically, so that although only a fairly narrow seam of clay shows at the surface, a great deal of usable material lies below. Digging clay is hard work, particularly if the clay is damp.

The following tests are suggested to determine the usefulness of a clay. Some of these tests are described in the Appendix.

1. Test for soluble impurities.
2. Test for excess sand or other mineral fragments.
3. Test for the presence of lime.
4. Test for plasticity.
5. Test for water of plasticity and for dry shrinkage.
6. Fire samples to various temperatures to determine the possible firing range of the material, and its fired color. Cones 08, 04, 1, 4, and 9 might be suitable intervals for the first tests.
7. Test for shrinkage and absorption on samples fired to various temperatures.
8. Deflocculation test.

The accumulated data from these tests, together with the experience gained from working samples of the clay in modeling and perhaps on the potter's wheel, should give an informed estimate of the value of the clay. Of course, clay which is good for one thing is worthless for some other purpose. For instance, clay which would be ideal for making common bricks would be quite unsuitable for wheel-thrown pottery. Most deposits of clay are of little or no commercial value. This is because of the abundance of the material and the cost of transporting common clay any distance from where it is mined. However, large commercial deposits of kaolin and ball clays are very valuable.

In testing clay to determine whether it can be used or not, it is not usually necessary to make a chemical analysis. While such an analysis may be essential in determining and controlling the composition of commercial clay, the physical nature of the clay and its reaction to firing are much more important to the ceramist. Chemical analysis rarely gives any surprising data which could not have been guessed at by an experienced person who had actually worked with the material.

In most situations, it is preferable, in the long run, to buy clay from suppliers rather than to dig it. The man-hours spent in digging, screening, and mixing clay by hand are usually not justified, even considering the relatively high cost of clay and freight.

2. Mixing Clay

No involved or complicated procedures are required in preparing clay for use. As a material, it is essentially readied by nature and needs only to be mixed with the right amount of water and cleaned of foreign matter, such as sand or rocks.

Where two or more materials are to be mixed together to form a clay body, or where the clay must be screened to remove impurities, it is best to first mix the clay with an excess of water. Water is put into a barrel, vat, bucket, or other container of a suitable size, and the clay is added to the water. Adding the clay to the water, rather than the water to the clay, ensures that each particle of clay gets thoroughly wet and does not ball up into a sticky mass of partly wet, partly dry clay, as would be the case if water were poured on dry clay. If a clay body is being made which contains both clay and non-plastic material such as flint, it is best to add the clay first, so that it can slake in a maximum amount of water. If the clay is in lump form, it will take some time and considerable stirring to break down and disperse the lumps. Enough water should be used to produce a fluid slip about the consistency of thick cream.

Mechanical mixers for clay are of two types. The blunger is a mixing machine which has paddles which revolve at slow speeds, keeping the slip under constant but not violent agitation. Sometimes two sets of revolving paddles are employed to increase the turbulence. The other type is the propeller mixer, which is made up of a propeller not unlike that of a marine screw, which revolves at relatively high speed and agitates the slip violently in one area of the mixing vessel. Such a mixer works exactly like a malted-milk mixer, and is extremely rapid and efficient in making slip from clays which have no very large lumps in them. If the material to be mixed is lumpy, such as would be the case with clay which one had dug out of the ground, the slower action of the blunger is to be preferred. The blunger will take very coarse and lumpy material and, by agitating it gently in the water over a period of time, will produce a thorough mixture.

For small batches, clay may be mixed by hand with a paddle or stick. This goes faster than one might think, but a machine is certainly desirable to do the work. Or an old washing machine may be used. The back-and-forth swishing action of a washing machine is quite efficient in mixing clay.

If the clay slip must be screened to remove granular impurities, this can be done after the fluid slip is thoroughly mixed and smooth. Two barrels or containers are convenient; the slip is poured from one barrel, through a screen, into the other barrel. Screens of various mesh sizes can be used. For most clays a screening through the 60-mesh screen will remove all objectionable matter. Porcelain bodies, or whiteware bodies which must be of great purity, may be screened through a 100-mesh screen, or one even finer. Screening removes not only the sand and rock fragments which may be in the clay but also the bits of lignite or carbon.

When the slip has been screened, some or all of the water must be removed. This is a troublesome problem, even where the best equipment is available. If plastic clay is desired, enough water must be removed from the clay to bring it to a stiff, plastic condition. If casting slip is to be made, it may be best to remove all the water, so that a carefully proportioned mix can be made for the deflocculated slip. One simple way to remove a good deal of the water from slip is by settling. If the slip is allowed to sit in the barrel for several days, the clay goes to the bottom and clear water will rise to the top. The water may then be siphoned off, leaving the relatively heavier slip in the barrel. This process, though effective, may take more time than is available. Plaster of Paris bats, or drying vessels, may be used to suck off the excess water. Plaster is very absorbent and draws the water rapidly from the slip. For small batches, this method works very well. The difficulty is that the drying bats soon become soaked with water. Also, putting the clay into and taking it out of the bats can be a rather messy job. Sometimes one large plaster vessel is used, which may be in the form of a square vat with sides about two inches thick and held together with an iron or wooden frame. The slip is poured into this, and when the sides of the vat have become saturated with water, the water drips off, gradually stiffening the slip. Still another method of drying slip is to put it into stout canvas bags which are hung from the ceiling. The water seeps through the canvas and drips down, and the slip in the bag gradually becomes thicker. This is a rather awkward method, and the slip bags soon become unsightly. Without any machinery for pressing the water out of clay, the best method is undoubtedly to put the slip out into drying bats of plaster or of soft-fired clay. If these bats are in a position where the air can get to them, and where the temperature is fairly high, they work quite efficiently and can be rapidly re-dried between batches. If clay is allowed to settle until it is a heavy mud and is then put into the drying bats, it will take only a short while to stiffen to a plastic condition ready for use.

Water can be removed from slip with the filter-press. This machine forces the clay under pressure into fabric-lined chambers which permit the water to be squeezed out but retain the clay. The slip is put into a pressure tank and forced to the press under 50 to 100 pounds of pressure. The individual leaves of the press are not large, which permits the water to escape fairly rapidly. After no more water will squeeze from the clay, the pressure is released, and the leaves of the press are opened up, revealing in each a cake of plastic clay. While the filter press works well enough for large batches of clay, it is not a very practical machine for making small batches, especially where various compositions are being made and where the press must be cleaned between batches. This is a tedious job.

If casting slip is to be made, it is

common practice to continue to dry the plastic clay until it is bone dry, and then to make the slip by adding just the right amount of water and electrolyte to the dry clay.

If the raw materials are in the right condition, it may be possible and desirable to mix the plastic clay or the slip directly, without going through the stage of making a fluid slip with an excess of water as described above. After all, the only purpose of such a step is to ensure the thorough intermixture of the ingredients of the clay and to make possible the screening of the clay to remove impurities. If the clay and the other materials of the body are already free from impurities and are in the form of fine flour or dust, it may be better to skip the step of making a thin slip. Many clays are now furnished to the trade in air-floated form. Air-floated clay has been pulverized and bagged, after having gone through an air classifier which removes and returns for further grinding all particles above a certain size. Such material is in the form of a very fine dust and needs no further screening.

Where only air-floated clays and other finely pulverized materials are to be used in a clay body, they can be mixed directly in a mixer with just enough water added to give the desired degree of plasticity. A wet-pan or Simpson type mixer may be used for this purpose. These mixers employ wheels or mullers which revolve in a pan, pressing, turning, and mixing the plastic material. The mixing can be done quite rapidly on such a machine. There is one difficulty, however: if different batches are to be made on the same mixer, a great deal of time is lost in cleaning the machine. If no machine is available for mixing, finely ground clays may be made up by hand. The dry ingredients are first sifted or shoveled together to thoroughly intermingle the dry powders. Then water is sprinkled on gradually, while the mass of clay is turned and mixed with a spade or hoe. Clay is a very sticky substance, and mixing it by this method is a good deal of work. When the desired degree of plasticity is reached, the clay is put into a container to temper, and after a day or two it may be wedged up for use. Methods of clay mixing which aim at arriving directly at plastic clay are successful only if the raw materials are already free from impurities and in a finely ground form.

If casting slip is to be made up directly from the raw materials, the water is weighed out and the deflocculant, dry clay, and non-plastic ingredients are added to the mix in that order, stirring all the while.

To illustrate the method of mixing a relatively refined clay body, the following steps are outlined for the preparation of porcelain slip:

1. The ball clay is mixed on a blunger or agitator with a great excess of water, then screened through a 200-mesh screen.
2. The resultant ball clay slip is then dried and pulverized to small lumps.
3. The water for the slip and the deflocculant are weighed out and put in a ball mill.
4. The ball clay and the kaolin are added to the water and the mixture is ground for several hours.
5. The non-plastic ingredients are added and the slip is further ground for about three hours.
6. Before casting, the slip is strained through a 30-mesh screen to make sure no lumps are present.

Ball-milling a slip serves to pulverize all particles in the mix to a very finely ground state and to give a thorough intermingling of all the materials. In the case of porcelain and whiteware slips, milling helps to break up and to disperse the particles of carbon or lignite which are usually present in the ball clay.

Magnetic filters are used when clay bodies of exceptional whiteness are desired. The slip is passed over a magnet which draws out particles of iron. This method is particularly effective in removing specks of tramp iron, which get into clay from machinery used during mining and processing.

3. Aging, De-airing, and Kneading Clay

The workability of clay improves with aging. The properties of plasticity and workability are rather difficult to measure exactly, but all experienced clayworkers agree that when a clay is first made up it is difficult to work with, and that when it has aged or tempered for a while it becomes easier to work with. One reason for this is probably that it takes quite a while for all the particles of a clay body to become throughly wet. Water must penetrate to each individual particle of clay and must wet over the surface of each particle before the maximum of plasticity will be reached. Mixing the clay up first as a fluid slip facilitates this wetting. Another effect of aging is to develop organic compounds in the clay which contribute to its plasticity. Damp clay, especially if it is kept in a warm place, is a good culture medium, and bacteria grow rapidly in it. These bacteria produce acid residues and promote the formation of gels, which undoubtedly affect the clay. If new clay is mixed with a bit of old clay, or if it is stored in old containers or under old cloths used on previous batches, it will age more rapidly. The effects of aging are quite noticeable after about one week. Beyond that, the improvement in the clay will be much less noticeable, and it is doubtful if aging beyond a certain point will have any beneficial effect.

As described in the section on earthenware bodies, some clays which have in them materials which contain slightly soluble alkalies will suffer from aging and will, in fact, deflocculate so that they cannot be used as plastic clay.

Clay should be stored in air-tight containers. Bins or pits made of concrete or brick are suitable for large amounts of clay. Smaller batches may be stored in stoneware crocks or galvanized iron containers with lids.

For modeling and particularly for throwing, clay must be kneaded or wedged to remove the pockets of air and to disperse lumps and make the clay smooth and homogeneous. The clay is rolled or kneaded by hand on a plank or plaster table, or is repeatedly cut and recombined, which has the effect of crushing out all pockets of air. These methods are age-old and have been used by potters everywhere. They involve, however, considerable work, particularly if quantities of clay are being prepared.

For large scale production, the pug mill performs the mixing and kneading operation. It is a machine which forces the clay through a chamber with a revolving screw, operating very much in the manner of a meat-grinder. The old country potter of a hundred years ago used a crude forerunner of this device, powered by a mule. A further refinement is the de-airing pug-mill. This machine holds the clay under a vacuum while it is being mixed and extruded, thus effectively removing all air pockets and producing a smoothness and density which would be impossible to produce by hand methods.

Part Two—GLAZES

Chapter 8

The Nature of Glass and Glazes

1. Silica as the Basis of Glass

Glazes on pottery are similar to other kinds of glass, and to understand pottery glazes, we must first understand something of the nature of glass as such. Although glass is an extremely abundant and important substance in our daily lives, few people have much understanding of what it really is and what it is made of.

Glass is difficult to define in nontechnical terms. It is actually a noncrystalline substance of more or less transparency and transluscency, which has been formed in the cooling of a melt of earthy materials. Plastics, which may be transparent or translucent, are organic in origin, and thus would not come within this definition.

To get at the nature of glass, the phenomenon of melting and the tendency of matter to crystallize must be considered. All the materials of which the earth is formed were, at the beginning, in a vaporous or liquid state. This was because elevated temperatures prevailed during the early stages of the formation of the earth. As the earth cooled, it solidified or froze—at least the outer crust did; the interior may be assumed to be hot enough still to be in the liquid state. That is, it would be in the liquid state if the pressures prevailing deep in the earth were removed, as sometimes happens in the case of volcanic action.

The state of matter, then, is strictly dependent on its temperature, and the same substance may be a liquid, a vapor, or a solid, depending on how hot it is. Water is a very familiar example of this. We know it as steam, as a liquid, or as a solid (ice). And what we think of as being permanently solid, such as a rock, may be reduced to a liquid or to a vapor if sufficient heat is applied to it. At the first atomic explosion at Los Alamos the sands around the tower holding the bomb were liquefied by the heat.

When a substance cools from the liquid phase to the solid phase, it ordinarily assumes a crystalline state. Most of the earthy substances of the crust of the earth are crystalline. When a substance is in a crystalline state, its molecules are arranged in recurring sequences or patterns which repeat themselves three-dimensionally. A crystalline substance might be compared to a pile of building blocks in which each block is placed in a similar relationship to its neighboring blocks. Different substances form crystals of different shapes and arrangements. Salt, for example, crystallizes in forms whose planes meet at right angles. The recurring pattern of a crystalline substance is known as the crystal lattice. The form of the crystal may be repeated on a larger scale so that pieces of quartz, for example, will have a shape bounded by planes meeting at the angle characteristic for the crystal of that substance. It will be seen that if crystals are to pack closely, with their faces meeting, only a certain number of shapes are possible. It was, in fact, predicted mathematically how many different crystal forms were possible before this number was verified by observation.

When a crystalline substance is heated, the bonds between the molecules become weakened, and the molecules are no longer able to maintain their fixed relationship to one another. This decrease in bond and the more helter-skelter arrangement of the molecules, which makes for fluidity, we call melting. A melted substance has no crystalline structure.

When a melted or liquefied substance is cooled, the molecules tend to form into a regular lattice, and when the material solidifies or freezes, it is again in the crystalline state.

We now come to the idea of glass. When, as sometimes happens, a substance cools and solidifies without a crystalline structure reforming, it retains some of the characteristics of a liquid. This "solidified" or "supercooled" liquid is glass. It may be thought of as a melted liquid which has managed to cool and solidify without re-crystallizing.

Some oxides have a greater tendency to form glass than others. Most important among the glass-forming oxides is silica, which in practice is the basis for all useful glasses. Silica melts at 1710°. This is, of course, a relatively high temperature, and is beyond the reach of most kilns and furnaces used in ceramics. When silica melts, it is a clear liquid, without crystalline structure. When silica cools, it has a tendency to remain in the amorphous or glassy state; that is, the crystalline structure of the original material does not re-establish itself. This is particularly true if the silica is cooled rapidly. Silica, then, by itself, is a material which readily forms a glass when melted and cooled. Furthermore, pure silica glass is exceptionally hard, durable, resistant to the attack of acids, and resistant to breaking from heat shock. It would be the ideal glass for many practical purposes except for the difficulty of melting the material and the impracticality of forming it into useful objects when it is in the molten state.

In nature, glass is rather unusual. The normal geologic processes allowed molten material to cool very slowly; and as the molten liquids froze, they had a chance to crystallize. Obsidian, and some other minerals, however, are true glasses.

Glass, then, may be thought of as a chilled liquid from the melting of earthy substances. While it is a solid, it is nevertheless elastic, more or less transparent or translucent, and lacking in crystalline structure.

2. Making Glass

If it were possible to make glass objects from silica alone, they would be superior for most practical purposes. Some vessels for laboratory and special uses are in fact made from pure silica. But the difficulty of melting and forming such objects makes them too expensive for ordinary use.

Silica is, however, the basis of all practical glasses, and to facilitate its melting and fabrication, fluxes are added to it. These fluxes lower the melting point and make possible the melting and forming of the glass at reasonably low temperatures. Soda and lime are usually used for this purpose. All these materials—silica, soda, and lime—are very abundant and cheap, and as a result glass can be made in great quantity and at low cost. Silica is usually used in the form of a white sand. The soda is added as soda ash, and the lime as crushed and ground limestone. The ingredients are heated in a clay pot or tank until they melt and fuse together as a liquid. The temperature at which this fusion takes place will depend on the exact composition of the batch, but most commercial glasses are made at around 1500°. The tank or bath of glass is kept at a high enough temperature to prevent its freezing, and some of the molten material is then drawn off and fashioned into glass objects by blowing, pressing, drawing, or rolling. After the object is made, it is placed in a low-temperature furnace and allowed to cool slowly. This annealing is necessary to prevent strains in the glass which might cause it to crack.

Compounds of lead and potassium are also used in glass to obtain different properties in the finished material. Color is obtained by adding metallic oxides, such as iron oxide, manganese dioxide, or cobalt.

Ordinary glass is predominantly silica, fluxed by the additions of other materials which lower its melting point, facilitate making it into objects while molten, or lend other desirable properties to the finished product, such as color. The glass industry has developed a great many kinds of glass which, in addition to filling the practical need for containers and cooking vessels, has supplied the optical trade and other scientific consumers with glasses of many valuable specific properties.

3. The Distinction between Glass and Glazes

The subject of glass as such is only touched on above, since our primary concern is with glazes for pottery. A distinction must now be made between glass and glazes. Although pottery glazes are true glass, their composition is adjusted for the rather specialized function of sticking on to the surface of a pot. Glass which is to be fashioned into bottles, window glass, and the like, must be of quite a low viscosity, or, in other words, it must be fairly runny when molten. In pottery glazes, the glass must, on the other hand, be quite stiff when melted, so it will hold its position on the surface and not run off during the firing. This stiffness in pottery glazes is achieved by the addition of alumina to the mixture. Alumina has the property of increasing the viscosity of the glass, and for this reason it is present in small amounts in ordinary glass. It is possible to make pottery glazes from glass which is low in alumina, and in fact some special colors are achieved only in the absence of alumina.

Glazes, like any other glass, are predominantly silica, with just enough other material added to make them melt at the desired temperature and to give the desired texture and color. The art and science of glaze making involves the proper selection, apportioning, mixing, application, and firing of glaze materials to get the desired result.

An obvious distinction between glazes and glass is that glazes are made by blending the unmelted raw materials, the silica, and other constituents of the glaze, and spreading these blended materials on the surface of the pottery, where the glaze or glass is formed or melted in place. Glass, on the other hand, is melted up first into a bath of molten liquid material and then fashioned into objects. A glaze may be defined as a glassy coating melted in place on a ceramic body, which may render the body smooth, non-porous, and of a desired color or texture.

Enamels, which are outside the scope of the present work, are essentially the same as glazes, except that they are melted onto metals rather than onto ceramic bodies. Enamels are usually melted at lower temperatures than glazes.

Chapter 9

Early Types of Glazes

The knowledge of ways to form glazes on pottery is of great antiquity, dating back to at least 5000 B.C. Since glazes were made in many parts of the world long before the beginnings of any scientific knowledge of chemistry, it is clear that the processes involved must have been essentially simple and the raw materials abundant and widespread. Before discussing in more detail the chemical make-up of glazes, it might be well to consider the methods which were used by the ancients in glazing their pottery. Their results were in no way inferior to the best of present-day glazed ware. These results were achieved by strictly empirical methods which had no basis in scientific knowledge or theory.

1. Egyptian Glazes

The Egyptians, who undoubtedly made the first glazed ware, utilized the soda compounds which are found in abundance in the desert areas of the Near East. The turquoise glazed beads, ornaments, and small sculptures, which are known as Egyptian Paste, are probably the earliest glazed objects. The glaze on Egyptian paste is formed by mixing soluble sodium salts into the clay, which, during drying, deposits on the surface where it forms a glaze when fired. Such glazes may have been made accidentally at first. It is not unlikely that when objects were being modeled from the desert clays and talcs, some of the soda ash which is so prevalent in the desert could have gotten mixed in by chance. The observation of this phenomenon, and the capitalization of it in works of art and utility, is a good example of the way in which man has advanced his techniques. It was discovered that the addition of copper-bearing minerals to the mixture resulted in bright blue and turquoise glazes. The vibrant color of this type of glaze is irresistibly beautiful, yet technically there is no great difficulty in producing it from a few readily available materials. This type of glaze is discussed in more detail in a later chapter.

A great technical improvement over Egyptian paste, in which the glaze-forming materials were mixed right into the clay, is the practice of applying the glaze materials to the surface of the ware and thus enabling a more exact control over the thickness and color. This advance, which occurred in Egypt in very ancient times, resulted in the first glazes which were made, applied, and fired as we do today. The glazes were very simple in composition, probably being made up of soda ash, sand, and a little clay for adhesion. Such a combination of raw materials would be easily found in the Near East and would melt to a glaze at a very low heat.

2. Early Lead Glazes

The highly alkaline glazes which were invented and used by the Egyptians had some serious drawbacks, such as difficulty of application, a tendency to craze and even to peel or fall off the ware after firing, and a certain amount of solubility, especially if put to use in cooking. Many of these difficulties were overcome by the discovery of lead as a glaze material. This important advance probably occurred in ancient Syria or Babylonia. It was found that lead, probably in the form of lead sulfide, or galena, when ground to a powder and dusted or painted onto the surface of the clay, would fuse in the kiln to a smooth and shiny glaze. Lead compounds are quite common in nature, and the procuring of the raw materials must have presented no great problem. The lead glaze was superior to the alkaline glaze in practicality, if not in beauty. It was easy to apply, was not subject to so many flaws in firing, and it fitted the clay better and was more durable in use. Simple lead glazes are easy to make and may involve only a few materials. The potters of medieval England and Europe merely dusted galena powder on the damp pots, thus getting a sufficient coating of lead to form a glaze on the fired piece. A fairly practical glaze can be made from two parts of lead oxide together with one part pulverized sand and one part of common red clay. Such a glaze will be smooth, bright, and brown or amber in color, similar in appearance to lead-glazed country pottery commonly made in Europe and America during the last century.

In the Near East, the Syrians and Babylonians learned to make various colored lead glazes by mixing in various metallic oxides, such as copper, iron, and manganese; and some of their ceramics, notably the large architectural tiles and reliefs, represent a very high development in glaze making. The knowledge of lead glazes spread to China, and some of the earliest glazes in that country, dating from about 500 B.C., were made with lead. Some of the early lead-glazed wares have weathered and become iridescent as a result of the decomposition of the glaze, and now look quite unlike their original state.

3. Ash Glazes

In China the pottery kiln was improved, making possible the attainment of higher temperatures. All the wares of the Near East were fired at about 1050° or less. In China, kiln firings of 1200° or more became common in early times—as early, perhaps, as 500 B.C. This development, which was made possible by the down-draft chamber kiln, which conserved and utilized the heat from the wood fire rather than letting it escape from the chimney, permitted the development of new types of glazes that melted at higher temperatures.

An early type of glaze was formed by the ashes of the fire which were blown through the kiln by the draft of the fire, lit on the ware (if it were unprotected), and formed a glaze on its surface. Wood ashes contain considerable alkalies—such as potash and soda in addition to silica and some alumina—which gives them a relatively low fusion point. Some old Chinese pots have a glaze on one side only, or on the shoulder, which can be accounted for by the ashes in the firing chamber. Or ashes were sometimes dusted or painted on the surface of the ware before firing, which resulted in a thin glaze. If a sufficiently high firing temperature is employed, a very durable and satisfactory glaze can be made from wood ashes, feldspar, and clay, in about equal parts. This is a good example of the simplicity of glaze compounding, at least where a high degree of control is not essential. All of these materials were readily available to the ancient potter, and he needed only to discover them and to control them by rule-of-thumb methods. No knowledge of chemistry was involved. Further information about ash glazes is given in a later chapter.

4. Slip Glazes

Higher firing temperatures also made possible the slip glaze, or glaze which is made up mostly or entirely of clay. Some of the most beautiful of the old Chinese glazes are of this type. When higher firing temperatures were reached, potters found that some clays, such as common red earthenware clay, would melt in the kiln and form a brown glass. Such clays are relatively fusible, due to the presence of iron and other impurities. Most common clays will melt at about 1250°, and some will fuse at even lower temperatures. To make a slip glaze, one has merely to spread a fusible, iron-bearing clay over a pot made of a more refractory clay and then fire to a sufficiently high temperature to form a glaze from the coating clay. The fusion point of slip glazes may be lowered by adding some flux, such as ashes or feldspar.

5. Feldspathic Glazes

Another extremely simple kind of glaze is the feldspathic glaze, or glaze which is made up largely of feldspar. Here again, relatively high temperatures are required to melt such glazes, and for this reason they remained the exclusive property of the Chinese potters for over 2000 years, since only in China were kilns constructed which could reach the necessary heat. Feldspar by itself will melt to a glass at about 1250°. This one material, when pulverized and spread onto the surface of a pot, may give a very beautiful milky white glaze, and in fact some of the masterpieces of early Chinese pottery were no doubt glazed in this way. Feldspar is a very common mineral and very easy to identify and to crush into a fine powder. Its fusion point can be lowered by merely adding a little ground limestone, and some of the most beautiful glazes known to the art are simple combinations of only three materials: feldspar, limestone, and quartz, all of which are common minerals available almost everywhere.

6. Salt Glazes

Salt-glazing, which is described more fully later, may be mentioned here as an example of a glaze which is simple to make and does not require either numerous materials or a knowledge of chemical reactions.

We have considered some of the ways in which glazes were made in the past before any technology existed which made possible a technical knowledge of what the materials consisted of or of how they behaved in various combinations when melted. In general, potters combined various earthy minerals in proportions which, by trial and error, were known to give the desired result, and they fired their glazes to a temperature sufficient to fuse the glaze. Recipes were handed down from one generation to the next, and secrets of glaze making were closely guarded. That such methods worked well enough is evidenced by the magnificent achievements of the past. It is also evident that glaze making is not too difficult or technical; otherwise it could not have been done so successfully in the past. It has been, and still is, a matter of combining a few common materials and subjecting them to the right degree of heat. The most beautiful things in glazes come about quite naturally and are the outcome of reactions which the potter has, by and large, stumbled upon rather than invented.

Although good glazes were produced in the past without any exact knowledge, present-day technology has made glaze making immensely easier for the potter. For one thing, the raw materials can be obtained in prepared and ground form and can be assumed to be uniform in composition. In former times the potter had to dig, grind, and prepare his own materials; and the composition might vary, depending on the source. Our knowledge now permits the rapid compounding, adjusting, changing, and control of glazes for any desired result. This, together with the relatively exact control with which we can fire our ware, makes for more certain results than were formerly possible. However, there is still enough uncertainty left in the process to keep it interesting, as any experienced potter will testify.

It is very desirable for the ceramist to acquaint himself with the important facts about glaze materials and their behavior. Not only does such knowledge save time and make it possible for him to achieve desirable colors and textures in his glazes, but it also makes the work very much more enjoyable and fascinating. It is a mistake to think that such knowledge is the province of the technologist only. Of course it is also a mistake to think that art can come out of technique alone, but it seems quite certain that art cannot exist without technique.

Chapter 10

The Oxides and Their Function in Glaze Forming

1. Oxidation and the Oxides

Most earthy materials, including those which we use for glazes, are in the form of oxides. The finished, fired glaze is a mixture or melt of various elements, all in oxide form. Since in ceramics we are continuously dealing with oxides, an understanding of the term is essential. An oxide may be defined as the chemical combination of any element with oxygen. Oxygen is a very prevalent element, and in the course of geologic time, most of the elements on the surface of the earth have entered into combination with it. In some cases it has taken eons of time to effect this oxidation, but in the case of some other elements, such as silicon, oxidation is rapid and the element is unstable in the presence of oxygen. Oxygen is, of course, ever present in the atmosphere and in water, and is thus always available for chemical combination.

We are all familiar with oxidation, even if we do not know it by this term. Combustion is an example. The carbon of wood, coal, or oil combines with the oxygen of the air, and the result, burning, is a chemical reaction which gives off heat and light. The product, carbon dioxide, is a gas which becomes part of the atmosphere. The residues, such as ash, consist mostly of material which was already in oxide form and so did not enter into the reaction. Rusting is another familiar example of oxidation. The iron (Fe) combines with the oxygen of the atmosphere of the air or of water and becomes rust or iron oxide (Fe_2O_3). The metal chromium does not oxidize under ordinary atmospheric conditions; so it is added to steel to keep it from rusting—stainless steel is an alloy of steel and chromium.

Like most chemical reactions, oxidation is facilitated by heat. When the crust of the earth was still hot, oxidation of the elements which composed it was more rapid and complete than it would have been at lower temperatures. For this reason, almost all earthy materials are oxides. In ceramics, we subject the materials to relatively high temperatures, and finished ceramic products are composed altogether of oxides, even when materials which are not in oxide form, such as the carbonates, are used in compounding them.

The study and control of glazes is made much simpler and more understandable if the glaze is considered in its final, fired, melted state rather than in its unfired condition. After the glaze has been heated and fused, it is made up of elements in the oxide form. The relationships between these various oxides —that is, their relative amounts and the effect which they have on each other during fusion—are what we are really concerned with in glazes. The distinction must be kept in mind between these oxides in the fired glaze and the raw materials which we combine to make the glaze. For one thing, many glaze materials have more than one oxide in them. Clay, for example, has both alumina and silica, and feldspars commonly have three or more elements in them. Furthermore, some glaze materials, such as whiting ($CaCO_3$), are carbonates rather than oxides, although the end result from such a material in the finished glaze will be an oxide, in this case, CaO. In other words, there is a real distinction between the raw materials, which we combine to make glaze, and the finished, fired, melted glaze.

The oxides which enter into the finished glaze will be considered first, and then the raw materials from which these oxides are derived.

2. The Glaze Oxides

A listing of all the commonly used glaze oxides includes the following:

- PbO Lead Oxide
- Na_2O Sodium Oxide
- K_2O Potassium Oxide
- CaO Calcium Oxide
- MgO Magnesium Oxide
- BaO Barium Oxide
- Li_2O Lithium Oxide
- SrO Strontium Oxide
- SbO Antimony Oxide
- B_2O_3 Boric Oxide
- ZnO Zinc Oxide

- Al_2O_3 Aluminum Oxide
- TiO_2 Titanium Oxide

- SiO_2 Silicon Dioxide

It will be noted that a comparatively few oxides are found in glazes and glass. There are enough, however, so that an almost infinite number of combinations is possible. This is what accounts for the great variety of glazes. It should be emphasized that the oxides listed above are the oxides which form the glaze itself and that, with some exceptions, these oxides do not lend any color to the glaze. The exceptions are lead oxide, which gives a faint yellowish color to glazes, and combinations of lead and antimony, which give the color known as Naples yellow. It is convenient to study first the glaze itself, and later to study the way in which it may be colored; and in practice, glaze colorants are usually added in small percentages to the batch of materials which forms the glaze.

3. The Function of the Oxides in Glazes

Something should be said here in a general way about the oxides which have been listed as entering into glaze composition. For one thing, no two of them behave exactly alike. Each oxide has a particular contribution to make to the glaze. Calcium and strontium behave more nearly alike than any other pair, and sodium and potassium are similar. The only oxide which is indispensable to glaze making is silica, and all the rest are oxides which may, or may not, appear in any particular glaze. Sources for the various glaze oxides are abundant and relatively cheap.

Silica, the only oxide which is indispensable to glaze making, is much the most important of the oxides listed. By itself it will form glass, given enough temperature. It should be thought of as the material which forms the main body of the glaze and the other materials should be thought of as modifiers. Most glazes contain a preponderance of silica. The oxides which have been listed above in the first column may all be thought

TABLE OF CERAMIC RAW MATERIALS

Substance	*Formula*	*Molecular Weight*	*Equivalent Weight*	*Fired Formula*	*Fired Weight*
Barium Carbonate	$BaCO_3$	197	197	BaO	153
Bone Ash	$Ca_3(PO_4)_2$	310	103	CaO	56
Borax	$Na_2O \cdot 2B_2O_3 \cdot 10H_2O$	382	382	$Na_2O \cdot 2B_2O_3$	202
Boric Acid	$B_2O_3 \cdot 3H_2O$	124	124	B_2O_3	70
Calcium Borate (Colemanite)	$2CaO \cdot 3B_2O_3 \cdot 5H_2O$	412	206	$CaO \cdot 1.5B_2O_3$	161
China Clay	$Al_2O_3 \cdot 2SiO_2 \cdot 2H_2O$	258	258	$Al_2O_3 \cdot 2SiO_2$	222
Cryolite	Na_3AlF_6	210	420	$3Na_2O \cdot Al_2O_3$	288
Dolomite	$CaCO_3 \cdot MgCO_3$	184	184	$CaO \cdot MgO$	96
Feldspars					
Cornwall Stone	CaO .304 Na_2O .340 K_2O .356 } Al_2O_3 1.075 } SiO_2 8.10	667	667	Unchanged	667
Godfrey Spar	CaO .097 K_2O .426 Na_2O .377 } Al_2O_3 .985 } SiO_2 8.433		542	Same	542
Nepheline Syenite	K_2O .25 Na_2O .75 } Al_2O_3 1.11 } SiO_2 4.65	462	462	Unchanged	462
Orthoclase	$K_2O \cdot Al_2O_3 \cdot 6SiO_2$	556	556	Unchanged	556
Oxford Spar	K_2O .631 Na_2O .369 } Al_2O_3 1.125 } SiO_2 6.047	703	703	Same	703
Flint	SiO_2	60	60	Unchanged	60
Fluorspar	CaF_2	78	78	CaO	56
Lead, Red	Pb_3O_4	684	228	PbO	223
Lead, White	$2PbCO_3 \cdot Pb(OH)_2$	775	258	PbO	223
Lead, Yellow (Litharge)	PbO	223	223	Unchanged	223
Lithium Carbonate	Li_2CO_3	74	74	Li_2O	30
Magnesium Carbonate (Magnesite)	$MgCO_3$	84	84	MgO	40
Niter	KNO_3	101	202	K_2O	94
Pearl Ash	K_2CO_3	138	138	K_2O	94
Potassium Bichromate	$K_2Cr_2O_7$	294	294	$K_2O \cdot Cr_2O_3$	294
Silica	SiO_2	60	60	Unchanged	60
Soda Ash	Na_2CO_3	106	106	Na_2O	62
Sodium Nitrate	$NaNO_3$	85	170	Na_2O	62
Spodumene	$Li_2O \cdot Al_2O_3 \cdot 4SiO_2$	372	372	Same	372
Strontium Carbonate	$SrCO_3$	148	148	SrO	120
Talc (Steatite)	$3MgO \cdot 4SiO_2 \cdot H_2O$	378	378	$3MgO \cdot 4SiO_2$	360
Tin Oxide	SnO_2	151	151	Unchanged	151
Titanium Oxide (Rutile)	TiO_2	80	80	Unchanged	80
Whiting	$CaCO_3$	100	100	CaO	56
Zinc Oxide	ZnO	81	81	Unchanged	81
Zircon (Zircopax)	$ZrO_2 \cdot SiO_2$	183	183	Unchanged	183
Zirconium Oxide	ZrO_2	123	123	Unchanged	123

of as fluxes, or oxides which cause the silica to melt. It will be noted that the oxides in the first column are all metallic oxides or alkaline earths. Although they vary widely in melting point, and in chemical activity or inertness, they all have the effect of making silica melt at a lower temperature than it would by itself. The alumina, which is used only in quite small amounts in glazes, has the effect of stiffening the melt. It prevents the melted glaze from running down the vertical walls of pots, and it also serves to prevent the formation of crystals in the glaze when it is cooling. For this reason, it is left out of glazes which are meant to show crystals, but it is present in almost all other glazes.

4. How Glazes Melt in the Kiln

Before discussing the glaze-forming oxides in more detail, the actual history of a glaze should be described, from its compounding to its melting and solidifying. Such a description should help in visualizing the part which the various oxides actually take in making up the finished glaze. The raw materials of glazes, which will be described in detail later, are either rocks or minerals such as silica and feldspar, which have been ground up to a fine powder, or they are materials which have been prepared by precipitation or other chemical methods, and are supplied in the form of fine dry powder. Glaze materials are usually fine enough to pass through a screen having 200 meshes to the inch. When the various ingredients of the glaze have been combined and mixed with water, a mass of material is obtained which is composed of particles of various materials lying next to one another. In this state the glaze is applied to the ware in a coating which is uniformly composed of small particles of the various original raw materials. The finer the grinding of the raw materials, and the more thorough the mixing of the glaze, the more intimate the contact will be between the various materials.

As the glazed ware is heated to red heat and beyond, changes begin to occur in the glaze. Whatever volatile materials are contained in the glaze, such as carbon and sulfur, will be driven off, and the glaze will then be composed entirely of oxides. These oxides, as the heat advances, will begin to react with each other, chemically, and fusion will begin. Fusion may occur at first in the reaction of two or more of the materials, and the glass so formed may then promote the fusion of additional oxides until all are drawn into the melt. In most glazes, this fusion occurs rather gradually with the advancing heat. Finally, all the separate solids of the mixture will have lost their identity in the melt, which will be of uniform consistency. Fine particle size in the raw materials promotes fusion by bringing the various materials into more intimate contact. When the heat of the kiln subsides, the glaze chills into a solid mass of glass coating the ware. This glass or glaze is actually a complex solution or mixture of the various oxides rather than a chemical compound of definite composition.

When glazes are melted onto clay bodies, there is always a certain amount of reaction between the two, especially in higher-fired ware. As we have seen, when clay approaches vitrification in the kiln, there is a certain amount of glass formed in it, and the oxides which make up the clay are activated by the high temperature. The fluid glaze likewise is active and tends to eat down into the clay a bit, taking some of it into solution and perhaps dissolving iron and other impurities from the clay surface. Microscopic examination of a section of a glazed piece will show an intermediate zone between clay and glaze which is partly glaze, partly clay, called "interface." This reaction between clay and glaze serves to make the glaze adhere firmly to the clay body. In porcelain, it may be difficult to establish the line where clay leaves off and glaze begins, since the two in this case are nearly alike. Low-fired ware shows little reaction between glaze and clay, and for this reason it is sometimes very hard to fit a glaze onto an under-fired, soft clay body.

5. Silica SiO_2

Silica is the fundamental oxide of glass. Pottery glazes are preponderantly made up of silica, and the other ingredients which are put into glazes are really put in to modify it towards a lower melting point, or to lend to it some other property such as alkalinity, opacity, or matness. Low-fired glazes, those which mature at 1050° or less, contain about two parts of silica to one part of the combined other ingredients of the glaze. High-fired glazes, those melting at 1250° or higher, will have three or four times as much silica as the other ingredients combined.

About 60 percent of the crust of the earth is made up of silica—a fact which indicates the hardness, durability, and resistance to chemical change or solution of this oxide. These are the desirable properties which it adds to glazes, and it is a general rule of glaze making that as much silica as possible is added to the glaze. High-fired glazes are of superior hardness compared to low-fired glazes, because more silica can be incorporated in them.

Vitreous silica has a low coefficient of expansion, and for this reason its presence in the glaze controls the fit of the glaze to the body. This will be treated more fully in the section on glaze faults.

Silica has no undesirable properties when used in glazes, except that, when present in excessive amounts, it may cause the glaze to be under-fired at the intended temperature, or an excess may cause devitrification or the formation of crystals in the cooling glaze. No glaze colors are adversely effected by silica.

6. Alumina Al_2O_3

Although alumina is used in relatively small amounts in glazes, it contributes importantly to the working properties of the glaze, and the only glazes which are commonly made up without alumina are those which are intended to develop crystals during cooling.

Alumina is refractory and does not melt by itself until about 2040°. For this reason, not much alumina can be added to a glaze without causing it to be under-fired and dry in appearance.

The presence of alumina in a glaze makes the melted glaze more viscous and less apt to run down off vertical surfaces. This is an indispensable property in glazes for most useful purposes. Another valuable function of alumina is the prevention of recrystallization during the cooling of the glaze. Without alumina, many glazes would devitrify in cooling and would have rough surfaces, opacity, or mottled textures. Alumina in the molten glass acts as a retarder in keeping the other materials from getting together in the crystalline state.

Alumina also adds to the hardness, durability, and tensile strength of glazes. Alumina, because of its high melting point, lends opacity and matness to any glaze if used in amounts beyond a certain critical amount dependent on glaze composition and the firing temperature.

7. Sodium Oxide Na_2O

The oxide of sodium is very active chemically and functions in glazes as a strong flux or melter. It is a very useful oxide in glazes from the lowest temperature range to the higher-fired glazes. Glazes which have a lot of sodium in them may be brilliantly colored by the addition of metallic coloring oxides. The presence of the soda lends a strength and brilliance to the color. One of the most outstanding examples of this is the turquoise blue which results from the addition of copper oxide to a glaze which is high in soda. The so-called Egyptian blue is a color produced by this combination.

Soda has the disadvantage of a very high coefficient of expansion which causes glazes which are high in soda to craze on most pottery bodies. Other disadvantages of high soda glazes are their tendency to be soft and easily worn or scratched, their slight solubility in acid, and their tendency to weather and deteriorate. Many of the masterpieces of ancient Persian pottery are now in bad condition because of the weathering of the soda glazes. Still another difficulty with soda is that there are few natural sources which are insoluble. Many feldspars contain soda, however, and modest amounts can be added to a glaze in this form.

Used in moderate amounts and in combination with other fluxes, soda is a very useful oxide in glazes over a wide range of temperature. Soda is an important constituent of ordinary glass, which is largely composed of silica, soda, and lime.

8. Potassium Oxide K_2O

Potassium oxide is very similar in its action in glazes to sodium. Actually, these two oxides behave so much alike that they are frequently described by the symbol "KNaO," which means a blend of sodium and potassium in any proportion. Potassium has the same advantages and the same disadvantages as sodium. Its color response is brilliant and similar to that of soda, with some differences in color, depending on whether soda or potassium predominates in the mixture. Manganese in a soda glaze gives a reddish purple color, for example; while in the presence of potassium, it gives a blue-purple. Potassium has a slightly lower coefficient of expansion than sodium, but it is still very high and causes crazing.

Potassium is a very active flux and is useful in glazes at all temperatures. Its only natural source in insoluble form is feldspar, and when considerable amounts of potassium are required in a glaze, a frit is used.

9. Lead Oxide PbO

Lead oxide is used in glazes as a flux. Lead and silica alone will give a fairly good glaze, similar to that which is used on low-fired Mexican pottery. Most glazes the world over have contained lead as the principal fluxing ingredient. Generally speaking, it is the most useful and dependable melting flux in the lower and middle ranges of temperature.

Lead oxide has the advantages of a very low melting point, a favorable effect on most coloring oxides, and the tendency to produce a smooth, bright glaze free from blemishes. It has a fairly low coefficient of expansion, which makes lead glazes quite easy to fit to most pottery bodies without crazing. Lead glazes may easily be made clear, transparent, bright, opaque, mat, or textured by varying the composition and adding suitable opacifiers and matting agents.

Lead as a material for glazes is valued for its dependability. It melts gradually, surely, and smoothly; and glazes fluxed with it are relatively free from defects. In addition to these practical advantages, lead glazes can be used to produce rich, brilliant, deep colors in a very wide variety of hues.

There are some disadvantages in the use of lead oxide in glazes. None of these disadvantages in any way disqualifies it for use in pottery, however. For one thing, lead-glazed ware must be fired in an oxidizing atmosphere. In modern practice, this is hardly a disadvantage since kilns are ordinarily fired with a clear, smoke-free atmosphere. Lead oxide does reduce easily, however, and if ware is in direct contact with flame or smoke during firing, it may be blistered and blackened. Another limitation of lead oxide is that above about 1200° it becomes volatile. For this reason lead glazes are seldom used above about cone 6. Of course, at the higher temperatures, other fluxes, such as feldspar, are available; so the use of lead is unnecessary. The volatilization of lead oxide accounts for the tendency of the interior of kilns and kiln furniture to become glazed over after numerous firings of lead-glazed ware.

Lead glazes have the reputation of being harsh and shiny in surface, and the devotee of stoneware glazes tends to underestimate the creative possibilities of the lead glaze. Actually, lead glazes can easily be controlled to any degree of matness or dryness and do not need to be bright and garish in color and texture.

One serious drawback to the use of lead oxide in glazes is that as a raw material it is poisonous, and appropriate precautions must be taken in using it to avoid the possibility of lead poisoning. Lead poisoning is caused by the ingestion of lead compounds into the system, either by mouth, by breathing vapors or dusts, or by getting lead into open cuts in the skin. The symptoms of lead poisoning are various, and it is difficult to cure, since lead once taken into the system tends to remain there. Painters using lead paint have frequently suffered from lead poisoning, and in England during the last century pottery workers using lead glazes became so subject to lead poisoning that regulations were established prohibiting the use of raw lead compounds.

While lead poisoning is a serious matter, the possibility of getting it while working with glazes can be easily avoided by a few simple precautions. When raw lead glazes are being used, care must be taken not to breathe dust from spraying or to get glaze on the ends of cigarettes or on food. Well-vented spray booths with strong fans are essential if spraying is to be done. Lead poisoning is the result of accumulations of lead in the system, and even the smallest amount taken in daily will, over a period of years perhaps, reach the critical level.

Lead which has been fritted with silica or other oxides is not poisonous, and wherever possible, lead should be introduced into glazes as a frit. This is particularly true in classroom work where it may be difficult to enforce the safety rules which are necessary in the case of raw lead glazes.

Another side of the problem of the poisonous nature of lead oxide is the fact that some lead glazes, after being fired on the ware, are slightly soluble in weak acids, and the possibility exists of small quantities getting into food from the dishes. The only kind of lead glazes which might create such a hazard are very low-fired glazes which have a great deal of lead in them and not enough other oxides to produce a stable, insoluble glass. If kilns are available which will fire to 1000° or more, and if even a modest amount of knowledge goes into the compounding of the glaze, the fired pieces will not present any hazard in use. If ware is to be used with food, it is wise always to introduce some lime into the composition and to design the glaze so that there are at least two molecules of silica to each molecule of lead. Any lead glaze fired to above cone 06, and containing several oxides in addition to lead and silica, will be so slightly soluble as to be completely safe in ordinary use. Even in the case of the softest and most soluble lead glaze, it is difficult to take into the system enough lead from the dishes to cause poisoning.

10. Calcium Oxide CaO

Most glazes contain calcium oxide, and since it is a common and inexpensive material and contributes only desirable properties to glazes, it is one of the most valuable glaze ingredients.

Although calcium oxide has a very high melting point, 2572°, its principal function in glazes is that of a flux. In high-fired glazes, calcium oxide may be the principal flux, but in lower-temperature glazes, other fluxes such as lead, zinc, or sodium must be used along with calcium to cause the glaze to melt. Calcium contributes to the hardness and durability of glazes. It causes no difficulty in firing, and few glaze faults can be traced to it.

Calcium oxide has little effect upon the colors obtained from coloring oxides. In high-fired reduction glazes the grey-green color known as celedon is favored by the presence of considerable calcium oxide in the glaze.

The presence of calcium in low-fired glazes which are high in lead oxide or sodium oxide renders them harder and more insoluble.

When too high a percentage of calcium oxide is used in a glaze, it will produce a mat, dull, or rough surface. This is due to the refractory character of the material when present in more than the amount needed and to devitrification caused by the limited solubility of calcium silicate in the melt. Calcium oxide is useful in producing glaze surfaces which are slightly dull. By increasing the amount of calcium in some glazes a dulled surface can be achieved without much affecting the transparency of the glaze.

11. Barium Oxide BaO

The function of barium oxide and calcium oxide in glazes is somewhat similar. Barium is refractory, and it must be used in smaller amounts than calcium, especially in low-fired glazes. In high-fired glazes, barium oxide is a flux, though not a very active one.

Barium is commonly used to produce mat glazes. In most types of glazes, barium produces a soft satiny mat surface which is very pleasant. When the amount of barium is too great, very dry surfaces will result. When considerable boron is present in a glaze, additions of barium oxide will not produce matness.

The presence of barium oxide in high-fired glazes favors the development of celedon and iron-blue colors in reduction firing. Brilliant copper-blue glazes may be obtained in glazes which are high in barium.

12. Magnesium Oxide MgO

Magnesium oxide is used principally as a high-temperature flux. It is too refractory to be of much use in low-fired glazes, except to lend opacity and matness. In high-fired glazes, magnesium oxide may give a smooth, buttery surface to the glaze. This is especially the case in reduction firing. High-fired reduction glazes containing magnesium oxide are usually opaque, smooth and dense, and pleasant to the touch. An excess of magnesium oxide will cause dryness in a glaze and may also contribute to such difficulties as crawling and pinholing.

When cobalt is added to glazes containing magnesium oxide, the resultant color is purple rather than the usual blue. At very high temperatures, and where considerable magnesium oxide is present, this purple may be mottled with streaks of pink or brilliant red.

13. Zinc Oxide ZnO

Zinc oxide is a very useful flux in the middle and higher range of temperature. Used in small amounts, it may be a very active flux, and when added in larger quantities, it may produce matness and dryness. It is little used in glazes fired at temperatures below cone 01, because at the lower temperatures it does not have much fluxing power.

Although zinc oxide is not nearly as strong a flux as lead oxide, it has been employed as a substitute for lead. The so-called Bristol glaze was developed in England to avoid the use of lead. It is a type of glaze which employs zinc as the principal flux, with calcium, magnesium, and barium used as auxiliary fluxes.

As an additional flux in glazes which contain lead, feldspar or boric acid, zinc is a very valuable material. It is an aid to smooth, even, trouble-free glazing. However, glazes which rely mostly on zinc for flux are apt to crawl and may be subject to pitting and pinholing, and the colors may be mottled and broken. A little zinc is a good thing and a lot of it is likely to cause trouble.

The presence of zinc oxide has a pronounced effect on the colors obtained from several coloring oxides. When iron and zinc are both used, the resulting colors are apt to be dull and rather dingy. On the other hand, copper and zinc together produce brilliant turquoise greens. When zinc and chrome are used together, brown results rather than green. When zinc and tin are both used, the glaze may become slightly pink or brownish. Zinc and titania together are useful in promoting crystalline development in glazes. Because of these rather special color reactions, the high zinc glaze is not commonly used.

14. Strontium Oxide SrO

The function of strontium in a glaze is very similar to that of calcium. It is a little more fusible, however, and may be substituted for calcium oxide where a more active melt is desired in a glaze at a given temperature. Since strontium is more expensive than calcium and has no pronounced advantages over calcium, it is little used.

15. Antimony Oxide Sb_2O_3

Antimony is sometimes used as an opacifier, although it is in no way superior to tin or zircon for this purpose. It is used principally to produce Naples yellow, which results from the combination of lead oxide and antimony oxide.

16. Lithium Li_2O

Lithium oxide is useful as an active flux, and its action in glazes is somewhat similar to that of sodium. Its color response is similar to that of sodium and potassium. The sources of lithium oxide are rather expensive, which has kept the oxide from being much used.

17. Boric Oxide B_2O_3

Boric oxide is a low-melting-point substance with strong fluxing power comparable to lead oxide or sodium oxide. It is a very useful glaze ingredient which has come into common use in modern times. The only natural source of boric oxide which is not soluble is colemanite, and except where this material is used, boric oxide is introduced into the glaze in fritted form.

Boric oxide can be used as the main flux in a glaze, or as an auxiliary flux, and it can be used from the lowest to the highest temperatures. It forms borates that reduce the expansion of the glaze, and so is useful in the correction of crazing.

Boric oxide intensifies the effect of coloring oxides, and in this respect it is similar to sodium and potassium. When even a slight amount of iron is present, it may produce milky or opalescent blues. It may also cause broken or mottled color effects with the various coloring oxides.

Glazes for commercial tableware are commonly made with lead oxide and boric oxide both used for flux, and such glazes—the so-called "lead boro-silicate" glazes—are notable for their smoothness, freedom from pits or other blemishes, long firing range, and good wearing properties.

Chapter 11

Glaze Materials

1. Preparation of Raw Materials for Use in Glazes

The important oxides which enter into the composition of glazes have been briefly described. Next, the raw materials which are used to obtain these various oxides will be discussed. The distinction between the oxides which make up the fired glazes and the raw materials which are combined to make up the glaze batch must be kept in mind. Some raw materials yield only one oxide in the finished glaze. Whiting, which yields only CaO in the finished glaze, is an example. Other raw materials may yield several oxides in the finished glaze. Cornwall stone, for example, yields five different oxides. If the ceramist is to use his raw materials intelligently, he must know what oxides are in them and what they contribute to the final result.

While the beginner may feel that there are a bewildering number of materials from which glazes can be made, the number of possible materials is actually severely limited. About twenty-one materials include all those which are commonly used. Of these twenty-one, about nine are used relatively little. A good working knowledge of about a dozen materials is needed to approach the subject of glaze making intelligently. Here we are not considering the materials which color glazes and influence their texture, but only the materials which are used to make up the body of the glaze itself.

Most of the commonly used glaze materials are derived from common rocks and minerals. It is a mistake to think that glazes are made up from obscure, expensive, or rare materials. Actually glazes can in most localities be made up from the minerals which are common and easily obtained in nature. For example, some of the most beautiful of all high-fired glazes are composed of feldspar, flint, limestone, and clay. All of these minerals are common and can be located and identified easily. In practice, however, it is seldom worthwhile for the potter to prepare his own glaze materials, because the materials which he would be digging and laboriously grinding would be in no way different or superior to the prepared materials which he could get from a supplier.

Glaze materials are supplied and used in the form of finely ground powders. Some materials—such as flint, feldspar, dolomite, whiting, talc, and clay—are natural materials which are mined and then ground to the desired degree of fineness. Other materials are the product of chemical processes, such as precipitation. Whether the material is derived from natural minerals or is the result of chemical preparation, the common standard for particle size is a grind which will pass through the 200-mesh screen. Fine grinding tends to make all the materials used for glaze making look very much alike, and the potter must take care not to get materials mixed up or to lose the labels from sacks or bins.

With the exception of lead compounds and barium, all glaze materials are non-toxic. Some of the soluble materials are caustic, however, and care must be taken to avoid prolonged contact with the skin. Care must also be taken to avoid breathing silica dust. Prolonged breathing of dusts containing silica may cause silicosis, a disease of the lungs; to avoid this hazard, all glaze spraying should be done in well-ventilated spray booths, and the dust about the working areas should be kept to a minimum. Modern methods of dust control have practically eliminated the problem of silicosis from the pottery industry.

Glaze materials do not deteriorate either in the raw state or when mixed up with water into glaze slips, and they may be kept indefinitely. Most glaze materials are quite cheap, and the relatively much higher cost of prepared glazes, which may be purchased from some suppliers, represents more the cost of preparing, packaging, and selling the glaze than the cost of the raw materials. Coloring oxides and stains for glazes may be expensive, but these are used in relatively small quantities.

The materials used in glazes should be insoluble in water. This practical consideration rules out many common materials which otherwise might be useful in glazes. For example, sodium silicate could be used for glazes as a source of sodium were it not for its solubility in water. The problem of solubility in glazes is discussed in the section on frit.

2. Flint SiO_2

Flint is used in glazes as the main source of silica. In mineralogy, flint is a variety of quartz—usually grey, black, or brown—which has an extremely small crystalline structure (cryptocrystalline). Potter's flint may be made by grinding any form of crystalline quartz into a fine powder. Flint is insoluble and chemically inert. It is abundant and cheap.

3. Clay $Al_2O_3 \cdot 2SiO_2 \cdot 2H_2O$

Clay is used in glazes as a source of aluminum oxide, and since all glazes require silica, its silica content also contributes to the glaze. Clay also contributes some desirable physical properties to the raw glaze. Kaolin or china clay is ordinarily used, since it is relatively free from iron and thus does not give any color to the glaze. Ball clay, stoneware clay, or earthenware clay may be used in glazes, but the higher iron content of these clays will give a tan or brown tint to the glaze and may also lower its fusion point somewhat.

Besides furnishing alumina and silica to the glaze, clay acts as a floatative in the raw glaze batch, helping to keep the other ingredients from settling to the bottom of the slip. Clay also helps to give the raw glaze coat on the ware a toughness which makes it less apt to be smeared or damaged during placing in the kiln.

Ordinarily all of the alumina which is called for in a glaze is supplied by clay and by feldspar. However, it is possible to introduce alumina in the form of aluminum hydrate or aluminum oxide. But since these materials are much more expensive than clay, and do not lend the same desirable physical properties, there is no advantage in using them.

In calculating glazes, the theoretical composition of kaolin is used (Al_2O_3-

$2SiO_2$), although many clays are known from chemical analysis to be considerably different from this in formula. Ball clay, for example, always has more silica in it than the amount in the theoretical formula for kaolin. But such variations have a negligible effect on the glaze, since the amount of clay in a glaze is small in any case. When glaze recipes include more than about 12 percent of clay, calcined clay may be used to lessen shrinkage.

Slip glazes, which are composed entirely or largely of clay, are discussed in a later section.

4. Feldspar

Feldspar is one of the most important glaze materials. It is used in almost all glazes, and in high-fired glazes it is often the principal material and provides the principal flux. Feldspar, as has been noted, is one of the constituents of granite, and it is one of the most common and wide-spread minerals.

Feldspar is made up of (a) an alkaline portion consisting of sodium, potassium, or calcium, singly or in combination; (b) alumina; and (c) silica. Formulas for pure feldspars are as follows:

Orthoclase	$K_2O \cdot Al_2O_3 \cdot 6SiO_2$
Albite	$Na_2O \cdot Al_2O_3 \cdot 6SiO_2$
Anorthite	$CaO \cdot Al_2O_3 \cdot 2SiO_2$
Spodumene	$Li_2O \cdot Al_2O_3 \cdot 4SiO_2$

The formulas represent the theoretical composition of these minerals. Only hand-picked specimens in nature would have a composition corresponding to the formula.

A commercial feldspar would be more apt to have a formula something like this:

K_2O	.74	Al_2O_3	1.026	SiO_2	6.34
Na_2O	.26				

Here, the first column indicates that sodium as well as potassium is present. The alumina and the silica are both present in higher amounts than in the theoretical composition. Commercially available feldspars have trade names such as "Buckingham Feldspar" or "Minpro Spar." These trade names have no mineralogical significance, but the suppliers of feldspars maintain a reasonably uniform composition for any feldspar marketed under a given name. Producers may blend the rock from different parts of the same quarry, or from different quarries, to keep the material uniform in composition. The producers of feldspar furnish a chemical analysis of the material being sold, from which the formula can be calculated.

Different feldspars vary rather widely in composition. Those feldspars having a high amount of potassium are favored for additions to clay bodies. Feldspars which are high in soda are favored for glaze making because of their relatively lower fusion point. When a glaze recipe calls for just "feldspar" without specifying any particular brand or kind, various kinds may have to be tried to find out which gives the desired result. More exact methods of glaze calculation call for specific kinds of feldspar.

Feldspar is useful in glazes because of its relatively low melting point and its incorporation of the alkalies potassium and sodium in an insoluble mineral. It is in effect a kind of natural frit. Most feldspars will melt by themselves, with no material added, at about 1250°, and will sinter into a hard mass at considerably less than that temperature. Five or 10 percent of whiting, dolomite, or talc added to a feldspar will bring down its fusion point 50 degrees or more. The fusible nature of feldspar is due to its content of sodium, potassium, or lithium.

When temperatures of cone 10 or more are available, extremely simple glazes can be made largely of feldspar, with perhaps small additions of whiting, dolomite, or talc. Glazes which are very high in feldspar have a tendency to craze because of the quantity of sodium or potassium present, but they often have a milky, semi-opaque quality which is very beautiful. Some of the classic old Chinese ware, notably Lun Ch'uan ware of the Sung Dynasty, was probably glazed with highly feldspathic compositions. One of the advantages of high firing is that a few simple materials can be made to yield such beautiful glazes.

Some feldspathic materials are so different from the ordinary feldspar that they are called by other names. Nepheline syenite, for example, is a feldspar which has an unusually high amount of soda and potassium in relation to the amount of silica present. It has the formula:

K_2O	.254	Al_2O_3	SiO_2
Na_2O	.746	1.108	4.652

The lower melting point of this material makes it very useful in compounding glazes, especially those in the middle range of temperature. Nepheline syenite is also very useful as a body flux in clays where a lower maturing temperature is desired.

Cornwall stone is another feldspathic material in common use for both glazes and bodies. It is produced in Cornwall, England. A typical analysis is:

$$\left.\begin{matrix} CaO & .304 \\ Na_2O & .340 \\ K_2O & .356 \end{matrix}\right\} \begin{matrix} Al_2O_3 \\ 1.075 \end{matrix} \left\{ \begin{matrix} SiO_2 \\ 8.10 \end{matrix}\right.$$

In Cornwall stone, the lime, soda, and potassium are about equal, and the silica is higher in proportion to the alkalies than in most feldspars.

5. Whiting $CaCO_3$

Whiting, or calcium carbonate, is the most common source of calcium oxide in glazes. It is made by grinding limestone, chalk, marble, or other calcite minerals. Whiting of exceptional purity is made by precipitation.

6. Magnesium Carbonate $MgCO_3$

Magnesium carbonate is used as a source of magnesium oxide in glazes. Either it is made from magnesite, or it may be a precipitated material made from mixtures of magnesium sulphate and soda ash. The precipitated magnesium carbonate is very light and fluffy in texture. It tends to mix more easily into the raw glaze than the ground magnesite.

7. Dolomite $CaCO_3 \cdot MgCO_3$

Dolomite is a natural mineral containing calcium and magnesium carbonates in equivalent parts. It may be used in glazes whenever both magnesia and calcia are called for.

8. Barium Carbonate $BaCO_3$

Barium carbonate is the usual source of barium oxide in glazes. The material is prepared from the mineral barytes (barium sulphate) by precipitation with soda ash, following reduction to sulfide.

9. Talc $3MgO \cdot 4SiO_2 \cdot H_2O$

Talc may be used in glazes wherever both magnesia and silica are desired. It is prepared by grinding the natural mineral, steatite. Talc frequently contains some calcium as an impurity, which contributes to its action as a flux in glazes. Talc is used as a flux for clay bodies, especially low-fired bodies.

10. Strontium Carbonate $SrCO_3$

Strontium carbonate is prepared from the mineral celesite ($Sr\ SO_4$). It is more expensive than whiting; and since its action in glazes is very similar, it is seldom used.

11. Colemanite $2CaO \cdot 3B_2O_3 \cdot 5H_2O$

Colemanite is a natural mineral containing both calcium and boron in a relatively insoluble form. It is valuable as a glaze material since it is the only source of boric oxide in an insoluble form except for frit. Its composition tends to be somewhat variable, which has limited its use in large-scale pottery manufacture. It is, however, a favorite material of the studio potter. Colemanite, when it is used as the principal flux in glazes, gives them a broken, mottled texture which can be very attractive. This is particularly true if rutile also is used. Also, glazes which have considerable boric oxide in them tend to be bright and colorful. Colemanite may also lend a milky, blue opalescent quality to a glaze. When combinations of lead and colemanite are used, the resulting glaze may be very reliable, smooth, and of long-firing range. Colemanite may be used alone as the flux for very low-fired glazes. The slight solubility of colemanite may give it a tendency to flocculate the glaze slip. It may be noticed that a glaze which has been made up to a normal consistency with water will, after standing for a day or two, become thick and pudding-like, and will require more water to make it right for application. This excess of water may result in trouble by causing cracks in the dried raw glaze, and perhaps subsequent crawling.

12. Litharge PbO

Litharge, or lead monoxide, is made by spraying molten lead into a furnace with a current of air. Because of its relatively low oxygen content, litharge is perhaps more subject to reduction in firing. Besides this disadvantage, it is relatively coarse in particle size compared to the other materials yielding lead oxide.

13. White Lead $2PbCO_3 \cdot Pb(OH)_2$

White lead, or basic lead carbonate, is prepared by treating the metal lead with acid and carbon dioxide gas. The result is a finely divided white powder, free from impurities and insoluble in water.

White lead is the preferred form of lead for use in glazes. Its advantages are its purity of composition and its fine particle size. The fine particles keep the material from settling rapidly in the glaze slip. White lead fuses very readily, perhaps partly because of the mixing which results from the escape of carbon dioxide gas from the material during heating.

14. Red Lead Pb_3O_4

Red lead is prepared by roasting litharge (PbO). It is cheaper than white lead, but it is not commonly used in glazes because of its coarse particle size, its tendency to settle out in glaze slips, and its objectionable red color, which stains the hands, clothing, and tools. It does not fuse quite as readily in the kiln as white lead. Red lead is commonly used in preparing frits, where none of these disadvantages apply, and where its higher lead content is an advantage.

Both white lead and red lead are poisonous and must be handled with due precautions.

Lead silicates, made by a fusion process, are now commercially available. These are non-poisonous. They are reliable in composition and are easily incorporated in glazes.

15. Zinc Oxide ZnO

Zinc oxide, the only available source of zinc for glazes, is made from the ore sphalerite (ZnS). Zinc oxide should be used in the calcined form. The raw zinc oxide may cause cracking and crawling of the glaze coating.

16. Antimony Oxide Sb_2O_3

Antimony oxide is the only common source of antimony in glazes. It is little used, except to produce Naples yellow stains from combinations of lead and antimony.

17. Soda Ash or Sodium Carbonate Na_2CO_3

Soda ash is soluble and is therefore little used in glazes. It is a major source of sodium in glass and in frits, however. It is used as a deflocculant for clay slips.

18. Bone Ash, Calcium Phosphate $4Ca_3(PO_4) \cdot 2CaCO_3$

Bone ash is sometimes used in glazes, although its most important use is in providing the flux in china bodies. The material is made by calcining bones or by precipitation. Bone china has been made in England since the early part of the last century, and it is known for its extreme thinness and translucency. In glazes, bone ash functions as an opacifier and as a source of calcium. The phosphorus in the glaze causes an opalescence which arises from the presence of countless small entrapped globules in the glaze. In a high-fired glaze, a small amount of bone ash may induce opacity and opalescence. Some famous old Chinese glazes, notably the glazes on Chun wares of the Sung Dynasty, are known to contain phosphorus, and their blue opalescence may be due to the presence of this material, which was possibly introduced into the glaze in the form of an ash.

19. Cryolite Na_3AlF_6

Cryolite, or sodium aluminum fluoride, is an interesting material because it makes sodium available in a natural and unfritted form. It may be used wherever sodium and alumina are called for in a glaze. It adds the characteristic color response of sodium or of highly alkaline fluxes. The fluorine content, however, may cause difficulties in the form of excessive boiling of the glaze during melting, with the possibilities of pitting or pinholes.

20. Lepidolite $(HO_2F)_2KLiAl_2Si_3O_{10}$

Lepidolite is a lithium mica and is sometimes used as a source of lithium in glazes. It has a lower fusion point than most feldspars, and the lithia will serve to make most glazes more shiny than when a potash or soda spar is used. Lepidolite, however, seems to cause boiling and pitting in some glazes.

21. Lithium Carbonate Li_2CO_3

Lithium carbonate is used as a source of lithium in glazes. It offers the possibility of making glazes which have a brilliant color response, without the necessity of resorting to soluble materials or to frits. However, lithium carbonate is quite expensive, and this has perhaps kept it from being more generally used. Lithium carbonate has been used in small amounts in glazes as an auxillary flux to improve brightness and to increase the firing range.

22. Fluorspar CaF_2

Fluorspar has been used in glazes as a source of calcium. While it is commonly used in the enamel and glass industry as a flux and decolorizer, its usefulness in glazes has not been definitely established.

23. Pearl Ash, Potassium Carbonate K_2CO_3

Pearl ash is soluble, and for this reason it is seldom used in glazes. It is used, however, as a source of potassium in frits.

24. Niter, Potassium Nitrate KNO_3

Niter is highly soluble and is seldom used raw in glazes. It is used in frits as a source of potassium.

25. Borax $Na_2O \cdot 2B_2O_3 \cdot 10H_2O$

Borax may be used in glazes as a source of both sodium and boric oxide. But it is soluble, and for this reason is of limited use except when it is incorporated into a frit. Small amounts of borax, however, are sometimes very useful in lowering the fusion point of a glaze slightly and making it heal over and melt more smoothly. Small amounts of borax in a glaze or slip help to form a tougher coating on the ware. A thin crust of borax crystals develops on the surface of the raw glaze or slip.

The materials described above include all the commonly used glaze materials. Of those listed, there are several which are very seldom used, and others which are used largely in the compounding of frits. All of these materials are best thought of as glass-makers and should not be confused either with the various oxides of which they are made up or with the materials, to be discussed later, which are used to color and to influence the texture of glazes.

The great variety of glazes which are possible and the variety in the temperatures at which they melt is achieved by blending these materials in various proportions. In the next chapter, methods of arriving at proper combinations of materials will be described.

Chapter 12

Glaze Calculations, Theory and Objectives

1. The Necessity for Different Recipes for Glazes

One might well ask why two or three recipes for glazes, once they had been found to be effective, would not do for all pottery making. To the uninitiated it would certainly seem that potters are too preoccupied with the matter of glaze composition. Actually, however, there is a real need for a great variety of glaze compositions. For one thing, pottery is fired over quite a wide range of temperature. The lowest-fired wares are heated to about 800°, and the highest are fired at about 1400°. Obviously, the same glaze would not be satisfactory at all temperatures, since a glaze which will melt at a low temperature will volatilize or run off a pot at a higher temperature. In practice, any one glaze composition is useful for a temperature range of, at most, about 30°. For this reason, various recipes are required for each range of temperature.

Another reason for numerous glaze compositions is the demand for a variety of surface qualities. Glazes may be bright or dull, opaque or transparent, shiny or mat, thick or thin, and all the gradations in between. All of these surface qualities result from varying the contents of the glaze.

Color in glazes results from the addition of small amounts of coloring oxides to the glaze. Various glaze compositions, however, strongly influence the resultant colors, and the make-up of the glaze itself must be controlled if certain desired colors are to be obtained. All of these factors have resulted in the great number of formulas and recipes which exist.

2. Grouping Oxides according to Their Function in Glazes

It has been noted that in formulating, changing, or studying glazes, it is convenient to think of the glaze as a completed melt, containing only oxides as they have resulted from the combining and melting of the raw materials. Some method of representing the relative amounts of these oxides in a glaze is a necessity, and also necessary is a method of determining what materials, and in what quantities, will yield the desired kind and amount of oxides in a glaze. The empirical formula and the calculation of glazes from the empirical formula have been devised to fill this practical need.

The empirical formula is a method of representing a finished or melted glaze in terms of the relative amounts of the various oxides which are present. "Empirical" here means that the formula is a device for convenience and calculation rather than a true chemical formula. In this sense the empirical formula, as it is used in work with glazes, is a somewhat arbitrary device. Nevertheless, it does represent a real relationship between the oxides in the glaze, and for this reason it is of great assistance to the ceramist in any work which deals with glaze composition. The convention of the empirical formula as a method of representing glaze composition has been universally accepted among ceramists, and it has been helpful not only in the practical problems of glaze composition but also as an aid to the understanding of glazes.

According to the empirical formula, the oxides which are common to glazes are grouped into three groups or columns as follows:

RO	*R_2O_3*	*RO_2*
PbO	Al_2O_3	SiO_2
Na_2O	B_2O_3	
K_2O		
ZnO		
CaO		
MgO		
BaO		
SrO		
Li_2O		

This classification groups together those oxides which in general perform a similar function in the melting of the glaze. The oxides in the first column tend to act as melters, or fluxes, and they promote the fusion of the silica, in the last column, which may be thought of as the more passive oxide in the reaction. The alumina, in the middle column, occupies a somewhat neutral position in the reaction. It does not act as a flux, and yet it influences the nature of the melt. The oxides in the first column are essentially basic or alkaline in their reaction, the silica in the last column is essentially acid, and the middle column oxides are neutral. The different groups are named according to the proportion with which the oxides of that group combine with oxygen. The first column is called the "RO" column, which means "radical combined with one atom of oxygen" or "some element combined with one of oxygen." The second column is called the "R_2O_3" column, which means some element combined with oxygen in the ratio of two to three. The last column is called the "RO_2" column.

This grouping of the oxides gives one a clearer picture of the function of the various oxides in a melting glaze. Of course, all the oxides in the first column are not equally active as fluxes, but that, in general, is their function. They serve to attack the silica and to cause it to melt. Some of the oxides in the first column, although they may function in glazes as fluxes, are in themselves very refractory substances.

3. The Theory of Atomic Weight, and the Method of Stating the Quantities of the Oxides in the Formula

Having briefly described the manner in which the oxides are grouped in a formula, the method of reporting the quantity of each oxide present in the glaze must now be considered. These quantities are expressed as the relative number of molecules of each oxide present rather than as the gross or actual weight of the oxide present. The reason for this will be clear when it is considered how widely differing are the weights of the various molecules. To make this more clear, a word should be said about atomic weights.

Ninety-six elements are known, and the smallest indivisible units of these elements are known as atoms. Chemists have discovered that the atoms of different elements vary widely in weight. The atoms of the element lead, for example, are very much heavier than the atoms of the element oxygen. Hydrogen is known to be the lightest element. In making a relative scale of weight, hydrogen was assigned the value of 1, and the weight of the atoms of all the other elements was expressed in terms of their relationship to the weight of the hydrogen atom. Oxygen, which is sixteen times as heavy as hydrogen is given the atomic weight of 16. Silicon is twenty-eight times as heavy as hydrogen. Thus all the elements have been assigned a weight. This weight does not refer to pounds or grams, but to the relative weights of the atoms of the elements in terms of the weight of the hydrogen atom.

Atoms combine in specific relationships to form the various substances of nature. These groups of atoms are called molecules. A molecule may be defined as the smallest part of a substance which can exist separately. Water, for example, is made up of hydrogen and oxygen. The water molecule consists of two atoms of hydrogen tied to one atom of oxygen, and it is written with the symbol H_2O, which simply means: two hydrogen atoms to one oxygen atom.

The weight of any molecule is expressed in chemistry as the sum of the weights of the atoms which it contains. Thus the water molecule H_2O is twice the weight of hydrogen, or 2, plus the weight of oxygen, which is 16, making a total weight of 18. The weights of the various atoms and the weights of the various oxides used in ceramics are easily determined by consulting a chart of atomic and molecular weights, and they therefore do not need to be calculated each time. But an understanding of the basic principle of atomic and molecular weight is necessary to an understanding of glaze calculation.

Another example of the calculation of the molecular weight of a substance will make the method clear. Suppose, for example, we wish to determine the weight of silica, SiO_2, which contains one atom of silicon to two atoms of oxygen. Multiplying the atomic weights by the number of atoms indicated in the formula and adding the total, we get the molecular weight as follows:

$$\begin{array}{ll} \text{Si} & 28 \times 1 = 28 \\ \text{O}_2 & 16 \times 2 = 32 \\ & \overline{60} \text{ — Molecular weight of SiO}_2 \end{array}$$

This same method is used in determining all molecular weights, and more complicated substances, such as feldspars or frits, merely involve more arithmetic.

The reader who has studied chemistry must forgive this brief digression on some very elementary facts. If, on the other hand, the reader does not know any chemistry, a certain amount of confusion about the method of dealing with substances in terms of atoms and molecules is to be expected. But unless some understanding of elementary chemistry is gained, calculating glazes may remain a meaningless juggling of numbers and symbols.

If the idea of molecular weight is understood, the method of stating the quantities of the various oxides in the formula can be described. These quantities are always expressed in the relative numbers of molecules present in the glaze rather than in terms of the weights

Korean wine pitcher, probably from about the welfth century. Although this piece is made rom a dense, thin porcelain, its form is won-lerfully fluid and plastic. The vertical fluting, which suggests a melon-shape, was impressed n the clay when it was still soft. *Courtesy of The Smithsonian Institution, Freer Gallery of Art, Washington, D.C.*

below)
orean bowl from the Yi Dynasty. The bowl, ade from a grey-brown stoneware clay, is overed with a thin white slip which has run rregularly at the foot. Painted on this slip with xquisite freedom is a leaf pattern in iron xide. The bowl is covered with a clear glaze. *ourtesy of The Smithsonian Institution, Freer allery of Art, Washington, D.C.*

Korean vase from the Yi Dynasty. The pie
has been coated with a white slip, and t
decoration carried out in brush strokes of ir
oxide. The glaze is thin and transparent. T
predominant color is a warm creamy grey, b
there are tinges of greenish tones from fi
flashing. Although the landscape is quite d
tailed, its adaptation to the form of the pie
is masterly. *Courtesy of The Smithsonian I
stitution, Freer Gallery of Art, Washingto
D.C.*

(below)
Korean bowl from the Yi Dynasty. This stur
pot was pushed into an ovoid shape by t
potter while it was still very soft, and his fing
mark shows prominently on the side of t
piece. The outside of the piece has eviden
been coated with a very rough clay, th
washed with white slip and glazed. The co
is a mingling of warm and cool greys. *Courte
of The Smithsonian Institution, Freer Galle
of Art, Washington, D.C.*

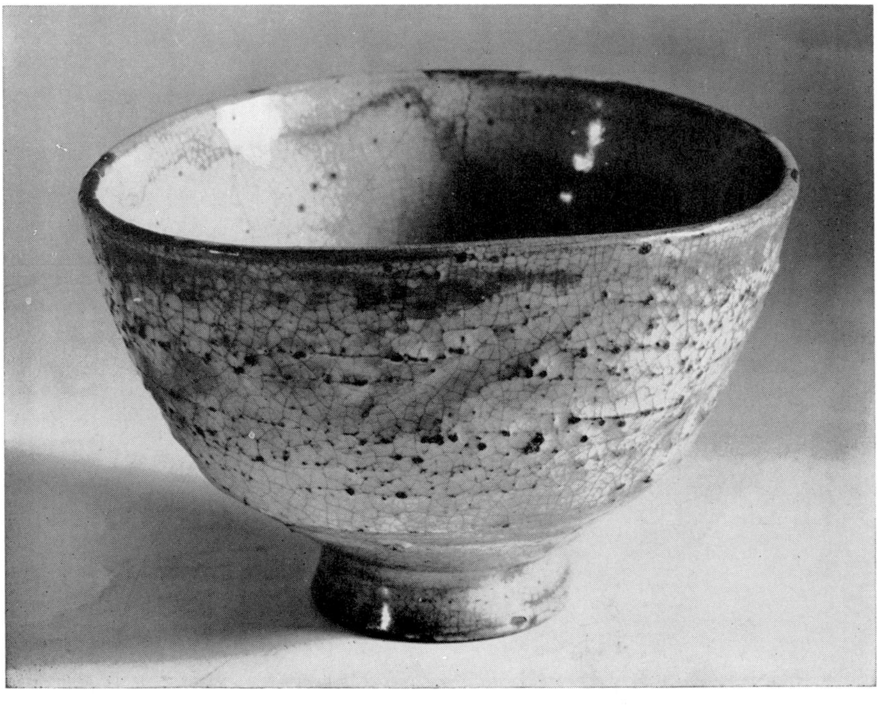

of the various oxides present. To make a simple analogy, suppose a basket is filled with apples and oranges. This is analogous to a glaze in which are melted two different oxides. If we wish to know the relative quantity of apples and of oranges, the best way is to make a count of each. Or, better, we might say that there is one orange for each two apples, for example, which gives an exact idea of the relative quantities. We would not say that there are five pounds of oranges and three pounds of apples. So it is in describing a glaze. What we want to know is how many molecules of silica there are in relation to the molecules of lead oxide, calcia, alumina, etc. In other words, the question is: what is the balance or relationship between the various things in the glaze? As we have seen, the molecules of the glaze are of widely varying weight, lead, for example, being several times heavier than silica. But in describing a glaze in a formula, the *relative number of molecules* of each substance is what is of interest, regardless of their weight.

For example, the formula for a simple lead glaze might be:

$$PbO \quad 1 \qquad Al_2O_3 \quad .2 \qquad SiO_2 \quad 1$$

This formula means that, in relative quantity, there is present in the finished glaze one molecule of lead oxide, two-tenths of a molecule of alumina, and one molecule of silica. The fact that the alumina is reported as being less than one molecule will give an idea of the rather arbitrary nature of the empirical formula, since we know that in actuality parts of molecules do not exist in this way. However, the formula may give an exact idea of the numbers of molecules in the glaze relative to each other.

A graphic representation of the glaze given above may help to make the meaning of the formula more clear:

Here, the molecules of the various oxides are represented by circles of various sizes which correspond to the discrepancy in weight of the different substances. Lead is heavier than silica. One circle each of lead and silica are shown, since the formula calls for a relationship of one to one. The alumina is represented as a fifth (.2) of the whole alumina molecule. Of course, in actuality, even the smallest visible fragment of a glaze would contain billions of molecules; so the formula does not tell anything about the total number of molecules in any given quantity of glaze. But it does give an idea of how many molecules of one thing there are in relation to the molecules of the other substances present.

4. The Unity Formula

As a basis for comparison, it has been accepted as a convention that all the oxides in the first column of the empirical formula be made to add up to one. This greatly facilitates the comparison of one formula with another. Since all the oxides in the first column act in general as fluxes, the numerical relation between the flux in a glaze formula and the silica can be seen at a glance. According to the unity formula, a glaze which contained lead oxide and calcium oxide in the proportion of one molecule of lead oxide to one molecule of calcium would be written:

$$\begin{matrix} PbO & .5 \\ CaO & .5 \end{matrix}$$

And if these two oxides were present in a glaze in this proportion, the formula might be:

$$\begin{matrix} PbO & .5 \\ CaO & .5 \end{matrix} \quad Al_2O_3 \quad .5 \quad SiO_2 \quad 1$$

In this formula there is one molecule of silica for each half-molecule of lead oxide, calcia, and alumina. When the sum of the fractional amounts in the first column adds up to one, we say that the formula is a unity formula.

Since the oxides in the first column perform a roughly similar function in the glaze, it is convenient for these always to add up to one, as a basis of comparison with silica. We can then see at a glance how many silica molecules are associated with the fluxing portion of the glaze. Of course, it would be possible always to write the silica portion of the glaze as the figure one and to state the other oxides as quantities relative to one. One trouble with such a system would be that the amounts of oxides in the first column would turn out to be such small fractional amounts that calculation would be more difficult and inexact.

Most of the confusion about the calculation of glazes centers about two points. One point is that the figures refer to molecules or parts of molecules rather than to weights or fractions of weights. The other point is that the amounts in the first column are arbitrarily made to add up to one and that all the other quantities are expressed in amounts relative to this.

5. Calculating Recipes of Glazes from Their Formula

Glaze calculation is a method of finding out what raw materials to mix up to yield, in a melted glaze, the balance of oxides indicated in a formula. It also is a method of determining the formula of any glaze recipe. It is important to distinguish between the formula of a glaze, which reports only the oxides present and their quantities, and the batch or recipe of a glaze, which tells only what raw materials go into making up the glaze, and their quantities.

Suppose, for example, that the following formula is given, and we wish to find out what materials to weigh out in the laboratory to make a glaze which, when fused, will have this composition:

$$PbO—1 \quad SiO_2—1$$

Although there is no alumina present, and only one oxide present in the first column, this is a correct unity formula, since the sum of the first column is one. One might think at first that the way to make up a batch of this glaze would be to take one pound (or gram) of lead oxide and one pound or gram of silica and mix them together. But one cannot do it this way, because, since the lead oxide molecule is much heavier than the silica molecule, one would get too many silica molecules and not enough lead oxide. Therefore, to find out what to weigh out to arrive at a glaze formula, one must first choose raw materials which will yield the desired oxides and then weigh them out in quantities which will yield the right molecular ratio between the oxides as called for in the formula. In this case, we want a ratio of one lead oxide molecule to one silica molecule. We might use for the glaze litharge, PbO, and Flint, SiO_2. To get the right quantity, the molecular weight of the material is multiplied by the quantity called for in the formula.

PbO 1 × 223 (molecular weight of litharge) = 223, amount of litharge
SiO_2 1 × 60 (molecular weight of flint) = 60, amount of flint

The answer, 223 parts of litharge and 60 parts of flint, may be weighed out in ounces, pounds, or carloads, and if this proportion were kept, the resultant glaze would have the proportion of one molecule of lead oxide to one of silica.

It will be seen that the calculation is made necessary by the difference in the molecular weights of the substances involved.

To give a slightly more involved example, suppose we wish to determine the batch or recipe of the following formula:

PbO .8	SiO_2 1
CaO .2	

Here, for each .8 molecules of lead oxide and .2 molecules of calcium oxide, there is one molecule of silica present in the finished glaze. The problem of calculating the batch or recipe for this glaze is to find the proper quantity and kind of raw materials to furnish the oxides in the amounts shown in the formula. Looking over the list of available raw materials, we note that lead oxide can be supplied by litharge, whose formula is PbO and whose molecular weight is 223. Calcium oxide can be supplied by whiting, whose formula is $CaCO_3$ and whose molecular weight is 100. Silica can be supplied by flint SiO_2, whose molecular weight is 60. Actually there is some latitude of choice in filling most formulas—choices which are governed mostly by common sense, as we shall see. Having decided what materials to use, the next problem is to find out how much of each material is needed to fill the formula. As in the previous example, this can be calculated by multiplying the amount of the oxide called for in the glaze by the molecular weight of the raw material which supplies this oxide.

PbO .8 × 223 = 178.4 parts of litharge
CaO .2 × 100 = 20 parts of whiting
SiO_2 1 × 60 = 60 parts of flint

The answers constitute the batch weight of the glaze, i.e., the relative amount of raw materials which must be weighed out to fill the formula.

It will be noted that the batch does not add up to 100 and is not a percentage composition. But it is a recipe which shows the relative amounts of each material. If it is desired to make the total come to 100, so that each quantity in the recipe will be a percentage of the whole, the sum of the recipe is divided into each figure in the recipe and then multiplied by 100, as follows:

Litharge	178.4	÷ 258.4 = .690 × 100 =	69.0
Whiting	20	÷ 258.4 = .077 × 100 =	7.7
Flint	60	÷ 258.4 = .233 × 100 =	23.3
	258.4		100.0%

The two simple examples given above illustrate how the formula can be converted into a recipe. This procedure would be followed when, for example, a new glaze had been formulated on paper and it was desired to find out what ingredients to weigh out for an actual sample.

6. An Example of Calculating from the Batch to the Formula

Glaze calculation makes possible the determination of the formula of any given batch or recipe of raw materials. Suppose, for example, that one wished to determine the empirical formula for the following mixture:

Whiting	10 parts by weight
Litharge	50 parts by weight
Flint	40 parts by weight
	100 total

This recipe tells the amount of each raw material to weigh out for the glaze, but it does not tell how many molecules of silica there are in the mixture relative to the number of molecules of lead oxide and calcium oxide. It is this relationship which we need to know if we are to deal intelligently with the composition.

To find the empirical formula of the above recipe, we divide each quantity of material by the molecular weight of that material:

Whiting	$10 \div 100 = .100$
Litharge	$50 \div 223 = .224$
Flint	$40 \div 60 = .666$

The answers here are known as molecular equivalents. We have already solved the problem in effect, because the relationship between .100, .224, and .666 tells the relative quantity of molecules of each substance in the glaze. It remains only to arrange these answers according to the empirical formula and to make the first column add up to one, or reduce it to unity. So the formula is written:

PbO	.224	SiO_2	.666
CaO	.100		
	.324 total		

As the formula now appears, the first column falls short of one. The next step is to divide each quantity in the whole formula by the sum of the quantities in the first column, which in this case is .324:

PbO	$.224 \div .324 = .691$
CaO	$.100 \div .324 = .309$
SiO_2	$.666 \div .324 = 2.05$

We may now write the formula in final form:

PbO	.691	SiO_2	2.05
CaO	.309		
	1.000		

Unless the division and multiplication be carried out to the fourth place, the sum of the first column is apt to be short of one by one or two thousandths. This is too small a quantity to be of any significance in glazes.

The essential methods of glaze calculation are illustrated in the examples given thus far, and if the principles involved in them are understood, more complicated problems can be dealt with without difficulty. The objectives of glaze calculation are: (a) to state the molecular formula in a clear way which will give a basis for comparison, (b) to translate the molecular formula into a recipe of materials which will yield in the finished glaze what the formula calls for, and (c) to arrive at a molecular formula from any given recipe of raw materials.

Chapter 13

Glaze Calculation Using Materials Containing More Than One Oxide

1. The Table of Raw Materials

A table is given (p. 63) which gives some of the necessary facts about the raw materials of glazes for use in glaze calculation. In practice, we refer to some such chart for atomic weights and other information which it is difficult and in fact unnecessary to commit to memory. Two formulas are given for each material: its formula as a raw material, and its formula after having been fired. This is necessary since many glaze materials are altered in composition by firing. Volatile constituents such as the carbonates are lost in firing. Whiting in the raw is calcium carbonate, $CaCO_3$; but when fired, it becomes calcium oxide, CaO. All the materials in their fired state are in oxide form. The molecular weight of a material may be different after it has been calcined, fired, or melted into a glass.

2. Equivalent Weight

The column labeled "equivalent weight" refers to the molecular weight of material which must be taken to yield one complete unit of the oxide which is desired in the glaze. In most cases, the equivalent weight is the same as the molecular weight of the material. There are, however, six exceptions where the equivalent weight is either more or less than the molecular weight. These are given below:

Bone Ash	$Ca_3(PO_4)_2$
Colemanite	$2CaO \cdot 3B_2O_3 \cdot 5H_2O$
White lead	$2PbCO_3 \cdot Pb(OH)_2$
Red lead	$Pb3O_4$
Nitre	KNO_3
Cryolite	Na_3AlF_6

In all of these six materials, the given formula of the material yields, when fired, either more or less than one molecule of the oxide which enters into the composition of the glaze. The molecular weight of the material has therefore been adjusted either to a higher or to a lower figure so as to give one molecule of the oxide in question. This adjusted, or equivalent, weight may be defined as that weight of a raw material which must be taken to obtain, in the glaze, one molecule of the desired oxide in fired form.

For example, red lead has the formula Pb_3O_4 and a molecular weight of 685. When red lead is fired, it becomes PbO. Note that PbO has more atoms of lead relative to those of oxygen than has Pb_3O_4. Also note that the formula of raw red lead is written "Pb_3," which means three atoms of lead. Therefore for a yield of one atom of Pb we must divide the molecular weight of the red lead by three, giving an equivalent weight of 228.

In the case of white lead, we must divide by three also. White lead has the formula $2PbCO_3 \cdot Pb(OH)_2$. When fired, the carbonate (CO_3) and the hydroxide $(OH)_2$ radicals are lost, leaving three PbO. To obtain, therefore, the equivalent weight of white lead, we divide its molecular weight, 775, by three, which gives 258.

In the case of niter, the raw formula contains but one atom of potassium. Since the fired unit, K_2O, has two atoms of potassium, we must multiply the molecular weight of the raw niter, 101, by two to get the equivalent weight, 202.

A similar situation obtains in the case of cryolite, Na_3AlF_6. Here, we wish to obtain one molecule of Al_2O_3. Since cryolite contains only one atom of Al, we must double its weight. Doubling Na_3 gives, in the fired formula, $3Na_2O$.

Colemanite as a raw material is conveniently written $2CaO{\cdot}3B_2O_3{\cdot}5H_2O$. It is awkward to handle this formula in calculating because there are two units of calcium; so the formula is split in two, giving instead one unit of CaO and one and one-half units of B_2O_3. This cuts the weight from 412 to 206.

The equivalent weight which is used in the case of these six materials is admittedly a rather arbitrary device, chemically. But it does simplify calculating, and if the equivalent weight is used consistently for all materials, no discrepancies in calculating will arise from this source. If the figure equivalent weight is not used, the six materials discussed above must be calculated each time with reference to their formula and to the fact that they do not yield one oxide unit.

3. Feldspar Formulas

The feldspars in the raw material table are represented by formulas which are identical with the empirical formula already described. The alkalies and alkaline earths are grouped in the first column, which adds up to one, and the alumina and the silica are given values relative to those of the first column. The formula of a feldspar, or of any other material for that matter, is computed in the same way as the example described above in which a glaze batch was converted to a formula.

An example is now given of the manner in which the formula of a feldspar is derived from its chemical analysis. Suppose that a feldspar has been given quantitative analysis and is found to have the following composition:

SiO_2	66.2
Al_2O_3	18.4
CaO	1.6
K_2O	10.8
Na_2O	2.0

These figures, as reported by the chemist, refer to the actual percentages by weight of the various oxides found in the particular feldspar. They do not mean that there are 66.2 molecules of silica to each 18.4 molecules of alumina, but rather that there are 66.2 grams or pounds of silica to each 18.4 grams or pounds of alumina. The purpose of converting the analysis as given above into a formula is to get at the relative quantity of molecules of each oxide present.

As in the example involving lead oxide and silica in a glaze, we divide each item in the percentage composition by the molecular weight of the oxide, which gives us the molecular equivalent or relative number of molecules of each oxide.

	% Composition	÷	*Molecular Weight*	=	*Molecular Equivalents*
SiO_2	66.2	÷	60	=	1.103
Al_2O_3	18.4	÷	102	=	.180
CaO	1.6	÷	56	=	.028
Na_2O	2.0	÷	62	=	.032
K_2O	10.8	÷	94	=	.114

The molecular equivalents can now be set down in their appropriate columns:

CaO .028			
	Al_2O_3 .180	SiO_2 1.103	
Na_2O .032			
K_2O .114			
.174			

Since the first column adds up to .174, this is not a unity formula; and to make it come to unity, all quantities of the formula are divided by .174, resulting in the formula in its final form:

CaO .160		
	Al_2O_3 1.04	SiO_2 6.39
Na_2O .184		
K_2O .655		

We now have the formula of the feldspar in terms of the relative numbers of molecules of the various oxides present. To obtain the formula weight of the feldspar, the quantity of each oxide present in the formula is multiplied by the molecular weight of that oxide, and the resultant sums are totalled, as follows:

CaO	.16	× 56 =	89.6	
Na_2O	.184	× 62 =	11.40	
K_2O	.665	× 94 =	61.6	
Al_2O_3	1.04	× 102 =	106.1	
SiO_2	6.39	× 60 =	383.4	
			571.5	formula weight of the feldspar

One of the feldspars which is listed on the raw materials chart is a theoretical, or typical, composition rather than a commercially available material. This is orthoclase. Most of the minerals found in nature do not conform exactly to the composition which has been determined by mineralogists to be typical. In the case of feldspars, only hand-picked specimens would be apt to conform exactly to the theoretical composition. Commercially mined feldspars usually have two or three alkaline constituents, and the proportion of alumina and silica is rarely like the ideal composition. To make an accurate calculation of a glaze, the formula derived from the analysis must be used.

4. Calculation of the Batch from the Formula of a Simple Lead Glaze

When glazes contain materials which have more than one oxide in them—and this is true of almost all workable glazes—the arithmetic or calculation becomes somewhat more complex. For example, the following glaze, although it is a very simple one, involves the addition of clay as a material, and since clay contains both alumina and silica, it will serve to illustrate the method of calculation where one material yields two different oxides.

PbO 1 Al_2O_3 .2 SiO_2 2.5

The experienced glaze maker can see at a glance that this glaze could best be made up by combining some material which yields lead oxide, such as litharge or white lead; clay, which would take care of the alumina; and flint, which would satisfy the silica. The problem is to determine how much of these materials to use to get the ratio of oxides indicated in the molecular formula. Let us say that litharge is chosen for the lead content of the glaze. As in the previous examples, the quantity of lead oxide called for, 1, is multiplied by the equivalent of litharge, 223, giving 223 parts as the amount of litharge to use in the recipe. The clay used to supply the alumina has the formula $Al_2O_3 \cdot$

$2SiO_2{\cdot}2H_2O$ and the equivalent weight of 258. Taking .2, the amount of alumina called for in the formula, and multiplying it by 258, we obtain the batch weight for the clay, 51.6. But with each molecule of alumina in clay, there are associated two molecules of silica. Therefore when we supply our formula with .2 of alumina, we get along with it .4 of silica. This amount partially fills the amount of silica called for in the formula, but there still remain 2.1 molecules of silica to be filled with the material flint. Taking then, 2.1, the amount of silica needed, and multiplying it by 60, the equivalent weight of the flint, we get the batch weight for the flint, 126.

The arithmetic involved in this simple calculation will be made more clear if the calculation is arranged in tabular form, placing across the top all the oxides in the formula and their quantity; and in the vertical column to the left, arranging the raw materials which are to be used in satisfying the formula.

	PbO 1	Al_2O_3 .2	SiO_2 2.5
Litharge 1	1		
	0		
Clay .2		.2	.4
		0	2.1
Flint 2.1			2.1
			000

Litharge 1 × 223 = 223
Clay .2 × 258 = 51.6
Flint 2.1 × 60 = 126 Batch weights or recipe

A table such as this is usually kept in calculating glazes to help keep track of the amount of the various oxides which are supplied by the raw materials.

The important method involved in the above calculation is the manner in which the amount of clay is figured, since it is supplying two different oxides to the glaze. It should be noted that when we take .2 of the material, we are actually taking a fractional amount of the material, less than one part. With this .2 we, of course, get .2 of everything in the material, not only .2 of alumina but .2 of the silica as well. When a quantity of a material is introduced, the quantity applies to all the components of the material. Actually, what was done in this example is to introduce .2, or one-fifth, of the clay molecule, and naturally this one-fifth part contains one-fifth of the alumina, or .2, and one-fifth of the silica, or .4. Of course, a molecule cannot actually be divided in this fashion, and the arbitrary nature of the calculation should be kept in mind. But, as we have said, the method does permit an accurate translation of the formula into terms of actual raw materials.

5. Calculation of a Glaze Containing Both Clay and Feldspar

The method of handling materials which supply more than one oxide to the glaze will be clarified by another example involving both clay and a feldspar. Suppose we need to calculate the recipe of a lead glaze with the following formula:

PbO .8 Al_2O_3 .25 SiO_2 2.00
K_2O .2

The first step is to construct a chart in which the oxides can be tabulated and kept track of as they are filled or satisfied by the raw materials. As before, the oxides of the formula are posted horizontally at the top, and the raw materials are placed in a vertical column at the left.

	PbO .8	K_2O .2	Al_2O_3 .25	SiO_2 2.00
White Lead .8	.8			
Potash Feldspar .2			.2	1.2
		.2	.05	.8
Clay .05			.05	.1
			00	.7
Flint .7				.7
				0

Here, we start with the lead oxide in the formula and fill it with .8 of white lead. Then the potassium oxide, K_2O, is filled by taking .2 of potash feldspar (orthoclase). In this case, for the sake of simplicity of calculating, we have used the theoretical composition of orthoclase as shown on the raw materials chart, even though such a material is not available commercially. With the .2 of feldspar, we get .2 of everything in the feldspar, which has the formula K_2O 1, Al_2O_3 1 and SiO_2 6. This adds to the formula .2 K_2O, (lx.2), .2 of Al_2O_3 (lx.2), and 1.2 of SiO_2 (.2x6), which quantities are posted in the chart as shown above.

The next problem is to find out how much alumina and silica still remain to be added to the glaze. This is determined by subtracting the amount which came with the feldspar from the amount called for by the formula, namely, .05 of alumina and .8 of silica. The alumina is then filled with the material clay ($Al_2O_3 \cdot 2SiO_2 \cdot 2H_2O$). As in the previous example, .05 of clay, which satisfies the alumina of the formula, brings along with it twice that amount of SiO_2, or .1. Subtracting this amount from the remaining silica gives the quantity .7, the amount of silica which must be added with flint.

The molecular equivalents obtained by this procedure are now multiplied by the equivalent weights of the various raw materials involved, which gives the batch weights or recipe of the glaze, as shown below:

White lead	.8 × 258	=	206.4	
Orthoclase	.2 × 556	=	111.2	
Clay	.05 × 258	=	12.9	
Flint	.7 × 60	=	42.0	

No matter how complicated the glaze is, or how many materials there are in it which contain two or more oxides, the procedure given in the above example is followed. Before giving a more complicated example of calculating, the following steps in calculating a glaze recipe from a formula are listed:

(1) First, a chart is constructed, as in the previous examples, which makes it possible to keep track of the quantities as they are added. Then all those oxides in the first column of the glaze which occur singly in the raw materials are satisfied. Such oxides as lead, barium, and zinc occur in raw materials which yield no other oxide. If they are taken care of first, only those oxides which are

found in materials containing two or more oxides will remain to be calculated.

(2) Next, the oxides in the first column are filled, which come from materials having more than one oxide in them.
(3) Next, the feldspar is calculated.
(4) Next, the remaining alumina is satisfied with clay.
(5) And finally, what silica remains to be satisfied after the addition of feldspar and clay is filled with flint.

6. Selection of Raw Materials for Glazes

One who has not become quite familiar with glaze materials may feel puzzled as to what raw materials to use to satisfy a glaze formula. Questions are apt to arise, such as: Should the sodium in the glaze be filled with borax, or with feldspar? The following general rules may make the reasons behind most choices more clear:

(1) Soluble materials are avoided, and the glaze is satisfied wherever possible with insoluble natural raw materials or with frits.
(2) As few materials as possible are used.
(3) Use of natural raw materials which contain two oxides is to be preferred to adding the two oxides in separate form. For example, it is better to satisfy a glaze containing both calcia and magnesia with dolomite, which contains both of these oxides, than it would be to add whiting and magnesium carbonate.
(4) Alumina is added in the form of clay or feldspar.
(5) The silica which is still needed after the clay and feldspar have been added is added in the form of flint.

It will be seen that the glaze formula may be filled with raw materials in different ways. For example, the same lead glaze formula could be made up with either red lead or white lead. While it is true that the quantity and kind of oxides should be the same, the two glazes might not have exactly the same maturing temperature or the same characteristics. Different raw materials, in other words, influence the glaze, even though they may yield the same oxides in the finished glaze. This is due to the melting characteristics of the various materials and their interaction on each other during melting. Oxides which are added to the glaze in the form of naturally combined materials, such as feldspars, will cause a somewhat lower fusion point than if the same oxides had been added to the glaze in single materials. The selection of raw materials is critically important in glaze making, and if any glaze is to be duplicated exactly, the batch as well as the formula must be known.

7. Calculation of a More Complex Glaze

An example will be given next of the calculation of a more complex glaze. Suppose we wish to obtain the batch or recipe for a glaze whose formula is:

PbO	.5				
		Al_2O_3	.25	SiO_2	2.8
CaO	.2				
		B_2O_3	.15		
K_2O	.2				
MgO	.1				

In studying this formula, one notes that several oxides in it can be supplied by materials which contain more than one oxide. The B_2O_3 may be supplied by colemanite, since there is also CaO in the formula. The MgO may be supplied by talc, since this material yields both MgO and SiO_2. The K_2O would be best supplied by feldspar. A logical choice of materials would be white lead, feldspar, colemanite, whiting, talc, clay, and flint.

As before, we set up a chart which indicates the oxides called for in the glaze and the raw materials which have been chosen to fill the formula. The calculation is given below:

	PbO .5	CaO .2	B_2O_3 .15	K_2O .2	MgO .1	Al_2O_3 .25	SiO_2 2.80
White lead .5	.5 0						
Colemanite .1		.1 .1	.15 0				
Whiting .1		.1 0					
Talc .03					.1 0		.132 2.668
Feldspar .2				.2 0		.2 .05	1.2 1.47
Clay .05						.05 x	.1 1.37
Flint 1.37							1.37 0

of the material in order to get the .15 called for in the glaze. In this case it will be seen that we must divide the formula of colemanite by 10 if we are to get .15 of B_2O_3, which is one-tenth of 1.5, the amount of B_2O_3 in the formula of the material. Using the decimal system, we multiply colemanite by .1, which is, of course, the same as dividing it by 10.

This situation arises frequently in calculating. We must divide the formula of some material so as to get the desired

In this calculation, some new problems are encountered. It will be clear how the .5 of white lead was arrived at. When we come to colemanite, the question is: how much colemanite must we use to satisfy the .15 molecules of B_2O_3 called for in the formula. The formula of colemanite, CaO 1, B_2O_3 1.5, will be seen to contain one and one-half times more B_2O_3 than CaO. We must divide the B_2O_3 as shown in the formula fraction of some one oxide present. In this case the amount of B_2O_3 controls the amount of colemanite to be put in the glaze, since all the B_2O_3 is to come from colemanite. To find the factor, or amount, of colemanite which will yield the right amount of B_2O_3, we divide the amount which is called for in the formula by the amount which occurs in the material. Thus, in the case of the following calculation:

$$\frac{.15\ B_2O_3\ \text{(called for in the formula)}}{1.5\ B_2O_3\ \text{(in the material colemanite)}} = .1\ \text{(the amount of colemanite which will yield } .15\ B_2O_3\text{)}$$

Having determined how much colemanite may be used, namely .1, we then multiply all the oxides in colemanite by .1 and post the answers on the chart. This gives a value of .1 for CaO (.1x1=.1) and, as expected, a value of .15 for B_2O_3 (.1x1.5).

Whiting is next added to take care of the remaining CaO.

Next we come to the MgO in the formula, which is to be supplied by talc. The formula of talc is 3MgO, $4SiO_2$; so again we must find a factor, or amount, for talc, which when multiplied by the formula of talc gives .1 MgO, the oxide needed. Following the procedure given above we get:

$$\frac{.1\ \text{(amount of MgO needed in formula)}}{3\ \text{(amount of MgO in talc formula)}} = .033\ \text{(amount of talc which can be used)}$$

Multiplying now all the oxides in talc by .033, we get .033x3=.099, which is as near to .1 as our arithmetic will take us, and .033x4=.132 SiO_2.

The method used here for determining the amount of colemanite and talc which can be used to fill a formula is used whenever the raw material contains an oxide in its formula which is either more or less than 1, provided that this oxide is the one we are using to fill entirely some oxide requirement in the formula. The rule-of-thumb for finding the amount of a material to use may be stated:

$$\frac{\text{What is wanted in the formula}}{\text{What is present in the material}} = \text{the amount of the material which may be used}$$

After subtracting the amount of silica which was obtained with the talc, the calculation of the above problem is carried out in the same fashion as the preceding example. It remains, then, to multiply each of the figures obtained for the raw materials by its equivalent weight to obtain the batch of the glaze as follows:

Feldspar	.2	× 556	=	111.2
White lead	.5	× 258	=	129.0
Colemanite	.1	× 206	=	20.6
Whiting	.1	× 100	=	10.0
Talc	.033	× 378	=	12.4
Clay	.05	× 258	=	12.9
Flint	1.37	× 60	=	81.6

8. A Calculation Involving a Complex Feldspar

An example is now given of a calculation involving a glaze which includes a particular feldspar, whose exact formula has been determined by chemical analysis and converted into a molecular formula. The problem is to calculate the batch of the following glaze:

K_2O .243			
	Al_2O_3 .35		SiO_2 3.5
CaO .6			
MgO .157			

"Buckingham Feldspar" is to be used, which has the formula:

K_2O .74	Al_2O_3 1.026	SiO_2 6.34
CaO .26		

and a formula weight of 571.

In this example, it will be seen that all of the K_2O and some of the CaO, Al_2O_3, and SiO_2 will be supplied by the feldspar. The rest of the formula can be made up with magnesium carbonate, dolomite, or talc to satisfy the MgO, and with clay and flint for satisfying the remaining alumina and silica.

A chart is constructed for ease of calculating:

Each oxide in the feldspar formula is now multiplied by the figure we have obtained, .33, and the amounts are tabulated in the appropriate column. The MgO is then filled with dolomite, which brings with it an equal amount of CaO. The remaining CaO is filled with whiting, and clay and flint are used to complete the formula. The batch is determined in the usual way by multiplying the molecular equivalents of the various materials by the equivalent weights of the materials to obtain the batch weights:

Buckingham Feldspar	.33 × 571 = 177.43
Dolomite	.157 × 184 = 28.88
Whiting	.357 × 100 = 35.7
Clay	.012 × 258 = 3.09
Flint	1.486 × 60 = 89.2

	K_2O	CaO	MgO	Al_2O_3	SiO_2
	.243	.600	.157	.350	3.50
Buckingham Feldspar .33	.243	.086		.338	1.99
	0	.514		.012	1.51
Dolomite .157		.157	.157		
		.357	0		
Whiting .357		.357			
		0			
Clay 0.12				.012	.024
				0	1.486
Flint 1.486					1.486
					0

In order to find out how much Buckingham feldspar can be used in this formula, the figure of K_2O .243 must be divided by .74, the amount of K_2O in the feldspar. This follows the method given in the previous problem, namely, that of dividing the amount of the oxide needed in the formula by the amount which is supplied by the raw material. In this case, the answer is:

$$\frac{\text{Wanted in the formula—.243}}{\text{Have in the material— .74}} = .33 \text{ mol. equivalent of feldspar to use to fill the formula.}$$

The examples of calculating which are given above cover all the problems which are ever encountered in calculating the batches of glazes from their formulas. Frits, which will be described further on, are calculated in the same manner as feldspars.

Chapter 14

Calculating Glaze Formulas from Batches or Recipes

1. An Example of Determining the Formula of a Glaze from a Recipe

An example is now given which will illustrate the derivation of a glaze formula from the batch or recipe. This has already been illustrated by a simple problem in Chapter 6. The following will indicate the method when numerous oxides are involved. Suppose that we are using a glaze with the following composition and we wish to know what its formula is:

Buckingham Feldspar	45
Colemanite	10
Talc	10
Dolomite	10
Whiting	5
Zinc Oxide	5
Clay	5
Flint	30

To find the formula of this combination of raw materials, we start by dividing the quantity of each material by its equivalent weight. It will be seen that the procedure in solving this problem is essentially the reverse of the method used for calculating the batch from the formula.

Buckingham Spar	$45 \div 571 = .078$
Colemanite	$10 \div 206 = .048$
Talc	$10 \div 378 = .026$
Dolomite	$10 \div 184 = .054$
Whiting	$5 \div 100 = .05$
Zinc Oxide	$5 \div 81 = .061$
Clay	$5 \div 258 = .019$
Flint	$30 \div 60 = .5$

Next, a chart is constructed which allows for the tabulation of the molecular equivalents of the various materials in a vertical column at the left. Across

	K_2O	Na_2O	CaO	MgO	ZnO	Al_2O_3	B_2O_3	SiO_2
Buckingham Spar .078	.057	.02				.079		.494
Colemanite .048			.048				.072	
Talc .026				.078				.104
Dolomite .054			.054	.054				
Whiting .05			.05					
Zinc Oxide .061					.061			
Clay .019						.019		.038
Flint .5								.5
Totals =	.057	.02	.152	.132	.061	.098	.072	1.136

the top are arranged horizontally the oxides which are known to occur in the raw materials. Then the molecular equivalent of each raw material is multiplied by the quantity of each oxide in its formula, and the answer posted in the appropriate column. The totals of the columns are the number of molecular weights of the various oxides in the glaze.

The totals of the various oxides are now arranged as a formula:

K_2O	.057	Al_2O_3	.098	SiO_2	1.136
Na_2O	.020				
CaO	.152	B_2O_3	.072		
MgO	.132				
ZnO	.061				
	.422				

The formula is now brought to unity by dividing every number in it by the sum of the first column, which gives us our final formula:

K_2O	.132				
Na_2O	.047	Al_2O_3	.23	SiO_2	2.69
CaO	.360				
MgO	.312	B_2O_3	.17		
ZnO	.144				

2. Steps in Calculating from the Batch to the Formula

The steps in calculating from the batch or recipe of a glaze to the formula may be summarized as follows:

1. Divide the quantity of each material by the equivalent weight of that material.
2. Construct a chart with all the oxides which are contained in the materials arranged horizontally across the top and the raw materials listed vertically at the left.
3. Multiply the molecular equivalent of each raw material as determined in step one by the quantity of each oxide in its formula, and post the answers in the appropriate columns.
4. Add the columns for each oxide.
5. Arrange the quantities of the oxides in the manner of a formula.
6. Bring the formula to unity by dividing all quantities in it by the sum of the first column.

Chapter 15

Practical Problems in Glaze Calculation

Some practical problems will make the reasons for calculating glazes more clear. Glaze calculation is a method of arriving at suitable compositions of materials for glazes, and for changing, adjusting, and comparing glazes without resorting to more trial and error in the laboratory than is necessary. Methods of arriving at original glaze compositions will be discussed in a later chapter.

1. Comparison of Glazes

It is very difficult to compare two glaze recipes, because the list of raw materials does not tell the relative amount of the oxides present, and it is the proportion of oxides in a glaze which is the controlling factor in melting and in surface quality. Glaze formulas, on the other hand, are easy to compare.

For example, suppose one were comparing the two recipes for cone 9 glazes given below:

Glaze A		*Glaze B*	
Minpro Spar	52.2	Buckingham Spar	149
Buckingham Spar	42.8	Dolomite	46
56 Spar	93.9	Whiting	25
Dolomite	18.8	Clay	25.8
Talc	30.2	Flint	120
Whiting	45.0		
Zinc Oxide	2.0		
Clay	30.9		
Flint	74.1		

Actually, glaze A is a semi-opaque, satiny glaze, and glaze B is opaque and quite mat. But in the recipes as shown, it is rather hard to account for this difference, especially since in this case the recipes are not given in percentage amounts. One can only make a guess as to how much calcium oxide, or magnesium oxide, percentage-wise, there is in the two glazes.

Reduced to formula, the two glazes have the following composition:

Glaze A

KNaO	.275				
CaO	.565				
MgO	.135	Al_2O_3	.45	SiO_2	3.75
ZnO	.025				

Glaze B

K_2O	.25	Al_2O_3	.38	SiO_2	3.8
CaO	.50				
MgO	.25				

In the formulas, we are able to see at once the relative amounts of the various oxides in the glazes and can compare them intelligently. It is clear in this case that the greater amount of MgO in Glaze B accounts for most of the difference in quality between the two glazes. The presence of more KNaO, ZnO, and CaO in Glaze A makes it more fusible, even though it has more Al_2O_3 than Glaze B.

2. Substitution of Materials

Glaze calculation is useful in making substitutions of materials in glazes. If, for example, a particular frit or feldspar becomes unavailable, one can easily substitute another material and know exactly how to change the recipe without altering the balance of oxides present in the glaze. To make such a substitution by trial and error would involve considerable laboratory work. One would have to make numerous tests and fire them until the correct amount of new materials was arrived at.

Suppose, for example, that one wished to continue using the following glaze even though "Ontario" spar was no longer available.

"Ontario" Spar

K_2O	.75	Al_2O_3	1.1	SiO_2	7.5	Formula weight = 647
Na_2O	.25					

Glaze

K_2O	.3	Al_2O_3	.44	SiO_2	3.50
Na_2O	.1				
CaO	.5				
MgO	.1				

Batch

Ontario Spar	258.8
Whiting	40.0
Dolomite	18.4
Flint	30.0

Substituting Nepheline Syenite for "Ontario" spar:

nepheline syenite = KNaO 1 Al_2O_3 1.108 SiO_2 4.652

The revised batch is, therefore:

Nepheline Syenite	184.8
Dolomite	18.4
Whiting	40.0
Flint	98.4

Although these two glazes are made up of different raw materials, their formula is the same.

3. Altering Glaze Formulas

There are many times when a potter feels that it is desirable or necessary to change a glaze in order to alter its appearance, to make it mature at a different temperature, or to improve its fit to the clay body. Glaze calculation provides a method for making such changes rationally, with a minimum of trial and error. It is very difficult to make changes by altering the batch of a glaze, because the changed balance of oxides in the finished glaze cannot be accurately known. It is very simple, on the other hand, to make changes in the formula and to calculate the new glaze batch.

In practice, it is possible, and sometimes desirable, to change a glaze by simply adding some material. If one wished to make a glaze more mat, for instance, clay could be added to the glaze in progressively larger amounts until the right surface quality had been achieved. But if the proposed alteration requires exact readjustment, it is much more logical to make the change in the formula. When making a change in the formula, one can see at a glance just how the ratio of the various oxides has been altered.

A simple example will illustrate the usefulness of glaze calculation in this connection. Suppose the following glaze at cone 04 is not bright and shiny enough:

White Lead	154.8
Whiting	20.0
Potash Spar	55.6
Zinc Oxide	8.1
Clay	50.6
Flint	108.0

Calculating the formula of this recipe, the formula is found to be:

PbO	.6	Al_2O_3	.3	SiO_2	2.8
CaO	.2				
KNaO	.1				
ZnO	.1				

The formula reveals too much alumina and too much silica for a bright glaze at cone 04. The formula might be re-written:

PbO	.6	Al_2O_3	.2	SiO_2	2.00
CaO	.2				
KNaO	.1				
ZnO	.1				

Calculating the batch from this formula, the revised glaze is:

White Lead	154.8
Whiting	20.0
Potash Spar	55.6
Zinc Oxide	8.1
Clay	25.8
Flint	72.0

4. Trying Out New Materials

Glaze calculation is very useful when some new material is being tried out in a glaze. If the chemical composition of the new material is known, it can be introduced into the glaze in the proper amount with a minimum of trial and error. Suppose, for example, that one wished to try out some wood ash in a glaze. If the chemical analysis of the ash were available, its formula could be calculated according to the method described in section 3 of Chapter 13.

Chemical composition of an ash:

SiO_2	42.3%
Al_2O_3	12.8
Fe_2O_3	1.4
CaO	26.3
K_2O	10.2
MgO	7.0

Formula derived from the chemical composition:

$$\left.\begin{array}{ll} K_2O & .15 \\ CaO & .63 \\ MgO & .21 \end{array}\right\} \begin{array}{l} Al_2O_3 \\ .15 \end{array} \left\{ \begin{array}{l} SiO_2 \\ .94 \end{array}\right.$$

When the formula of the ash has been obtained, it can be used in a glaze with due regard for the amounts of various oxides present. In the ash given above, it will be seen that the material by itself is too low in alumina and silica to be, by itself, a successful high-fired glaze. It would need the addition of clay, flint, and perhaps feldspar to make it practical as a glaze.

In a later section, the method of originating new glazes will be described, and according to this procedure, the ash described above could easily be incorporated into a new glaze which would be likely to perform in a predictable way. The method of originating new glazes will be more understandable in the light of more information about the composition of glazes and the make-up of various types of glazes as discussed in the next two chapters.

Chapter 16

The Composition of Glazes

1. Fusion Points of Glazes

It is now necessary to consider in more detail the composition of glazes and the design of glaze formulas to control the temperature of melting, the texture, and the response to the addition of coloring oxides.

Combinations of oxides ordinarily have lower melting points than some of the oxides in the mixtures. When two oxides are intimately mixed and then subjected to heat, their melting point is usually considerably below that of either of the oxides when heated separately. The proportion of two oxides which has the lowest melting point is called the eutectic. This tendency of combinations of materials to have a lower melting point than either of the materials making up the combination is of great importance in glaze making, since it enables fluid mixtures to be made from combinations of largely refractory oxides. If the ceramist wishes to verify this fact, he can make the following experiment: feldspar and whiting are mixed dry in three different proportions, 50-50, 25 percent feldspar and 75 percent whiting, and 25 percent whiting and 75 percent feldspar. If these mixtures, together with pure whiting and pure feldspar, are made into mounds and fired on tiles in a kiln to about cone 8, it will be seen that the proportion of 25 percent whiting and 75 percent feldspar will have melted into a glass, while the feldspar will have only sintered into a stiff mass; and the whiting, changed by the fire into quick lime, will not have melted at all. Such "fusion button" tests are actually very useful in determining the effect on melting of various combinations of materials.

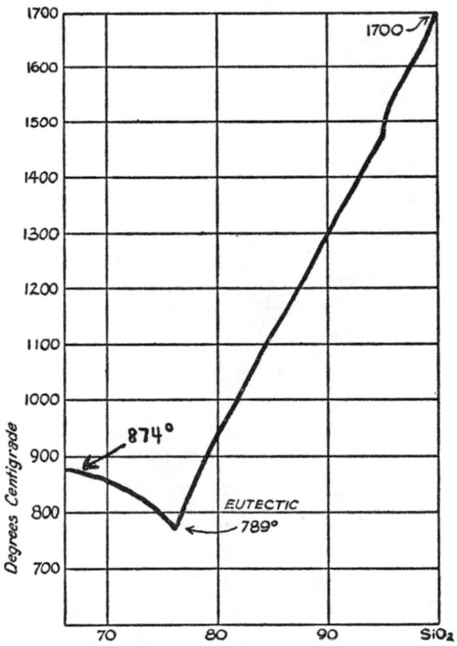

Eutectic between Sodium bi-silicate and silica.

The accompanying diagram illustrates the eutectic between sodium bi-silicate and silica. Sodium bi-silicate has a melting point of 874°. Silica has a melting point in the neighborhood of 1700°, yet when more silica is added to sodium bi-silicate, its melting point is lowered to 789°.

Glaze composition must be controlled so that, at the desired temperature, the glaze will melt and smooth itself out over the ware in a glassy coating. This fusion point is controlled by (a) the kinds of oxides present in the glaze, and (b) the relative amount of these oxides. Melting is brought about by the interaction of the various oxides on each other when subjected to heat. Since most glazes contain numerous oxides, the reactions involved in the fusion of the materials into a glass are complex, and it is difficult to predict the exact temperature at which any given combination of glaze materials will melt. The formula of a glaze, however, gives a reasonably certain basis for predicting the melting point of the glaze within a cone or two.

The fusion point of a glaze may be lowered by—

(1) Increasing the amount of active fluxes such as lead oxide, soda, or potash.
(2) Adding more fluxing oxides to the composition of the glaze. For example, a glaze may be made to melt at a lower temperature by adding lead oxide, soda, potash, zinc oxide, or boric oxide.
(3) Decreasing the amount of silica and alumina in the glaze.
(4) Decreasing the more inactive fluxes, such as magnesia and barium oxide, in favor of more active fluxes.
(5) Adding coloring oxides, such as iron, cobalt, or copper, which in themselves are active fluxes.
(6) Grinding the materials more finely or introducing the oxides in the form of a frit rather than in the raw state may lower the melting point of the glaze.

The fusion point of a glaze may be raised by a reverse of these procedures.

It will be obvious that the melting point of any glaze must be known and under control before it can be successfully used, and that a glaze suitable for the lower ranges of temperatures will not be suitable for higher temperatures.

2. Fluxing Action of the Various Oxides

Chart No. 1 gives the approximate temperature range of the fluxes which are commonly used in glazes. Each of these oxides, of course, has a specific melting point, and it will be seen that these melting points vary widely. MgO, for instance, has a melting point of 2800°, while PbO melts at 886°. It must be remembered, however, that in combination with other oxides, even a material which, by itself, has a very high melting point may function as a flux.

The chart shows each oxide represented by a solid line in that range of temperature, indicated by pyrometric cones, where it may be useful as a flux. The dotted portion of the line shows the temperature range at which the oxide may be less useful. The temperature range of these fluxes may be summarized as follows:

1. Lead oxide is an active flux from the lowest temperatures up to about cone 5. Beyond this temperature, lead becomes increasingly volatile and is seldom used.
2. K_2O and Na_2O are useful as fluxes throughout the temperature range. Both of these oxides are very potent fluxes.
3. The alkaline earths CaO, MgO, and BaO are active fluxes only at high temperatures, and below cone 4 they

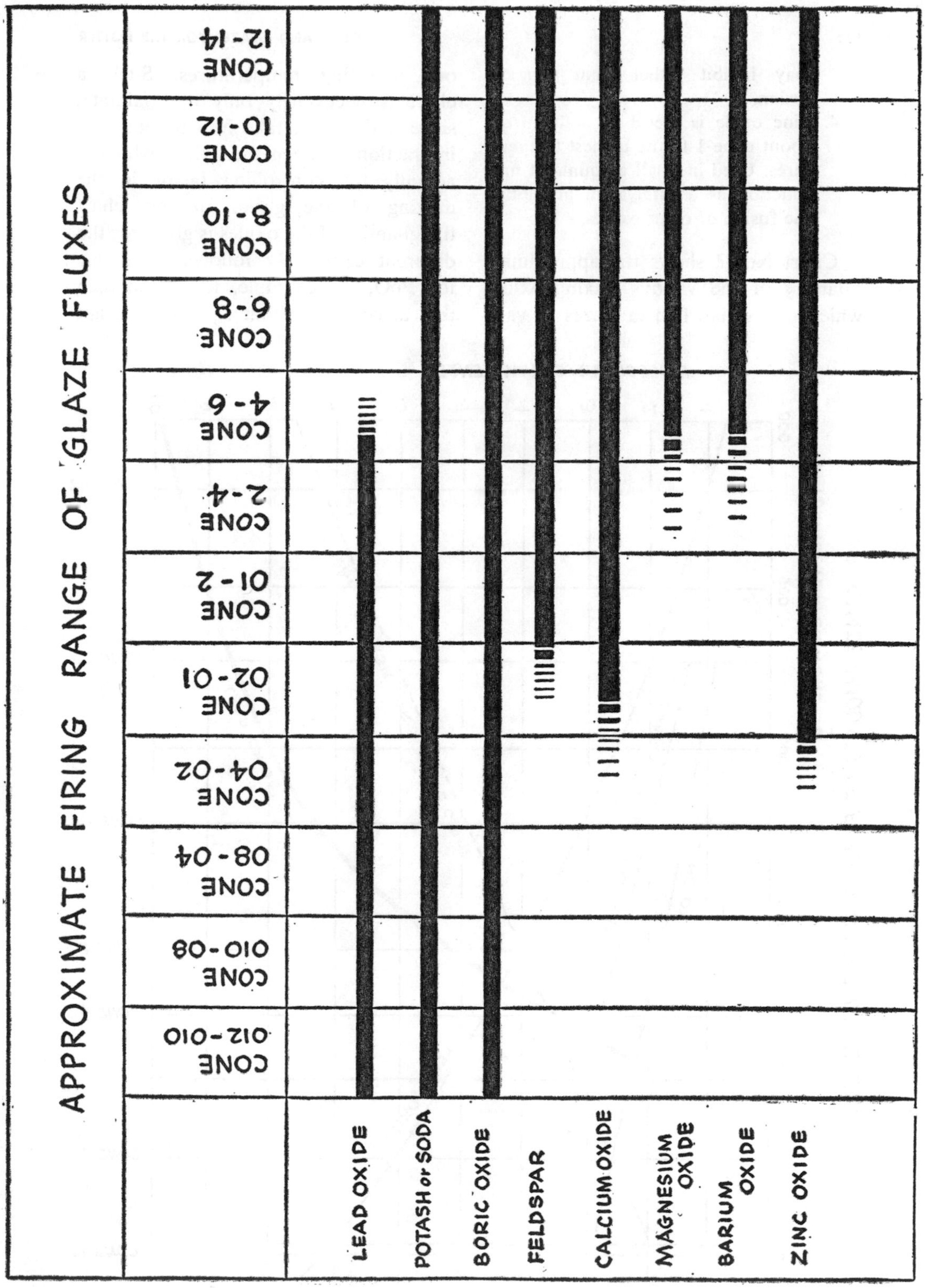
APPROXIMATE FIRING RANGE OF GLAZE FLUXES
CONE 12-14
CONE 10-12
CONE 8-10
CONE 6-8
CONE 4-6
CONE 2-4
CONE 01-2
CONE 02-01
CONE 04-02
CONE 08-04
CONE 010-08
CONE 012-010
LEAD OXIDE
POTASH or SODA
BORIC OXIDE
FELDSPAR
CALCIUM OXIDE
MAGNESIUM OXIDE
BARIUM OXIDE
ZINC OXIDE

CHART 1

may inhibit rather than promote fusion.

4. Zinc oxide is useful as a flux from about cone 1 to the highest temperatures. Used in small amounts, it may function as a catalyst in promoting the fusion of other oxides.

Chart No. 2 shows the approximate quantity of the various fluxing oxides which one would find in glazes of various maturing temperatures. Such a chart is necessarily only approximate, since it does not take into account the interaction between the oxides which is actually the controlling factor in the melting of the glaze. In this chart the quantity of the oxides is given for the different cones. By following the line for PbO, for example, it will be seen that at cone 04 about .7 of lead is apt

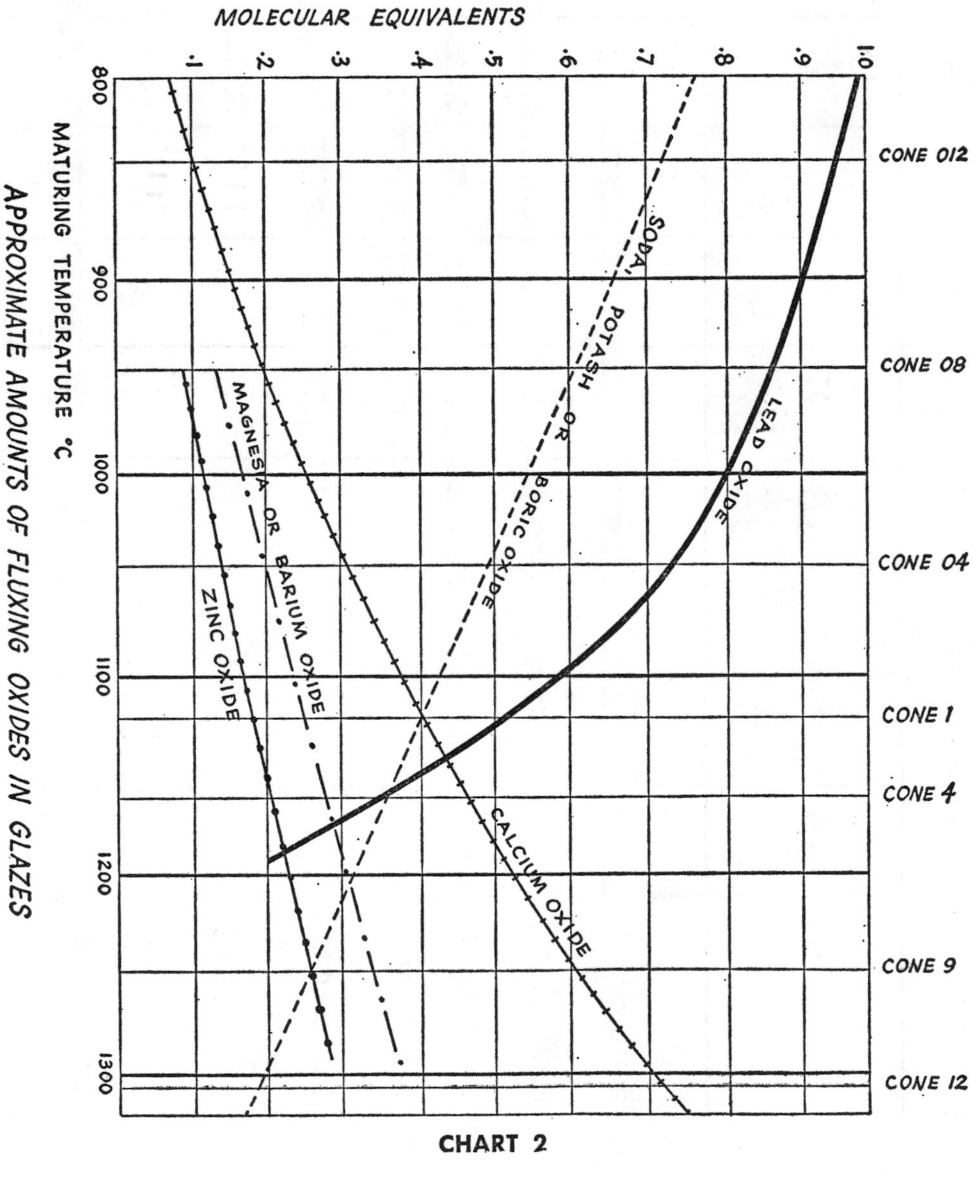

CHART 2

to be found in a formula. Of course, if B_2O_3 were present in the glaze also, the amount of lead would be much less. The chart illustrates the fact that as the temperature advances, the more active fluxes—lead, soda, and potash—must be present in diminishing quantities, and the less active fluxes—such as CaO and MgO—may be increased in amount as the temperature becomes higher. It must be emphasized that such a chart may be used only as an approximate guide.

3. The Amounts of Silica and Alumina in Glazes

The amount of silica and alumina is always critical in glazes, since the amount of silica relative to the amount

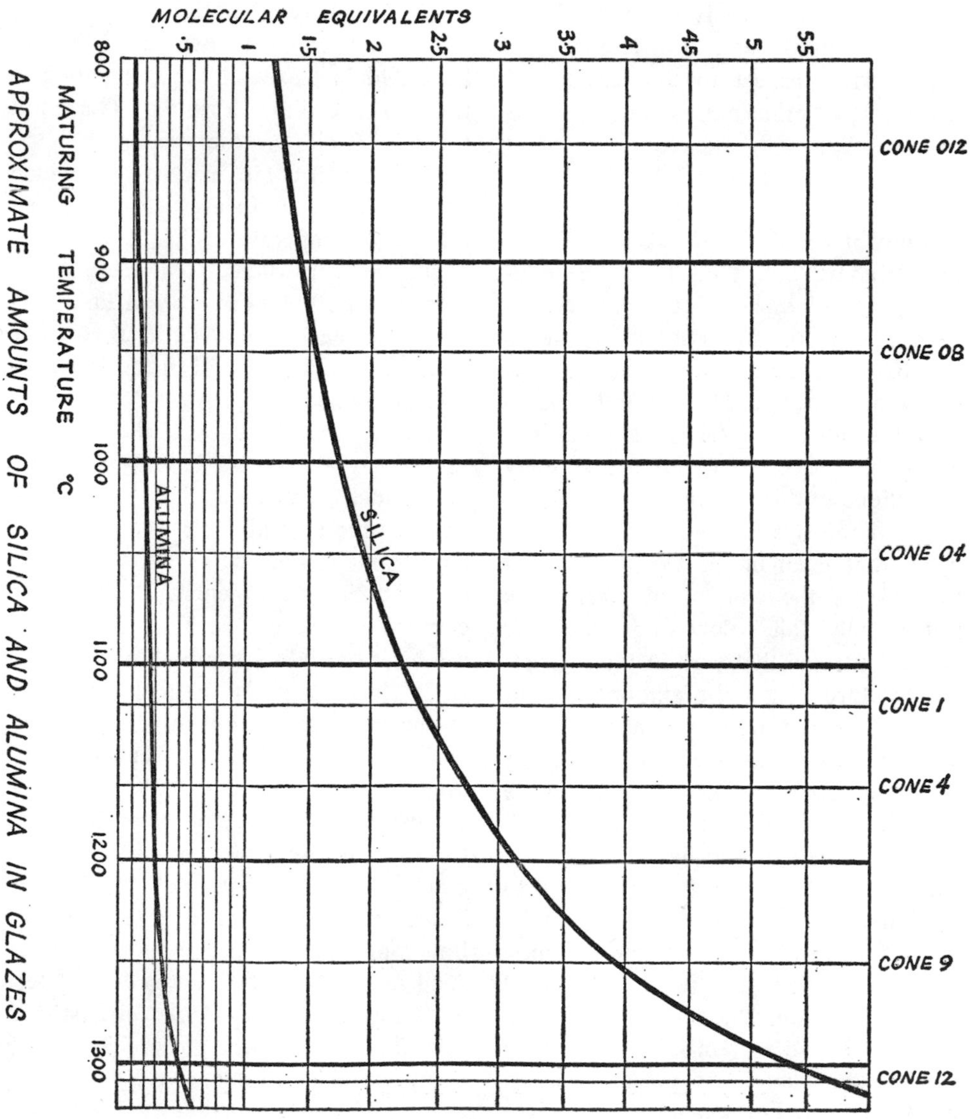

CHART 3

of the combined fluxes is the factor which largely controls the melting point. The amount of alumina has, always, a significant influence on the surface and texture of the glaze. Chart No. 3, which is constructed similarly to Chart No. 2, shows the probable amounts of silica and alumina which are found in glazes of various maturing temperatures. The amount of these two oxides increases with the temperature. However, it will be noted that there is more similarity between high- and low-temperature glazes with respect to the amount of silica and alumina present than there is with respect to the makeup of the RO column and the amount of oxides in it. The amount of silica relative to the amount of alumina is shown graphically in this chart, and it illustrates the relative preponderance of the former. In general, the relative quantity of these two oxides is quite constant at the various temperatures. The general rule is that the silica will be three times the alumina, plus one, but there are so many exceptions to this rule that it can seldom be applied. It will be noted from the chart that even in the lowest-temperature glazes the amount of silica does not usually fall below one molecular equivalent, and that even in the highest-temperature glazes the amount of alumina does not exceed one molecular equivalent. An excess of silica in a glaze makes it too refractory and may cause devitrification. Not enough silica will make a glaze soft and liable to crazing. Too much alumina will cause glazes to be harsh, mat, opaque, and scratchy in surface, while not enough alumina will cause the glaze to run from vertical surfaces. Again, the amount of silica and alumina in a glaze is dependent on what other oxides are present and in what amount. For example, if a large amount of some powerful flux such as lead is present in a glaze, the amount of silica and alumina can be correspondingly higher. Since silica and alumina lend the valuable properties of hardness, durability, and fit to glazes, they are introduced in as large amounts as possible.

4. Limit Formulas

Another way of stating the amounts of the various oxides which are apt to be found in glazes of various temperatures is the limit formula. The limit formula indicates the maximum and minimum amount of each oxide which is likely to occur in a glaze of a given maturing temperature. Limit formulas could be constructed for each pyrometric cone, but in practice a limit formula for each range of four or five cones is sufficient to aid in the formulation of glazes.

Since, as we have seen, the amounts of the various oxides in any glaze are very much determined by the kind of oxides present and their relative quantity, limit formulas can serve to indicate only in the most general fashion the composition of glazes. For example, if the limit formula for cone 9 glazes indicates that magnesia may be found in amounts ranging from nothing to .35 molecular equivalents, it serves to remind us only of the outside limits for the use of magnesia; and when it comes to assigning an exact amount for this oxide, we need to know how much B_2O_3 is present, how mat the glaze must be, how much alumina is present, and other such facts which, taken together, determine the amount of MgO which is correct for a particular glaze. There are many variables to consider.

In spite of the fact that limit formulas

assign values to the various oxides only within broad limits, they are useful in indicating the composition of glazes in a general way. The following limit formulas are given for the different temperature ranges and types of glazes.

012 – 08 Lead Glazes

PbO	.7 –1	Al_2O_3	.05 – .2	SiO_2	1. – 1.5
KNaO	0 – .3				
ZnO	0 – .1				
CaO	0 – .2				

08 – 01 Lead Glazes

PbO	.7 –1	Al_2O_3	.1 – .25	SiO_2	1.5 – 2.00
KNaO	0 – .3				
ZnO	0 – .2				
CaO	0 – .3				

08 – 04 Alkaline Glazes

PbO	0 – .5	Al_2O_3	.05 – .25	SiO_2	1.5 – 2.5
KNaO	.4 – .8				
CaO	0 – .3				
ZnO	0 – .2				

08 – 04 Lead-Colemanite

PbO	.2 – .60	Al_2O_3	.15 – .2	SiO_2	1.5 – 2.5
KNaO	.1 – .25	B_2O_3	.15 – .6		
CaO	.3 – .60				
ZnO	.1 – .25				
BaO	0 – .15				

Cone 2 – 5 Lead Glazes

PbO	.4 – .60	Al_2O_3	.2 – .28	SiO_2	2. – 3.
CaO	.1 – .40				
ZnO	0 – .25				
KNaO	.1 – .25				

Cone 2 – 5 Colemanite

CaO	.2 – .50	Al_2O_3	.2 – .28	SiO_2	2. – 3.
ZnO	.1 – .25	B_2O_3	.3 – .6		
BaO	.1 – .25				
KNaO	.1 – .25				

Cone 2 – 5 Lead Boro-Silicate

PbO	.2 – .3	Al_2O_3	.25 – .35	SiO_2	2.5 – 3.5
KNaO	.2 – .3	B_2O_3	.2 – .6		
CaO	.35– .5				
ZnO	.0 – .1				

Cone 8 – 12 Stoneware or Porcelain

KNaO	.2 – .40	Al_2O_3	.3 – .5	SiO_2	3.0 – 5.0
CaO	.4 – .70	B_2O_3	.1 – .3		
MgO	.0 – .35				
ZnO	.0 – .30				
BaO	.0 – .30				

Chapter 17

Types of Glazes

What has been said so far about glaze composition applies in a general way to all glazes. A more detailed examination of various types of glazes will help to clarify the reasons behind the use of the various materials. These various types of glazes will be considered as base, or colorless, glazes. The coloring oxides will be described later.

Glazes are extremely various in appearance. They have a wide range of possible color and texture. However, all glazes do fall into a few distinct types. These types shade into one another, which makes any exact system of classification rather arbitrary, but an understanding of glazes is greatly advanced by learning the characteristics of the most important types.

Glazes can, of course, be classified according to the temperature at which they mature. Glazes are also classified as to whether they are raw or fritted—an important distinction in the consideration of glaze batches. Fritted glazes will be treated more fully in a later section.

1. Low-Temperature Alkaline Glazes

An alkaline glaze is one which depends on the alkalies, i.e., sodium, potassium or lithium, for its flux rather than on lead, the alkaline earths, or boric oxide. Any glaze which matures below about cone 02 might be called a low-fired glaze.

Low-temperature alkaline glazes have been used for centuries to obtain colorful decorative surfaces for pottery. This is the general type of glaze which was used for the most beautiful of Persian, Egyptian, and Hispano-Mooresque wares, as well as some of the more colorful types of Chinese and Japanese pottery.

The characteristics of glazes of this general classification are (1) fluid melting and a tendency toward a glassy appearance, (2) softness, (3) a tendency to craze on most clay bodies, and (4) the property of brilliant color when coloring oxides are added to the glaze. Soda and potash are very active fluxes, and their presence in considerable quantity in a glaze makes for rather sudden melting at low temperatures. The danger of over-firing is naturally increased by the presence of violent fluxes in the glaze; and highly alkaline glazes, especially if the alumina content is low, may be difficult to fire and may run excessively if the intended temperature is even slightly overreached. As will be seen from the limit formula for this type of glaze, the sodium or potassium content may be as high as .7 molecular equivalents.

The presence of sodium or potassium in a glaze favors the production of brilliant strong colors from the addition of various coloring oxides. In alkaline glazes, copper oxide gives intense hues of blue-green, turquoise, or blue. The famous "Egyptian Blue" color which appears on ancient Egyptian faience is an alkaline glaze colored by copper. Cobalt in an alkaline glaze gives an intense blue. Iron gives strong shades of straw color or brown, and manganese gives rich hues of violet and grape-purple. The color from these coloring oxides are more intense and scintillating in low-fired alkaline glazes than in any other type of glaze.

Although the alkaline glaze is tempting from the standpoint of color, some practical disadvantages must be allowed for. For one thing, the highly alkaline glaze is almost impossible to fit to a clay body without crazing. The causes and cures of crazing are discussed in detail later, but in this connection it may be said that the only way alkaline glazes can be made to fit is by bringing the composition of the clay so near to that of the glaze that the working properties and plasticity of the clay are seriously impaired. However, on decorative wares which do not need to be impervious to liquids, and on vitreous wares which have an impermeable body, the tendency of alkaline glazes to craze may not be a serious disadvantage. Their color and brilliance, in any case, are at their best on decorative rather than on utilitarian ware. The network of lines formed by the crazed glaze may in itself be considered a decorative embellishment.

Another difficulty with highly alkaline glazes is the fact that, outside of the feldspars, insoluble sources of potassium and sodium are few. In low-temperature alkaline glazes the feldspars cannot be used as a source of significant amounts of alkali because they bring in too much alumina and silica. The use of feldspar as the principal flux is therefore limited to the high-temperature glazes. The choice, then, in compounding low-fired alkaline glazes is one of either using soluble materials such as soda ash or borax, or of using frits containing the desired soda and potash. Considering the practical difficulties encountered in the use of soluble glaze materials, it is usually best to use fritted material.

Highly alkaline glazes are soft and easily scratched, and for this reason they are not suitable for use on ware which is intended for hard usage. Such glazes may also be slightly soluble, even after they are fired. Glass which is composed of soda and silica alone, without any other oxide being present, is soluble. In glazes, solubility is highly undesirable because it leads to the deterioration and destruction of the glaze by weathering in contact with water or the weak acids which are found in foods. For this reason, alkaline glazes must contain enough of the alkaline earths or alumina to prevent solubility. Alkaline glazes sometimes come from the kiln with a slight scum on them which can be scraped off. This is a sign of solubility, as is the tendency to become dull after a little use or exposure to water. Such glazes need more lime, zinc, magnesia, or alumina in them to stabilize the glass and render it insoluble.

Alkaline glazes may be either transparent or opaque, depending on the presence of opacifiers or on the balance of oxides in the glaze. If an alkaline glaze contains an excess of silica, it may have an opaque sugary texture. If a clear alkaline glaze is desired which will give the bluest color obtainable from copper, the alumina content of the glaze must be kept very low. This will, of course, make the glaze subject to running and therefore short in firing range.

Highly alkaline glazes have a high surface tension when melted, and this makes them subject to crawling. The glaze may draw up into beads of glass on the surface, leaving bare spots on the ware. This is most apt to happen when the glaze is being melted on already vitrified ware.

2. Lead Glazes

Lead glazes are extremely useful at temperatures ranging from the lowest ordinarily used for pottery glazes, about cone 012, up to about cone 6. Lead glazes have many advantages. They are reliable, easy to control, colorful, and durable enough for most purposes. The invention of lead glazes in the Near East, which occurred about 1000 B.C., was a milestone in the history of ceramics because for the first time really practical glazed ware became possible. Since then, most of the glazed earthenware in all parts of the world has been glazed with lead. Familiar historic lead-glazed wares include the glazed architectural terra cottas of ancient Syria, the glazed tomb sculptures of the Tang Dynasty in China, the tankards and jugs of Medieval Europe, the peasant wares of central Europe and England, Bennington pottery in the United States, and the colorful majolica and slip-decorated wares of Mexico.

Lead oxide melts by itself at 886° and cools to form a glass. The glass formed from fused lead oxide alone is too soft, however, to form a durable and insoluble glaze for pottery. But when lead is melted with silica and other oxides, it forms a practical and beautiful glass. The "crystal" used for the finest glasswares is a lead glass, and it is valued for its exceptional clarity and luster. The low melting point of lead oxide makes it possible to fuse lead glazes at relatively very low temperatures, not much above red heat.

The charts and the limit formulas which have been given indicate the approximate amounts of lead oxide required in glazes at various temperatures. In the low-fired glazes, the amount of lead may be nearly all of the RO portion of the glaze. In the cone 4 to 6 range the amount of lead will be about .3 molecular equivalents. Beyond cone 6, lead begins to reach its volatilization point and can no longer be used with consistent results. Above cone 6, feldspar, rather than lead, is the most commonly used flux. When lead glazes are used at temperatures above cone 6, some of the lead content of the glaze is lost by volatilization, and the glaze which remains on the piece may be dry and under-fired in appearance.

Lead glazes flow to a smooth, even, glassy surface, and one of the distinguishing characteristics of lead glazed ware is a bright shiny surface. Lead glazes are not necessarily shiny, however, since they can easily be matted or dulled by the addition of barium oxide or alumina. But the lead glaze is normally bright and smooth, and in ware which is to be used for food, this is a definite advantage.

The color range of lead glazes is wide. Most of the coloring oxides when added to lead glazes yield soft, bright, pleasing colors. Copper produces a rich grassy-green color. While this green can be quite beautiful, it perhaps lacks the appeal of the turquoise color which copper produces in an alkaline glaze. Manganese in a lead glaze is a soft brownish purple. Iron yields exceptionally warm and beautiful hues of tan, brown, and reddish brown. Small amounts of iron, up to 2 percent, give pleasing tan, honey color, or amber. Higher percentages of iron will give deep amber, brown, or red-brown, depending on the amount used. Transparent lead glaze used over red clay gives the familiar red-brown color of Mexican pottery, or the more subdued tan or brown of old European or Pennsylvania Dutch slip ware.

Lead glazes which are opacified with tin oxide have a pleasant creamy quality. Iron and tin together in a high lead glaze give a warm, mottled cream to rust color which is often very beautiful, especially over textures or patterns in relief in the clay, which are emphasized by the glaze.

Base glazes fluxed with lead are used to produce the so-called "aventurine" glaze, which is a crystalline glaze colored with iron, and also chrome-red glazes, which are made at very low temperatures. Both of these kinds of glazes will be described in more detail in the section on special glazes.

Lead glazes which are fired at cone 2 to cone 6 have a more subdued color than the very active high-lead glazes at the lower temperatures. But the whole range of lead glazes can be handsome and adaptable to many purposes. When transparent, lead glazes may beautifully reveal slips or underglaze color; and when opacified, particularly with tin oxide, they make ideal majolica backgrounds or solid-color glazes.

The disadvantages of lead glazes include the danger of poisoning, which has already been described. A more serious disadvantage is the softness of lead glazes. Low-fired lead-glazed ware is easily scratched and in hard use will become covered with fine scratches which give the glaze a dull appearance. Frequently the lead glaze on old pieces is badly worn or decomposed. In the case of ancient wares such as the pottery as a fuel, lead-glazed ware is ordinarily Medieval Europe, the glaze may be mostly worn off or disintegrated by the solvent action of time and centuries of exposure to atmosphere and dampness. Lead glazes, after long exposure to moisture, may take on an iridescent color, which, in the case of some old wares, has undoubtedly enhanced a glaze that may originally have been quite garish and harsh in color when it first came from the kiln.

Lead glazes which are fired above cone 01 are relatively durable and give good service in all ordinary usage. Admittedly, lead glazes are not as durable as the more highly fired stoneware and porcelain glazes, but their color range and reliability may more than outweigh any deficiency in hardness.

Glazes containing some raw lead oxide are easy to apply because the lead, particularly if lead carbonate is used, makes the raw glaze dry on the ware in a hard coating, not easily dusted off or damaged in setting the ware in the kiln. However, if a glaze contains a very high percentage of white lead, cracking may be noted in the raw glaze coat. This is caused by the shrinkage of the white lead and can be corrected by replacing some of the raw lead with a frit, or by adding a gum to the glaze.

Lead glazes will not withstand reducing atmospheres in the kiln and must be fired with an excess of air. Lead oxide is easily reduced to the metal, lead. In a reducing atmosphere it turns grey or black, and the escape of gases from the glaze causes it to boil and blister. Prominent blisters on a lead-glazed piece may almost always be traced to reduction in the kiln. In electric kilns, or in kilns which can be controlled to give a clear atmosphere, lead glazes should not blister. Where gas, oil, or wood is used as a fuel, lead-glazed ware is ordinarily protected from direct contact with the flame by muffles or saggers. Fritted lead glazes are less liable to blister from contact with flame than are raw lead glazes.

3. Glazes Containing Boron

Boric oxide is a strong flux, and many glazes depend principally on it for fusion. There are few natural sources of boric oxide which are insoluble, and for this reason the oxide is commonly introduced into the glaze batch in the form of a frit. Colemanite, however, does provide a source of B_2O_3, which is practically insoluble, and for this reason it has become a very popular glaze material, especially with studio potters.

Very low-temperature glazes may be made with boric oxide, since its melting point is low, about 600°. Combinations of boric oxide, soda, and lead may produce very fluid glazes at dull red heat.

The color response of glazes which contain considerable B_2O_3 is strong, with a tendency toward high-keyed color, more akin to the alkaline type of glaze than to lead glazes. Copper, in a high boron glaze, gives a brilliant greenish turquoise, and cobalt a rich deep blue. Iron colors, however, tend to be rather dull and undistinguished compared to their brilliance in high lead glazes.

Boric oxide may give a milky opacity to glazes. This opacity or opalescence results from the optical properties of the glaze. When traces of iron are present in the glaze—and this is usually the case—the glaze may be bluish in color. This tendency of high B_2O_3 glazes to turn a milky blue may be exploited to advantage by the addition of small amounts of coloring oxides such as copper, iron-bearing rutile, and ilmenite. The result may be spectacularly varied glaze surfaces of considerable interest. Such highly colored and textured glazes are rather difficult to use on pottery, however, without unduly detracting from the form of the piece.

Glazes which are high in boric oxide have a tendency to boil during melting; and when they reach complete fusion and smooth out, the remains of the boiling phase may appear as mottled spots or alligator-skin patterns. This surface texture is favored by the presence of rutile and zinc. Although the breakup of color may be very noticeable on a flat tile, the flow which occurs when the glaze is put on a vertical surface usually destroys it and results merely in some streaks.

The lead-boro-silicate glaze is commonly used on tableware. It is smooth, reasonably hard, and has a bright blemish-free surface. Such glazes, in the range of cone 2 to cone 6, are made by combining lead frits and boric oxide frits with feldspar, whiting, zinc, and other raw ingredients. In the tableware industry, glazes are carefully milled, precisely applied, and accurately fired in a clear atmosphere. This results in the flawless surface demanded by commercial standards.

4. Bristol Glazes

Bristol glazes are middle-temperature glazes, cone 2 to cone 6, which depend on zinc oxide as their principal flux. This type of glaze was developed in England to replace the lead glaze when the poisonous nature of raw lead compounds had become a health hazard in the growing pottery industry. In the middle range of temperature, it is possible to make fairly fluid glazes without lead by carefully proportioning zinc oxide, whiting, and feldspar. The Bristol type of glaze is opaque, rather stiff, and not as smooth and bright as the typical lead glaze. It has the color response which is typical of high-zinc glazes, namely, rather poor and muddy colors from iron oxide, good greens and blues from copper and cobalt, and brown colors from chrome.

Calcined zinc oxide should be used in Bristol glazes to avoid the high shrinkage and possible cracking and crawling which may result from too much raw zinc in the batch. The Bristol glaze, because of its rather viscous and pasty consistency when melted, is very subject to pitting and pinholes. Since lead oxide is now available in fritted form, and since the Bristol type of glaze is difficult to use, it is actually an outmoded kind of glaze. The Bristol glaze can be handsome, however. It is at its best on ware which is light in color, rather thickly glazed, and colorful.

5. Porcelain and Stoneware Glazes

Leadless glazes fired above cone 6 or cone 7 may be called porcelain or stoneware glazes, depending on the kind of ware upon which they are used. Porcelain glazes are generally considered to be clear, smooth, colorless glazes made up with feldspar and lime as the principal flux and fired to cone 9 or higher.

Porcelain glazes can be relatively simple in composition. Feldspar alone melts at around cone 9 or 10, and little material need be added to it to make an acceptable glaze. For this reason, high-fired glazes are generally simpler in composition than low-fired glazes. It is a simpler problem to make a glaze at cone 9 than it is to make one at cone 06. Heat works for the potter, causing simple combinations of materials to fuse, and the chemically more active and temperamental fluxes—such as soda, lead, and boric oxide—may be replaced by the more slow-melting alkaline earths and the minor amount of alkalies which are combined in feldspar.

Good high-fired glazes can be made from such simple combinations as: feldspar, 85 parts, whiting 15 parts; or feldspar, 60 parts, flint 20 parts, and whiting 20 parts. Some porcelain bodies are not too far from a glaze in composition and can be made into a glaze by the addition of about 20 percent more feldspar and 10 percent of whiting. Feldspar is the most important ingredient of most high-fired glazes. Feldspar is really a natural glaze by itself, a frit formed by nature which combines the alkalies needed for flux with alumina and silica. Although all the different feldspars are quite similar in melting point, there is enough difference to make them not interchangeable in high-fired glazes, although in low-fired glazes, a different feldspar may sometimes be substituted without any difference in the fired result being noted.

High-fired glazes which contain considerable calcium oxide—.5 to .7 molecular equivalents—are usually transparent and tend to be bright. They have the dense, smooth, hard, jade-like surface which is admired on porcelain. In glazes of this type, small amounts of iron will produce beautiful celedon colors in reduction firing, especially if barium is also present. Copper reds may also be produced in glazes which are high in calcium oxide, especially if considerable soda and potash are present.

High-fired glazes which are high in magnesia tend to be somewhat opaque, smooth, and "fat" in surface. The Chinese likened such glazes to "congealed mutton fat," and glazes of this character have been much admired on old Chinese stoneware. Certainly the high-magnesia glaze is one of the most beautiful in the whole range of pottery glazes. There is some danger of pitting and pinholing, however, because of the high viscosity of the glaze and also because there is some chance that over-firing will radically alter the appearance of the glaze by making it shiny and transparent.

High-fired glazes which contain considerable zinc oxide, .15 to .3, may have a rather sugary look, with areas of matness and shine on the same piece. Color is apt to be broken; and if the glaze contains rutile, the result may be highly textured. High-zinc glazes are temperamental, and pitting and pinholing may be hard to control.

In general, high-fired glazes have the advantages of being very hard, durable, and resistant to acids and to decay, and, if they are properly compounded and fired, they may be free from defects such as crazing and irregularities of surface. Besides these practical advantages, high-fired glazes have a sensuous appeal because of their dense hard surface and their characteristic soft muted colors. High-fired glazes appear to be more a part of the piece, more related to the clay of the pot, than do glazes matured at lower temperatures. In the case of porcelain, where the body itself is approaching a glassy condition, body and glaze may be very similar, and the line between the two is hard to detect even on a broken piece. At the higher temperatures, there is more reaction between body and glaze. Stoneware glazes may be rock-like in color and texture and may reflect and reveal the earthy origins of pottery. The character of stoneware glazes is very difficult to simulate at lower temperatures.

Brilliant color is not characteristic of high-fired glazes, which are best suited for greyed subtle colors. Strong colors are possible from copper and cobalt, but they do not have the vibrancy of the colors of low-fired alkaline glazes. At higher temperatures, manganese, iron, and vanadium yield noticeably more subdued colors than at the lower temperatures.

High-fired glazes have an appeal for the potter quite aside from the inherent practical advantages of the finished ware. Part of this appeal lies in the drama of extreme heat, which can melt and fuse hard earthy materials. At about cone 9 the color in the kiln becomes a bright yellow, and this color seems to symbolize the transmutations of the fire. Then, too, the traditions of pottery reserve a special place for high-fired stoneware and porcelain, since these represented in their origin a magnificent technical achievement. The classic stonewares and porcelains of the Sung Dynasty in China will probably always stand as pinnacles of excellence in the potter's art.

Persian earthenware pitcher from the fifteenth century. The decoration is in black underglaze, and the glaze is a brilliant transparent turquoise. Alkaline glazes of this type, which are typical of Persian pottery, were fired at a relatively low temperature. *Courtesy of The Smithsonian Institution, Freer Gallery of Art, Washington, D.C.*

Mesopotamian earthenware bowl from the twelfth century. The heron, which is painted with great elegance, is in black under a deep turquoise glaze. *Courtesy of The Smithsonian Institution, Freer Gallery of Art, Washington, D.C.*

Persian earthenware bowl from the thirteenth century. This piece is a good example of masterly integration of form and decoration. The whole piece is covered with a white slip, and the decoration is done in blue and black underglaze color. The glaze is a clear alkaline glaze thinly applied. *Courtesy of The Smithsonian Institution, Freer Gallery of Art, Washington, D.C.*

Chapter 18

Originating Glaze Formulas

1. Originating Glazes as Percentage Recipes

The question may arise as to how glaze formulas are arrived at and how the exact amounts in the formula are decided upon. Some information on this may be inferred from the charts already given and from the limit formulas. But here specific procedures will be outlined for originating new formulas.

Historically, glazes were originated by cut-and-try methods. Potters simply tried various materials in various percentages, rejecting those which did not work and making the most of those which did. We have the story of Bernard Palissy's long search after glazes which would simulate those then in use in Italy. He simply tried everything, hoping to hit upon the secret. Until late in the last century, the whole art of glaze making was dependent on blind experiment of this sort, and there was little scientific understanding of the results.

One can, then, originate glazes very much in the manner of the old potters, by mixing, percentage-wise, various materials, trying them out in the fire, then changing the mix and trying it again as many times as necessary until it works. Even a rudimentary knowledge of the materials will enable one to proceed in this way. Suppose, for example, one were to set about making an original glaze recipe for a low-fired lead glaze. An elementary knowledge of glazes provides some information as to the probable composition of glazes of this type. For one thing, it could be assumed that lead would be present in about 25 to 60 percent of the batch. Flint would have to be present and would probably make up about 15 to 30 percent of the batch. Whiting would be desirable and could be present in about 5 to 15 percent of the batch. Feldspar would also be desirable and could be added up to about 25 percent of the batch. Clay, which aids in the working properties of the raw glaze, should be added and could make up to 15 percent of the batch. With general limits such as these in mind, one could postulate a glaze which might be as follows:

White Lead	50	(for flux)
Flint	20	(for hardness, stability, and insolubility)
Whiting	10	(for insolubility, hardness)
Feldspar	10	(for insolubility, auxiliary flux)
Clay	10	(for suspension, to slow the melt)

This mixture would represent a guess, founded on some knowledge and experience, as to what materials would give a satisfactory glaze at the intended temperature. The next step would be to try the glaze in the fire to see how it melted. It might be found to be too fluid, runny, and glassy, in which case the amount of lead could be cut to, say, 40 parts, and the feldspar increased to 20. Or the clay might be raised at the expense of the lead. If a more fusible glaze was desired, the amount of lead could be raised, and the clay, feldspar, and flint lowered. If a number of corrected recipes were fired and the results studied, a workable composition could result.

Similar procedures could be followed for any type of glaze. One must, of course, know the typical composition of glazes to avoid missing the mark by a wide margin, but even if the first tries are not successful, adjustments can be made in the light of a few simple principles of glaze formulation. If the glaze is too dry and appears rough and underfired, more flux is needed. If, on the other hand, the glaze is too soft and fluid and tends to run, the more refractory and hard-to-melt materials in the glaze, such as flint, clay, barium, magnesia, and whiting must be increased. The composition may, of course, be altered to make it more opaque, more transparent, more mat, or more shiny.

In originating low-fired formulas, it is logical to start with some active flux—such as lead, soda, or boron—and make additions to it. For high-fired glazes, feldspar is the best starting point, and other materials can be added to this to bring about the desired fusion and surface texture.

2. Using the Molecular Formula in Originating Glazes

The method of arriving at the composition of glazes by adjusting the percentage of materials as outlined above is necessarily somewhat hit-or-miss. The reason for this is that when we add, say, 10 percent of feldspar, it is very difficult to keep track of the oxides which have been added with this material. In the recipe, the balance of oxides is not indicated, and there is no logical way of comparing formulas or of making changes intelligently with reference to the oxide content of the glaze. When the formula is used, on the other hand, it is easy to originate glazes of known molecular composition, and the control over the amounts of the various oxides in the glaze makes the result much more likely to be practical. By using the formula, so much of one oxide can be put into the glaze and so much of another, until the formula is filled according to the balance of oxides which is known to melt at a given temperature, and then the recipe or batch can be calculated in terms of the various raw materials. The limits of the amounts of the various oxides which can be used at the various temperatures and for the various kinds of glazes is indicated in the limit formulas already given and in the graphs showing the probable amounts of the various oxides in glazes of different melting points. The amounts given in the limit formulas are determined experimentally and have no significance other than the fact that these amounts generally give glazes which melt at the indicated temperature. As has been pointed out, the limit formula can only state in a general way the composition of glazes, since there are so many materials involved that their interaction creates a great many variables. For this reason, it is not possible to formulate glazes on paper with very much assurance that such compositions will work in practice. All new compositions must be tried, and, more likely than not, adjusted before they perform as desired. In this sense, making up new glazes is always experimental, and although the use of the molecular formula makes the result more certain to be successful, it by no means eliminates the necessity for testing and for trial-and-error experiment.

3. An Example of Writing a New Formula for a Glaze

To formulate a new glaze intelligently, some one temperature and kind of glaze should be aimed at. The temperature at which a glaze is to be fired is, of course, a critical factor in determining its composition. And, as we have seen, the different qualities of texture, opacity, and response to coloring oxides are critically influenced by the composition of the glaze. For example, a typical problem might be the development of a transparent cone 04 lead glaze. To make up a formula for this type of glaze one might proceed as follows:

The limit formula for cone 04 glazes indicates that the amount of lead oxide is apt to be between .3 and .8 molecular equivalents. Within this rather wide latitude of choice, .6 might be taken as a likely amount. If a mat or rough-surfaced glaze was desired, a smaller amount might be tried. If the lead is assigned a quantity of .6 molecular equivalents, .4 equivalents remain to be satisfied in the RO column. Since it is desirable to include feldspar in practically all glazes, a figure of .15 might be assigned to "KNaO," which means either Na_2O or K_2O or both in indefinite ratio. These alkalies are associated with feldspar and in raw glazes are usually added in the form of feldspar or in some fritted material. There are now .25 equivalents yet to be added to bring the RO column up to one. Again consulting the limit formulas, it is noted that CaO may be present in glazes of this type in amounts from 0 to .3. Since this oxide is a valuable one to have in any lead glaze, .2 might be the amount decided upon. After this addition of CaO, .05 remain to be added. This might be filled with zinc oxide, barium, or magnesia. In this case let us say that zinc is added for promoting a smooth clear glaze. The RO column of the proposed glaze is now:

PbO	.6
KNaO	.15
CaO	.2
ZnO	.05

The limit formula indicates that the alumina in a glaze of this type may be between .1 and .25 equivalents. Since we are designing a clear glaze, a figure of .15 might be estimated. Less alumina than this might make the glaze too fluid; more might cause opacity in the glaze.

Silica, according to the limit formula, may vary between 1.5 and 3. Since we have indicated a high figure for the lead, the silica can be quite high also, and a figure of 2.5 might be decided upon. Our glaze now reads:

PbO	.6				
KNaO	.15	Al_2O_3	.15	SiO_2	2.5
CaO	.2				
ZnO	.05				

Having arrived at a formula for the projected glaze, the next step is to calculate the glaze into terms of raw materials. From such a batch recipe, a small amount of glaze can be weighed out and fired on a test tile. Sometimes a new glaze formula will come from the fire with just the intended properties, but more often some adjustments have to be made in the composition.

4. Originating a Formula Based on the Properties of a Particular Material

It will be noted that in the above example, when a value was assigned to the oxide "KNaO," the material feldspar was intended. Actually, when a new glaze formula is written, the raw materials must be carefully considered as well as the oxides, and new glazes commonly have as their starting point some raw material or combination of raw materials. Suppose, for example, we have observed the relatively low melting point of the material, nepheline syenite, and wish to make a cone 9 glaze incorporating a high percentage of this material into its composition. The formula of nepheline syenite is:

.75	Na_2O	Al_2O_3	1.1	SiO_2	4.5
.25	K_2O				

This formula is fairly close to a cone 9 formula as it stands, and in fact nepheline syenite melts to a stiff glass at cone 9. However, it is too high in alumina and silica to be a practical cone 9 glaze, and the alkaline ingredients of the RO column make it craze on most bodies. We may decide, then, since most cone 9 glazes have, at the most, about .5 Al_2O_3, that our new glaze could be made up of about half nepheline syenite. Taking half of the nepheline syenite formula (.5), all the way through, gives us the following quantities:

.375	Na_2O	Al_2O_3	.55	SiO_2	2.25
.125	K_2O				

Here we have in effect split the formula of the material in two. We must now fill in the formula to bring it to unity. We might add .4 CaO, since in cone 9 formulas it is common for this oxide to be as high as .7 equivalents. To fill in the remaining .1 we might add MgO which could be satisfied with talc, since the silica in the formula must be increased. The formula now stands:

.375	Na_2O	Al_2O_3	.55	SiO_2	2.38
.125	K_2O				
.4	CaO				
.1	MgO				

The glaze now appears to be workable except for the silica which, even after the addition of the talc, is too low. By bringing the silica up to a figure of 3.00, the glaze might be considered complete, and the glaze batch could be calculated using nepheline syenite, whiting, talc, and flint.

In this example, the procedure was to (1) start with some material of known formula and melting characteristic, (2) decide how much of it can be used and divide its formula accordingly and (3) fill in the rest of the formula with other materials.

After some acquaintance with the glaze forming oxides and their quantitative balance in typical glazes, it is not difficult to write on paper glazes which are very apt to work. There are, after all, a limited number of variables, and long experience has established within general limits the proportions which are most apt to be successful. The ceramist, in making up new glazes, will notice that there is actually a wide latitude in the proportions of materials in glazes. Glaze formulas may actually be altered considerably without radically changing the fired appearance or fit of the finished glaze. For instance, the amount of lead in a glaze may be cut down or increased by .2 or more molecular equivalents without making a noticeable difference. In making up new glaze formulas, we are aiming at rather broad targets, and one soon learns that combinations of glass-making oxides tend to melt rather easily in the fire, and that a little more of this and a little less of that may not make too much difference in the result.

On the other hand, when one is aiming at some specific quality in a glaze, such as a particular degree of matness or a certain response to color, a small change in the formula may have an important effect. It is in making such small adjustments that glaze calculation is an especially useful tool. For example, in a celedon glaze (this type will be discussed later), a small amount of barium is known to produce a pronounced cool blue or green color. In the formula of such a glaze, an increase of barium by as little as .05 equivalents may make a significant change in the color of the glaze. Similarly, the exact degree of surface brightness in a glaze may be controlled by a fairly minor adjustment in the amounts of one or two oxides.

Granting that for most practical purposes one can rely on existing and published glaze formulas, the origination of new ones is exciting and the results, properly interpreted, may be very revealing as to the behavior of ceramic materials in the fire. It will be seen that mathematically there are a great number of possible variations in materials and the proportioning of materials for glazes of any given firing temperature.

In addition to this possible variation in base glazes are the large number of variations brought about by the additions of coloring oxides and opacifying agents. The sum of these variables is almost infinite. It is the resulting unexplored territory of new glazes which is tempting for the potter. The healthy urge toward experimentation and the great variety of colors and textures which may result from it have for centuries lent a certain vitality and interest to the craft.

Chapter 19

Fritted Glazes

1. Reasons for the Use of Frits

A frit is a glass which has been melted, quenched, and ground to a powder ready to add as an ingredient to glazes or enamels. Various kinds of frits are of great usefulness to the glaze maker.

One reason for using frits in glazes is to obtain certain valuable alkaline oxides in insoluble form. There are few insoluble sources of K_2O, Na_2O, and B_2O_3. Although sodium and potassium do occur in feldspar, they are associated with such quantities of alumina and silica that, especially in low temperature glazes, their fluxing power is small. B_2O_3 is available to the potter in only one naturally occurring mineral which is insoluble: colemanite.

In order to make these desirable oxides available in insoluble form, they are fritted or melted up together with other oxides to form a stable, insoluble material which can be used like any other glaze ingredient.

Another reason for using fritted material is the poisonous nature of lead oxide. When lead oxide is fritted with sufficient quantities of other oxides, it becomes non-poisonous; and whenever possible, it is advisable to use lead as a frit rather than in the raw state.

2. Hazards of Soluble Glazes

Since making frit requires special equipment and at best is apt to be a time-consuming process, and since commercially available frits are rather expensive, the potter may be tempted to make use of soluble materials in his glazes, especially in those intended for low-temperature work. Soluble materials can be used successfully, provided the necessary precautions are taken, and it is likely that much of the pottery made in the ancient Near East, including some of the most beautiful pottery ever made, was glazed with mixtures containing highly soluble materials.

The difficulties inherent in the use of soluble materials in glazes are:

(1) Some of the soluble materials, such as pearl ash and soda ash, are caustic and may injure the skin unless rubber gloves are worn for protection.

(2) If a glaze contains soluble material, the material dissolves in the water with which the glaze is mixed. This water must therefore be kept and not decanted off the glaze when the glaze has settled in storage.

(3) In glazing, some water usually soaks into the body of the ware. If soluble material is present, it penetrates with the water into the body of the piece, leaving the glaze on the surface deprived of some of its material, and altering, in effect, the composition of the clay and its behavior in the fire.

(4) When the piece dries after glazing, concentrations of the soluble ma-

terial may build up on edges, handles, or knobs. These concentrations of soluble materials may cause uneven melting.

(5) Soluble glazes, when stored for a time, may become lumpy or filled with hard crystals or crusts which are hard to grind or mix again into the glaze.

(6) Soluble materials are hard to keep in dry form. Some are hygroscopic, that is, they take on moisture from the atmosphere and become hard and caked, making the material difficult to mix and grind.

Preparation and application techniques will occur to the potter which overcome all of these difficulties in the use of soluble materials. For example, materials can be stored in air-tight containers, and glazes in covered jars. Ware can be bisqued to the point of vitrification and can therefore be impervious to saturation by soluble glaze. Drying can be controlled. Masks and gloves can be worn to give protection from poisonous and caustic materials. But frits have been developed to get around all these difficulties, and, except in special cases, it is better to use them.

One advantage in using fritted material, in addition to the simplification of glaze-making and application techniques, is the smoother melting characteristics of already fired and melted material. Some of the volatiles of such materials have already been driven off, and as a result, fritted glazes do not go through as marked a boiling or gas expulsion stage as raw glazes, and they are consequently less subject to pitting and pinholing. Fritted lead glazes, furthermore, are not so subject to reduction as raw lead glazes and can be fired more safely in gas kilns.

3. Methods of Preparing Frit

The method of preparing frit is simple and is essentially the same as that used for making glass. The weighed-out materials are placed in a furnace or crucible and heated until they are fused together into a mass of liquid. This red-hot liquid is then tapped out of the furnace and is allowed to flow into a tank of water, where the sudden cooling chills it and shatters it into small fragments. The glass is then ground in a ball mill until it is fine enough for use. Small batches of frit may be made in a pottery kiln by putting the raw material into a clay vessel or crucible and firing it in a glaze fire. After cooling, the mass of glass inside the crucible may be broken out and ground.

4. Calculating a Frit Batch

Frit compositions are designed to give a high yield of the desired oxides, usually the active fluxes PbO, K_2O, Na_2O, and B_2O_3, and to contain in addition enough other oxides to make the glass stable and insoluble. These other oxides may include SiO_2, Al_2O_3, CaO, ZnO, or MgO. Some typical frit formulas are given below:

$$\left\{\begin{array}{ll} PbO & .94 \\ Na_2O & .02 \\ K_2O & .04 \end{array}\right. \quad Al_2O_3\ .08 \quad SiO_2\ 1.5$$

$$\left\{\begin{array}{ll} Na_2O & .38 \\ CaO & .62 \end{array}\right. \quad \begin{array}{l} Al_2O_3\ .38 \\ B_2O_3\ 1.2 \end{array} \quad SiO_2\ 2.8$$

$$\left\{\begin{array}{ll} PbO & .85 \\ Na_2O & .15 \end{array}\right. \quad Al_2O_3\ .18 \quad SiO_2\ 2.5$$

$$\left\{\begin{array}{ll} Na_2O & .65 \\ K_2O & .21 \\ ZnO & .08 \\ CaO & .06 \end{array}\right. \quad Al_2O_3\ 0 \quad SiO_2\ 2.3$$

It will be seen that the alkali content of some of these formulas is higher than could be obtained without recourse to some soluble materials. The silica and alumina are in low quantity relative to the RO groups. This relationship naturally makes for a low melting point.

The calculation of a frit batch is done in exactly the same manner as the calculation for a glaze. Suppose, for example, that a frit furnace is available and that we wish to make a frit of the following formula:

Na_2O	.6				
K_2O	.2	Al_2O_3	.15	SiO_2	2.5
CaO	.1				
BaO	.05				
ZnO	.05				

This formula cannot be made up from insoluble materials because of the high content of Na_2O relative to the alumina and silica. Since we are making a frit, however, soluble materials can be used in the batch and in this case we might choose as raw materials soda ash, feldspar, whiting, barium carbonate, zinc oxide, clay, and flint. The calculation is given below, using the same method as that already given for glaze calculation.

The materials are weighed out in the proportion indicated in this recipe and fused to a glass in the frit furnace. After quenching and grinding, the frit is ready to use as a glaze material.

5. Calculating a Glaze Which Includes a Frit in Its Composition

In calculating a frit as part of a glaze formula, we proceed exactly as with any other material. Frit formulas will be seen to resemble the formula of feldspar in that both contain some alkaline oxides associated with silica and alumina.

Before using a frit in a calculation, we must determine its total molecular or

	Na_2O .6	K_2O .2	CaO .1	BaO .05	ZnO .05	Al_2O_3 .15	SiO_2 2.5
Soda Ash .6	.6 x						
Niter .2		.2 x					
Whiting .1			.1 x				
Barium Carbonate .05				.05 x			
Zinc Oxide .05					.05 x		
Clay .15						.15 x	.3 2.2
Flint 2.2							2.2 x

Soda Ash	.6	× 106 =	63.6
Niter	.2	× 202 =	40.4
Whiting	.1	× 100 =	10.0
Barium Carbonate	.05	× 197 =	9.8
Zinc Oxide	.05	× 81 =	4.05
Clay	.15	× 258 =	38.7
Flint	2.2	× 60 =	132.0

formula weight. This is done in the same manner as for a feldspar or any other material, namely by multiplying the quantity of each oxide in the formula by the molecular weight of that oxide and adding them to secure a total, as follows:

Na_2O	.6	× 62 =	37.2
K_2O	.2	× 94 =	18.8
CaO	.1	× 56 =	5.6
BaO	.05	× 153 =	7.6
ZnO	.05	× 81 =	4.0
Al_2O_3	.15	× 102 =	15.3
SiO_2	2.5	× 60 =	150.0
			238.5 Formula weight of frit

As an example of calculating a fritted glaze, suppose we wish to incorporate our frit into some already established glaze formula. Such a glaze formula might be as follows:

Na_2O	.5	Al_2O_3	.25	SiO_2	2.8
K_2O	.2				
CaO	.2				
BaO	.05				
ZnO	.05				

Because of the relatively large amount of sodium in this glaze, it would be difficult to satisfy the formula with insoluble raw materials, and in this case the frit fills the practical requirements of the glaze. The calculation is carried out in the usual manner, the frit being treated exactly like any other raw material. (*See chart on following page.*)

6. The Use of Frit as a Glaze

Actually a frit is a pre-melted glaze, and in very low-temperature work, frits can be used alone to glaze pottery with no additions made to them. If no clay is added to the frit, it may be found difficult to keep the material in suspension in water during application. When a glazing temperature of above cone 06 is used, most commercial frits will be found to be too fluid and runny to be used by themselves as a glaze. However, for low-temperature work very satisfactory glazes can be made which are made up largely of commercial frit, with some additions of clay, flint, whiting, and feldspar. Good glazes of this type can be arrived at by a few simple tests. For example, any commercial glaze frit may be combined with increasing percentages of clay and flint, starting at, say 5 percent of each, until the right degree of fluidity at the desired temperature is reached. A base glaze arrived at by this method may be further altered by small additions of whiting, tin, or zinc oxide.

	Na_2O	K_2O	CaO	BaO	ZnO	Al_2O_3	SiO_2
	.5	.2	.2	.05	.05	.25	2.8
Frit .83	.5	.166	.08	.04	.04	.124	2.07
	x	.034	.12	.01	.01	.126	.73
Potash Spar .034		.034				.034	.2
		x				.092	.53
Whiting .12			.12				
			x				
Barium Carbonate .01				.01			
				x			
Zinc Oxide .01					.01		
					x		
Clay .092						.092	.18
						x	.35
Flint .35							.35
							x

Frit	$.83 \times 238 = 197.5$
Potash Spar	$.034 \times 556 = 18.9$
Whiting	$.12 \times 100 = 12$
Zinc Oxide	$.01 \times 81 = .8$
Barium Carbonate	$.01 \times 197 = 1.9$
Clay	$.092 \times 258 = 23.7$
Flint	$.35 \times 60 = 21.$

Another approach is to combine two commercial frits together with small amounts of clay, flint, or whiting. Such double-frit glazes are apt to have a very complex formula and may, because of the presence of so many oxides, have a very long, slow melting point and a long firing range.

Some manufacturers of glaze frits give the molecular formula of their product to the consumer. This makes it possible for the potter to calculate the material like any other raw material. Other manufacturers do not publish the formula of their frits, and these frits must therefore be used in amounts determined entirely by experimentation.

Chapter 20

Glaze Textures

1. Transparency and Opacity

So far, glazes have been considered as clear, colorless glass. Glazes, however, have a great variety of textures and colors, and the materials and firing treatments which determine these myriads of possible textures and colors must be understood by the ceramist. First, the varieties of textures will be considered, and later the problem of color.

Some glazes are clear; that is, we can look through the layer of glaze and see the clay body or slip underneath it. Other glazes are opaque and have the effect of an obscure or frosted glass, concealing what is under the glaze. Opacity in glazes may be due either to the nature of the glaze itself or to the presence in the glaze of opacifying agents.

Transparency may be thought of as the normal state of glazes; that is, if a glaze is fired to maturity and all the oxides in its composition reach a state of complete fusion, it will normally be clear and transparent. Many glazes, however, even though they do not contain any opacifying agent as such, are cloudy and opaque. Under-fired glazes, for example, are opaque because of the lack of complete fusion. If firing is halted before the glaze is completely melted, some unmelted material may be floating in the glaze. These particles of unmelted materials may cloud the glaze in much the same fashion as dirt added to water makes an opaque muddy mixture. Glazes which are opaque because they are under-fired will usually clear up and become transparent if the firing proceeds to the point of completely fusing the glaze.

Another cause of opacity is entrapped bubbles in the glaze. This may produce a cloudy or opalescent effect. Here the effect is analogous to suds in water, which may cause opacity without adding any actual solid particles. Bubbles in glazes are usually caused by the evolution of gas from the volatile materials of the glaze. Advancing temperature usually completes this reaction and clears up the glaze.

Opalescent, and hence cloudy, glazes may also be due to a mixture of glasses of differing indexes of refraction. This phenomenon frequently occurs in glazes which are high in B_2O_3 content. Such glazes may have a milky blue-white texture. In this case the glaze has the property of breaking up the light which passes through it, thus making it opaque.

Still another cause of opacity is the development of crystals in the glaze as it cools from a liquid to a solid. This phenomenon is known as devitrification. The crystalline solids, dispersed in the glaze or on the surface of the glaze, make it opaque. Such crystals may grow in the cooling glaze because of an excess of silica in the glaze, or the presence of rutile and zinc in glazes which are low in alumina, or from an excess or saturating amount of some coloring oxide such as iron or copper. Normally, the presence of alumina in glazes prevents the formation of crystals in the glaze.

If some oxides in the glaze are increased beyond their normal limits at any given temperature, opacity may result. Zinc oxide, calcium oxide, barium oxide, magnesium oxide, or aluminum oxide, if present in more than a normal amount, will cloud the glaze.

Glazes which are opaque as a result of under-firing, opalescence, refraction, devitrification, or the imbalance of oxides are apt to clear up if the firing is carried to a sufficient degree of heat. This makes for rather uncertain results if opacity is desired in a glaze, and a surer way to achieve opacity is to add an opacifying agent. There are two opacifiers in common use: tin oxide and zirconium oxide. Both of these materials have a low solubility in glass; that is, they are not easily taken into the melt and remain in the cooled glaze as minute suspended particles. These suspended, unmelted particles make the glaze white or opaque. Tin oxide and zirconium oxide are usually added to a base glaze which by itself is essentially clear and transparent.

In many ways tin oxide is the preferred material to use as an opacifier. The discovery of its use in glazes, which occurred in the Near East over a thousand years ago, represented a great advance in pottery; it made white glazes possible. Tin oxide imparts a soft, pleasant texture to glazes and it enhances the colors derived from most of the coloring oxides. "Tin glazed" ware has included much of the wares of Persia, Spain, southern Europe, and the peasant wares of central Europe. The white, opaque glaze which can be made by the addition of tin to lead glazes has offered the ideal background for majolica decoration. About 5 percent of tin added to most glazes renders them opaque. A small addition of tin, 1 to 3 percent, may make a glaze semi-opaque and cloudy.

Zirconium oxide also gives opacity to glazes and may be used instead of tin oxide. It is usually prepared as a silicate of zirconium, some silica being combined with the zirconium oxide. "Zircopax" and "Opax" are trade names for such combinations. A higher percentage of zirconium oxide than of tin oxide must be used in glazes to achieve the same degree of opacity. About 7 percent of zirconium oxide will make most glazes opaque, and about 12 percent will produce white glazes. Zirconium oxide may be chosen as an opacifying agent because it is cheaper than tin oxide. However, it may give a somewhat harsher texture to the glaze and may not favor certain colors as tin oxide does. Zirconium oxide may also be useful as an opacifier in certain glazes containing chrome, where the presence of tin oxide will produce unwanted pink or brown colors.

Recent work indicates that pure titanium oxide may have useful properties as an opacifier.

Semi-opaque glazes are those which partially reveal what is underneath them, like an obscure glass. They are among the most attractive of all glazes. Semi-opaque glazes reveal, yet partially conceal in a tantalizing way, the slips or clays beneath them. Unfortunately they are very hard to control, and for this reason, although they are popular with studio potters, they are little used in industry. A semi-opaque glaze can be made by adding only enough opacifier to cloud the glaze without making it completely opaque. In semi-opaque glazes, the thickness of the glaze coating and the firing temperature become critical factors. If the glaze is applied a little too thickly, it may be opaque; if applied too thinly, it may be transparent. Also, if a semi-opaque glaze is slightly over-fired it may clear up and become too transparent; and if it is slightly under-fired, it may be too opaque.

Semi-opaque glazes may result from any of the conditions described above as causes for opacity. In many cases, however, the effect is too dependent on exact firing temperature to be practical. The most practical semi-opaque glazes are those which are made by adding small amounts of tin oxide or zirconium oxide to an essentially clear transparent base glaze.

2. Bright and Mat Glazes

The surfaces of glazes may have more or less shine, reflectance, or brightness. A glaze with a dull surface, lacking in shine or reflections, is called a mat glaze. A completely melted glass or glaze is apt to have a bright shiny surface. This is because the glaze, as it melts, levels and flattens out to an exceedingly smooth surface. This smoothness of glazes is one of their practical features. A smooth surface is sanitary, is easily cleaned, and does not harbor dirt and germs in crevices or pits.

If a glaze is not completely melted in the fire, or if the viscosity of the glaze at the height of firing is still high, the surface of the glaze is apt to be slightly rough and therefore more or less mat. Under-fired glazes are commonly mat as well as opaque. The development of crystals on the surface of the glaze may also cause matness. Some of the most beautiful mat glazes are made in this way. Slow cooling naturally favors the mat glaze, especially if the matness is the result of crystals in the glaze. Such mat glazes are called "crypto-crystalline" glazes to distinguish them from glazes which have large visible crystals.

The addition of clay to glazes will cause matness by making them more refractory and therefore somewhat under-fired at the intended temperature. Similarly, additions of whiting to a bright glaze will give it a mat surface.

Barium oxide in excess of about .2 molecular equivalents will produce matness in most glazes. The barium mat is particularly soft and frosty in appearance and is pleasant to the touch. Lead glazes which are matted by the presence of barium oxide are among the favorite glazes of studio potters. Barium may not cause matness in glazes which are high in B_2O_3, since this oxide forms a eutectic with barium, producing a fluid glass.

Mat glazes, although they are very attractive, have some practical disadvantages. They are hard to clean; and when used on tableware, they may make an unpleasant scratchy noise when scraped by silver. For these reasons smooth, bright glazes are to be preferred for tableware. Mat glazes are often very beautiful and their soft-looking surface, without highlights or reflections, enhances the form of pottery.

The properties of matness and opacity are related. That is, a mat glaze must also be opaque, because the roughness of surface which causes matness does not permit transparency. An intriguing possibility would be a slightly mat glaze which was at the same time transparent enough to reveal the clay body or engobe beneath. Such effects are difficult to achieve. They are approximated by semi-opaque glazes which are applied thinly. The addition of calcium oxide may cause the dulling of the surface of a glaze without much affecting its transparency.

To summarize; matness may be induced in glazes by:

(1) Under-firing.
(2) Increasing the alumina.
(3) Increasing the calcium oxide or magnesia.
(4) Increasing the silica to the point where devitrification will occur in cooling.
(5) Including barium oxide in the glaze in amounts above about .2 molecular equivalents.

Chapter 21

Sources of Color in Glazes

1. Theory of Color in Glazes

Glazes on pottery, in addition to giving a tough, impervious, sanitary, and easily cleaned surface, have the virtue of an exceptionally wide range of color—color which has variety, depth, luminosity, and permanence.

Color in glazes may be due to the color of the clay, slip, or underglaze color under the glaze, as seen through the transparent glaze coating. Or glazes may be colored by metallic oxides which are dissolved in them. The latter is the most common and characteristic kind of glaze color. Glazes may also be colored by glassy coatings on their surface, such as overglaze enamels or luster films. "China painting" or the familiar decal decoration on tableware is composed of color fired onto the surface of the glaze.

Some metallic oxides—such as the oxides of iron, copper, manganese, and cobalt—are readily soluble in glass. When dissolved in glass, they lend to it a characteristic color. The solution may be quite complete, and the effect in the finished glaze may be compared to the effect of adding a dye to water.

The color of any transparent body is the result of selective absorptions of certain wave-lengths or color bands from white light. Some bands are absorbed more than others. The color that we see (in glaze or glass) is that of the color band, or a combination of color bands, least absorbed.

The color conferred on a glaze by a given metallic oxide is seldom related to the color of the oxide itself. Chrome is an exception, with its green. The color is sometimes that of the ion of the metal in a water solution of its salts. Here, cobalt is an exception. Cobalt salts are pink in water solution. The fact seems to be that the vehicle, or solvent, strongly influences ion colors. Hence the variety of tints and even variety in color, when the same element is in a silicate melt with different modifiers of the glaze or glass.

While only a few oxides are used as glaze colorants, the variables in the composition of the glaze, quantity of coloring oxide, application, and firing conditions are great, and in practice an almost unlimited number of colors can be made. It is this large variability which makes the study of glazes so fascinating.

The coloring oxides will be described first; later the methods of combining and blending these oxides to obtain desired colors will be described.

2. Iron Oxide

Iron oxide is perhaps the most important of the coloring oxides. It occurs in most earthy substances. The earth as a whole contains a very substantial percentage of iron, and, as we have seen, all clays either are fairly dark in color when fired, because of the presence of iron oxide, or have smaller amounts of iron oxide present as an impurity even when the fired color is light. The characteristic browns, rust colors, yellows, or greys of most rocks, sands, and soils are the result of the iron oxide which is present in these earthy materials.

Clear glazes which appear over clay containing iron oxide reveal colors of tan, brown, reddish brown, or yellow. There is a good deal of variety in these glazed-clay colors—a variety dependent on the amount of iron oxide in the clay, the type of glaze, and the temperature and atmosphere of firing. If potters had only this range of color to work with, much could be done in subtle variations of color. Immature clay bodies which are glazed with a clear glaze are brown, reddish brown, salmon, ochre, or yellowish pink. When a high lead content glaze is used, the color of the clay is apt to be warm in tone; while alkaline glazes give cooler but bright hues of red-brown and yellow. Clay bodies which have a small amount of iron oxide in them will appear buff, creamy, or yellow under clear glazes; while those containing considerable iron oxide will appear to be a dark reddish brown or chocolate color.

In the middle range of temperature, from cone 02 to 5, clays containing an appreciable amount of iron are apt to be hard-fired and mature, and under clear glazes they will be more grey and subdued in color than the lower-fired bodies.

Clay bodies fired at cone 5 or more are apt to be still more subdued in color. In such bodies, iron oxide causes a very subdued brown or grey. Reduction firing, as will be described later, gives still another range of color to clay.

In most of the tableware industry, iron oxide is regarded as an impurity, and a great deal of trouble is taken to avoid contamination of clays and glazes with iron. Many commercial ceramics, including tableware and sanitary ware, are traditionally white, and specks caused by traces of iron are regarded as serious defects. Ceramists have occupied themselves for generations in perfecting pure white porcelain—a feat which was mastered in China over 1000 years ago. Whiteness no doubt achieves a prestige value because of the difficulty of achieving it and because of its association with the fine wares of the Orient and with the expensive early porcelains of Europe.

Factories producing whitewares must be equipped to prevent contamination by iron particles. Grinding mills are lined with porcelain blocks, and magnetic filters remove the larger particles of iron which may have gotten in clays and slips. The studio potter, however, tends to accept iron in his materials and to make the most of the varied and sometimes earthy effects which it naturally lends to pottery.

Iron oxide dissolved in glazes produces a wide range of color. Again, if potters had only this one oxide to use as a glaze colorant, wares of great variety and color could be made. In fact, the Chinese potters of the classic Sung Dynasty period relied almost entirely on iron oxide as a colorant. The relatively wide range of glaze color which can be produced from iron is due to its ready solubility in glass, its sensitivity to changes in the composition of the glaze, and its sensitive response to atmosphere in the kiln.

Iron is usually added to glazes in the form of ferric oxide, Fe_2O_3. The mineral name for ferric oxide is hematite. It is commonly called red iron oxide because of its color, which is dense and strong, the color of barn paint, which is, in fact, made from iron oxide. Red iron oxide is the stable form of iron; and in no matter what form iron is put into the kiln, in bodies or glazes, the oxidizing effect of firing converts it largely into Fe_2O_3.

Ferrous iron, or black iron oxide, which has the formula Fe_3O_4, may also be used as a glaze colorant, and in most cases it gives the same color as red iron oxide. As will be seen from the formula, it has a higher ratio of iron to oxygen than the red iron oxide, and for this reason may be expected to give somewhat darker colors when used in the same amount. Red iron oxide is finer in particle size than black iron oxide, and for this reason it is preferred whenever complete dispersion in the glaze is desired.

Since common red clays contain as much as 8 percent of iron, such clays can be added to glazes as a source of iron oxide. Most glaze recipes call for some clay; and if red clay is used, the glaze will be colored as would be expected from a small addition of iron.

When rough, spotty, or speckled effects are desired, iron oxide may be added to the glaze in the form of crocus martis, an impure iron oxide, or in the form of red iron-bearing clay, slip-clay, or as rust scrapings or ground black mill-scale. Some clay-like minerals are loaded with iron, manganese, and other metallic oxides, and may be used to color engobes, bodies, or glazes. Barnard or "black-bird" clay is an example of this type of material. When used as a slip under high-fired glazes, the iron and other metallic oxides in barnard clay bleed through, producing brown, tan, or grey coloration.

Iron oxide will produce warm hues in glazes ranging from light tan or straw color to dark brown or black. One percent of iron oxide added to a glaze will give a noticeable tint. Three percent will give a medium tint, 5 percent a strong tint, and over 7 percent will usually produce a dark brown or black.

In lead glazes, iron oxide gives warm soft colors of tan, yellowish brown, amber, reddish brown, or dark mahogany-brown. In low-fired glazes which are high in lead, rather brilliant tones of amber can be produced by additions of 2 to 5 percent of iron oxide. At the higher temperatures, in the range of cone 01 to cone 5, when the lead content of the glaze is less, the colors produced by iron oxide are more subdued.

When iron oxide is used in a high lead glaze which contains also tin oxide, a mottled cream color results, with red-brown areas where the glaze is thin, as on the edges of pots. Such glazes can be very handsome, especially over clay surfaces which are textured.

In alkaline glazes, iron oxide gives cooler tones of yellow, tan, and brown.

If iron oxide is added to glazes which contain zinc oxide, the resultant color is apt to be rather dull and muddy. In general, base glazes which are high in lead oxide and are free of zinc oxide give the most handsome colors from iron additions.

When iron oxide is added to most glazes in excess of 7 percent, a very dark brown or black results. Such blacks may be very bright and almost mirror-like in surface. Iron oxide is an active flux in glazes, and even small amounts will make a glaze noticeably more fluid. Sometimes a glaze which is quite mat will become bright by the addition of 2 or 3 percent of iron oxide.

If considerable iron oxide is used in a glaze, it has a tendency to crystallize out upon cooling. In the case of high lead glazes, these iron crystals may be brilliantly tinted with colors of yellow and red. The so-called aventurine glazes are produced this way.

Iron is very useful in modifying colors derived from other oxides. For example, glazes which are colored yellow, blue, or green by additions of vanadium oxide, cobalt oxide, or copper oxide, may be greyed down and given depth and subtlety by the addition of small amounts of iron oxide.

In addition to producing a palette of warm colors, iron oxide also is used to produce the special and sometimes spectacular type of glazes known as celedon, saturated iron, and temmoku. These are described in a later section.

3. Copper Oxide

Copper oxide has been used since antiquity to produce colors of blue and green in glazes. Some of the earliest known examples of glazed pottery, made in Egypt about 3000 B.C., are glazed with alkaline glazes colored blue with copper oxide.

Copper carbonate, the most common source for copper oxide, is a light green powder, very fine in particle size, and having the formula $CuCO_3$. Black copper oxide is sometimes used. It is somewhat coarser in grain size, and, as will be seen from its formula, CuO, it yields more copper per unit of weight than does copper carbonate.

Copper oxide is highly soluble in glazes. It mixes thoroughly with the molten glaze during firing, even when not well ground into the raw glaze batch. Copper oxide, like iron oxide, is a strong flux, and its addition may make the glaze noticeably more fluid and bright in surface.

A 1-percent addition of copper oxide will give a light tint of color to most glazes. Two to 3 percent will give strong color. More than 5 percent of copper oxide will give a dark or metallic surface, green or black in color.

Copper oxide added to a strongly alkaline glaze will produce a turquoise or blue color. This is the beautiful and familiar color which we associate with Egyptian and Persian ceramics. The blue color is favored by the presence of little or no alumina, and for intense hues, the soda or potash content must be high. About 2 percent of copper oxide added to an alkaline glaze will give a strong color. Copper-blue glazes may be opaque or, if transparent, may appear over a light body or slip which gives a maximum of reflected light passing through the glaze. Highly alkaline glazes usually craze on any ordinary clay body, but this defect may be tolerated for the sake of a very desirable color such as copper-blue.

In lead glazes, copper oxide gives various shades of green. Such greens are soft, warm, and similar in range of color to the green of plants. These greens may be beautifully modified by the addition of small amounts of other coloring oxides, such as vanadium, rutile, iron, or nickel.

In glazes which rely largely on boron for their flux—such as colemanite glazes—copper oxide additions produce greenish turquoise colors. While these glazes may lack the singing brilliance of alkaline copper-blue, they can be very deep and beautiful in color, especially when opaque. When a base glaze which is very high in barium is colored by copper oxide, the result may be an unusually high-keyed blue or blue-green.

Above cone 8, copper oxide is quite volatile. It escapes from the glaze as a vapor which may influence the color of other glazed pieces in the kiln. In reduction firing, copper oxide gives the famous copper-red or ox-blood color, which will be described in a later section.

4. Cobalt Oxide

Cobalt oxide is the most stable and reliable glaze colorant. It gives a similar shade of blue in almost all types of glazes and under various firing conditions. The usual forms employed are cobalt carbonate, a light purple powder with the formula $CoCO_3$, or black cobalt oxide, CoO. The carbonate is usually preferred because of its fine particle size.

Cobalt oxide is the most powerful of the coloring oxides in tinting strength. One-fourth of 1 percent in a glaze is sufficient to give a medium blue. One-half percent gives a strong blue, and 1 percent ordinarily gives a very dark blue. Amounts of more than 1 percent produce dense blue-black or black.

In alkaline glazes, cobalt oxide produces an extremely brilliant blue. Other types of glazes colored with cobalt oxide are somewhat less intense in color. When magnesia is present in the glaze in fairly large amounts, 0.2 equivalents or more, cobalt oxide colors the glaze purple-blue. In glazes fired at cone 9 or more, combinations of magnesia and cobalt oxide may give mottled effects, marked with spots or splotches of red, pink, and purple. Glaze colors of this kind are very hard to control or duplicate because they occur within narrow ranges of temperature and atmospheric variation.

The color resulting from cobalt oxide in glazes is so strong, insistent, and uniform in hue that most potters tire of it and lose interest in it. It is certainly true that cobalt oxide alone gives a rather harsh color. But the blue of cobalt oxide can be beautifully and subtly varied by the addition of other coloring oxides such as iron, rutile, manganese, and nickel.

Glazes containing cobalt oxide may need to be thoroughly ball-milled to eliminate a speckled or mottled appearance in the finished glaze.

5. Chromium Oxide

Chrome oxide is the most versatile coloring oxide, a veritable turn-coat. It will produce red, yellow, pink, brown, or green glazes, depending on the kind of glaze used and the temperature of firing.

In glazes which are free of zinc oxide and not excessively high in lead, chrome oxide gives a green color. This green is apt to be rather dense and heavy. It is usually not as attractive as the green resulting from copper oxide, especially if more than 1 percent of chrome oxide is used. Amounts of one-half to 3 percent of chrome oxide may be used for greens of various intensity.

In low-fired lead glazes which have above 0.7 equivalents of lead oxide and a low alumina content, chrome oxide may give brilliant orange or red color. The firing temperature of chrome-red glazes must be low, preferably below cone 08. One to 2 percent of chrome oxide is enough to produce the color, which tends to be somewhat sugary-looking because of crystals on the surface of the glaze. Or a soluble chromium compound may be used, such as potassium dichromate.

Low-fired lead glazes which contain some soda as well as lead oxide may give a brilliant yellow when about 1 percent of chrome oxide is present. Here again, as in the case of the chrome-red glaze, the firing temperature must be low.

Glazes which contain both chrome oxide and zinc oxide are brown. Brown underglaze stains are made from this combination of materials. Ordinarily only a small amount of chrome oxide is required to produce fairly strong tints in a zinc glaze, and when more than about 2 percent is used, the color is apt to be heavy and dingy.

When chrome oxide is added to a base glaze which also contains tin oxide, the resultant color is pink or brownish red. A small amount of chrome oxide, less than one-half of 1 percent, is sufficient to give a pink color in a glaze which contains 5 percent of tin oxide. Rich and varied tones of pink, greyed pink, and warm browns are possible with this combination, but true red cannot be achieved with chrome and tin. Red glazes are described in a later section.

When chrome oxide and cobalt oxide are both added to a glaze, especially a glaze of the magnesia type fired in reduction at cone 9 or above, beautiful hues of blue-green may be obtained. Small amounts of both chrome oxide and cobalt oxide give the most pleasing colors. The cobalt oxide should be held to less than one-half of 1 percent, and the chrome oxide to less than 1 percent.

Chrome oxide is quite volatile at cone 6 or above, and sometimes glazes containing tin oxide will be streaked with pink or brown by the volatilization of chrome from some piece nearby in the kiln. Chrome oxide alone is quite refractory and does not dissolve in the glaze as readily as the oxides of iron, copper, or cobalt. Chrome oxide may be used as the green oxide of chrome, Cr_2O_3, or as potassium dichromate, $K_2Cr_2O_7$. This later material, however, has the disadvantage of being soluble and poisonous.

6. Manganese Oxide

Manganese gives a purple or brown color in glazes. The usual source is manganese carbonate, $MnCO_3$, which is a very fine pink-colored powder, or black manganese dioxide, MnO_2. Black manganese is used in bodies and slips where its coarser grain size, which tends to cause specks, may be considered an advantage rather than a disadvantage. Manganese, compared to cobalt or copper, is a weak coloring oxide, and 2 or 3 percent is usually required to give a pronounced color.

In highly alkaline glazes, manganese gives a rich blue-purple or plum color. In lead glazes it gives a softer purple, less intense and tinged with brown. In glazes which are fired above cone 6, manganese tends to give rather neutral brown, and in a reducing fire it gives a very subdued brown.

In some lead glazes, manganese carbonate may cause blistering, especially if the atmosphere in the kiln is not strictly oxidizing.

Combined with small amounts of iron, manganese oxide may give rich shades of cool brown. Combined with small amounts of cobalt oxide it can produce deep violet or plum colors.

7. Nickel Oxide

The common forms of nickel oxide used in glazes are green nickel oxide, NiO, or black nickel oxide, Ni_2O_3. Nickel oxide gives quite a wide variety of colors in glazes, but its most typical color is brown. The colors derived from nickel are rather uncertain, and for this reason it is little used by itself in commercial production as a glaze colorant. Small amounts of nickel oxide—below 1 percent—will give a grey color in most base glazes. When the amount is increased to 2 or more percent, brown may be expected. The color obtained with nickel oxide alone tends to be rather quiet, and sometimes dull and dingy. It is really most useful in modifying or greying the colors derived from other coloring oxides, and when about one-half of 1 percent of nickel oxide is added to glazes in addition to coloring oxides such as cobalt, iron, or copper, beautifully greyed or modulated hues may result.

In some cases, nickel oxide may give strange and rather unpredictable color. In high-zinc base glazes, which are fired in reduction at cone 8 or higher, nickel may cause fairly bright yellowish or purplish tones, or even blue. These colors, however, are very uncertain and hard to repeat.

Nickel oxide is very refractory and if added to already mat glazes in amounts exceeding about 2 percent, may make them excessively dry and rough.

8. Vanadium Oxide

Vanadium oxide is ordinarily used in glazes as a stain which is prepared by combining vanadium pentoxide, V_2O_5, with tin oxide. In such a stain, the tin forms the bulk of the material. Vanadium stain gives a yellow color in glazes. Because of the rather small amount of vanadium oxide in vanadium stain, fairly large percentages are required to color glazes. Five percent will usually give a weak yellow, and 8 to 10 percent, a strong yellow. Since tin is present in the stain, it lends opacity to the glaze. If a base glaze already contains tin oxide and vanadium stain is added for color, the batch may have, as a result, too much tin, resulting in a pasty, under-fired appearance.

9. Rutile

Rutile is an ore containing titanium oxide and iron oxide. It is used in glazes as a source of titanium, provided the color contributed by the iron is not objectionable. Rutile gives a tan or brown color to glazes. Its tinting power, however, is weak, because of the relatively small amount of iron present, and it is more frequently used for its influence on the texture of the glaze than for its color. Rutile has the property of producing broken color or mottled color in glazes which would otherwise have a smooth color and texture. Three to 5 percent is the usual amount added to the glaze. In glazes containing B_2O_3, rutile may cause pronounced streaks or spots, particularly in those glazes which are opaque and lightly tinted with some other coloring oxide such as copper or iron. In lead glazes, the texture caused by rutile may be less prominent. Besides contributing to the break-up of surface color, and lending a tan or brown influence to the glaze, rutile also serves to increase opacity, especially if used in amounts of 5 percent or more.

Rutile added to glazes containing copper, iron, cobalt, or chrome may give beautifully greyed and textured colors, and rutile glazes of various kinds are rightly favored by the studio potter for their rich variety and surface interest.

The part which rutile plays in the formation of crystalline glazes is described in a later section.

10. Ilmenite

Like rutile, ilmenite is an ore containing both titanium and iron. Ilmenite is a cruder ore and contains a higher percentage of iron. As a colorant, it gives effects similar to those obtained from black iron oxide, especially if it is well ground into the glaze. Ilmenite is used mostly for its influence on texture and as a means of inducing spots or specks into bodies and glazes. When used in granular form, that is as a coarse grind which will not pass through an 80-mesh screen, ilmenite will produce prominent specks or spots in a glaze. If other coloring oxides are also present in the glaze, these spots may be surrounded with minute halos of yellow which can give the glaze a highly complex and interesting surface. One to 3 percent of ilmenite is sufficient to give a marked color and texture. When added to clay bodies or engobes, ilmenite produces a darkening of color and a speckled, peppery appearance.

11. Iron Chromate

Iron chromate is used in glazes to produce shades of grey, brown, or black. In most glazes, 2 percent will give a pronounced darkening of color. If the base glaze contains zinc, iron chromate will produce a brown color. If tin is present in the glaze, a pink or reddish brown may be expected from the addition of iron chromate. In general, iron chromate, which has the formula $FeCrO_4$, colors the glaze about as would be expected from the addition of the two materials, iron and chrome. It is most useful as a modifier of other colors, although when a neutral grey is desired, iron chromate will sometimes give hues which can be obtained by no other combination of oxides. Iron chromate is commonly used in engobes to give a grey color.

12. Uranium Oxide

Uranium can be added to glazes in the form of either uranium oxide or sodium uranate. Since 1944 the government has not released even small amounts of uranium for ceramic use; so potters are no longer able to use this valuable glaze colorant. Uranium oxide gives a yellow color. In contrast to vanadium, which gives rather warm yellow, uranium can be used to produce cool lemon-yellows. In low-fired, high-lead glazes, uranium gives an orange-red, similar in hue to chrome-red.

13. Cadmium and Selenium

Cadmium and selenium are used to produce red glazes. They are ordinarily used combined in a glaze stain which is added as a colorant to a low-fired fritted glaze. The stain may contain about 20 percent selenium and 80 percent cadmium sulphide. In fact, the prepared "color" is a solid solution of CdSe and CdS. Stains of cadmium and selenium give a bright, almost spectrum-red. The color is quite fugitive, however, and must be fired at a low temperature. Rapid cooling of the glazes is necessary to prevent the red color from disappearing. In producing red colors from cadmium and selenium, it is best to purchase a prepared stain and to rely on the supplier's recommendation of a suitable frit to use for the glaze.

Chapter 22

Methods of Compounding and Blending Colored Glazes

1. Additions of Single Oxides to Glazes

It is convenient to think of glaze colorants as materials which are added to an essentially colorless base glaze and to think of these added oxides as coloring or tinting the glaze to the desired hue. The glaze itself, minus any color influence, is referred to as the "base glaze." Sometimes the coloring oxides of a glaze are reported in its empirical formula in terms of molecular equivalents. In such cases, they are calculated like any other material. Usually, however, the coloring oxides are considered as additions to the base glaze and are expressed as an outside percentage. For example, a glaze which is said to contain 2 percent of iron will comprise 100 parts of glaze and 2 parts of iron. Using this method, the total of the glaze and the colorants added to it is more than 100. Since some glazes have numerous oxides added to them for color, it will be seen that it is more convenient and more logical to consider the base glaze as being 100 parts.

It is very simple to develop a series of colors using any base glaze which has been tried out and which has been found to melt properly at the intended temperature. When a new glaze is being worked out, it is common to concentrate first on the composition of the base glaze until it is working well, and then, as the next step, to develop various colors.

The first step in trying out some coloring oxides in a glaze is the simple addition to the glaze of a percentage of each of the coloring oxides. Amounts should be used which are known from previous experience to give an average concentration of color. If a separate test is made for each of the coloring oxides, the response of a new glaze to the various coloring oxides is determined at once, and further blending may be done more intelligently. The following list gives the approximate quantities of coloring oxides which are used to give tints of average strength:

Cobalt oxide or cobalt carbonate	½ to 1 %
Iron oxide	1 to 10%
Copper oxide	2 to 5 %
Chrome	2 to 5 %
Nickel	½ to 3 %
Manganese	2 to 6 %
Iron chromate	1 to 3 %
Vanadium stain	4 to 10%
Rutile	2 to 10%
Ilmenite	1 to 5 %

It is well to make several tests using iron, copper, and cobalt to determine the colors resulting from various amounts of these oxides.

When a transparent glaze is being tested, it may be advisable to try also a parallel series in which the glaze is made opaque by the addition of tin oxide or zirconium. When a transparent series is tried over dark clay, the results may be somewhat disappointing because some of the colors, particularly the blues and greens, will appear dark and dingy because of the dark color of the body underlying the glaze and influencing the color of the glaze.

2. Line Blends

Although some beautiful glazes may result from the addition of single coloring oxides to a glaze, the most exciting glaze colors are usually the result of the addition of two or more colorants to the base glaze. Such additions may be arrived at by methodical blending, or by adding combinations and quantities of oxides which are known to be congenial and promise to give good results. Or testing may proceed on a "hunch", or in the spirit of experimentation, by adding various materials to the base glaze just to see what will happen.

In methodical blending, the ceramist may anticipate that a certain percentage of his tests will prove to be unsatisfactory and will only produce muddy and unpromising colors. But there is also the probability that methodical blending will produce beautiful combinations which might not have been hit upon by other approaches.

The simplest type of methodical blend is the line blend. This kind of blend establishes a series of variations or mixes between two colors. Suppose, for example, we wish to determine the effect of diminishing amounts of cobalt in a glaze. A line blend could be planned as follows:

A	25% B	50% A	25% A	B
3% cobalt	75% A	50% B	50% B	0% cobalt

A is the glaze with 3 percent cobalt. B is the same glaze with no cobalt. Three other mixtures are made as shown. This is simply a method of establishing intermediary blends between the two end points. Such a blend may have as many steps or variations as desired.

A convenient method of blending glazes is to blend them in the wet state, mixed with water. The glazes which are to be blended are ground, with care being taken to use the same amount of water in each batch. After grinding, the specific gravity of each glaze can be checked by weighing 100 cc. of each glaze. If one of the glazes weighs more than the other, more water can be added to it until both weigh exactly the same. When blending, the right amount of each glaze can be carefully measured out in a graduate, then combined and shaken together until well mixed, and applied to the test tile.

A line blend may reveal interesting combinations between two different coloring oxides. A, for example, might be a glaze with 2 percent copper oxide; while B might be the same base glaze containing 5 percent rutile. Such a blend would illustrate the effect of diminishing copper oxide and increasing rutile, and vice versa. Line blends are frequently used to study combinations between different base glazes and to locate in-between points when solving some problem such as crazing, or when achieving a certain degree of matness or smoothness.

Another type of line blend may be illustrated as follows:

1	2	3	4	5	6
	1–2	1–3	1–4	1–5	1–6
		2–3	2–4	2–5	2–6
			3–4	3–5	3–6
				4–5	4–6
					5–6

The top numbers, One to Six, may be any set of variables, such as additions of single coloring oxides to some glaze. Number One, for example, might be a base glaze plus 2 percent of iron oxide. Number Two might be the same glaze plus 3 percent of copper oxide, and so on. In the next row down, 1-2 is a half-and-half mixture of Number One and Number Two; 1-3 is a half-and-half mixture of One and Three, and so on. What this type of blend actually accomplishes is to exhaust all the mathematically possible 50-50 combinations between the original variations in the top row. Such a blend can be rapidly prepared by wet blending after the glazes in the top row have been prepared with identical water content. This is a very valuable kind of blend, and it seldom fails to yield some subtle variations, particularly if the original variations are fairly numerous—say six or more.

3. Tri-axial Blending

When three materials or glazes are to be blended, a tri-axial blending diagram is used. It appears as follows:

In this diagram, the points on the line between A and B and between B and C and between A and C are, in effect, the same as straight line blends. The midway point in each line represents half of one member and half of the other. Other points on the outside lines of the triangle have more or less of the end members, depending on the position of the point, each point in this case representing one-tenth of the line. The composition of point Y, for example, will be 60 percent of A and 40 percent of C. The composition of a point on the inside of the tri-axial blend will depend on its distance away from the points at the corner. Point X, for example, will contain 50 percent of A, since it is five spaces removed from A. X will contain 30 percent of B, since it is seven spaces removed from B, and 20 percent of C, since it is eight spaces removed from C. Similarly, the composition of any other point in the diagram can be determined. Tri-axial diagrams are of great utility in tracking down some subtle variation in body or glaze composition. They are perhaps unnecessarily complex where color alone is being studied.

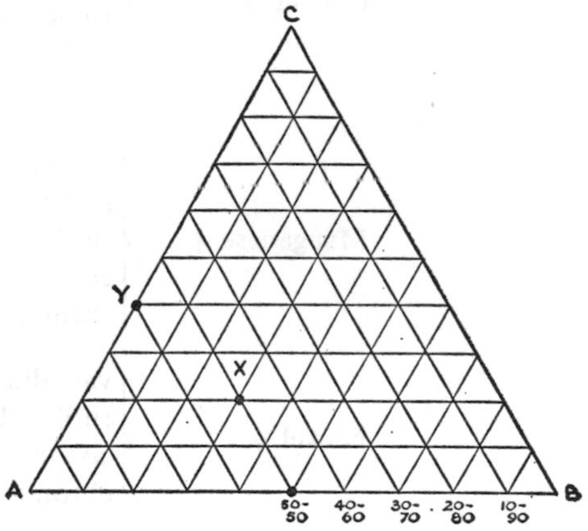

4. Methods of Making Glaze Variations without Blending

All sorts of variations may be made on any one base glaze without using any methodical method of blending, but by simply planning some intended additions and trying them out. However, unless the experimenter is experienced enough to avoid unlikely combinations, much time may be wasted. For instance, the inexperienced potter may waste a day making tests which combine manganese and chrome as colorants in a glaze, whereas anyone who has worked much with glazes would know that this combination could result only in muddy colors. With a little knowledge, however, the ceramist may go directly to potentially promising mixtures and arrive at good glaze colors with less time spent testing than would be required by following some system of blending. Such a method also allows for the following of hunches and the trying out of unusual and strange combinations, some of which may prove worthwhile.

The following list is given as a general guide to combinations of glaze colorants. It does not extend to three colorants, and it should be emphasized that some of the best glaze colors do result from three or more coloring oxides. The amount of colors used, has, of course,

Iron +
- cobalt—grey-blue
- copper—warm green, metallic green, black
- manganese—brown
- vanadium—ochre
- rutile—ochre, brown
- nickel—brown to grey
- chrome—blackish green

Copper +
- cobalt—blue-green
- manganese—brown, black
- vanadium—yellow-green
- rutile—warm or textured green
- nickel—grey-green
- chrome—green

Manganese +
- vanadium—yellowish brown
- nickel—grey or brown
- rutile—brown
- cobalt—blue-purple
- chrome—brown

Nickel +
- vanadium—grey, brown
- rutile—brown
- cobalt—grey-blue
- chrome—brown

Cobalt +
- vanadium—greyed yellow or mustard
- rutile—textured warm blue or grey-blue
- chrome—blue-green

Rutile +
- vanadium—ocherish yellow
- chrome—warm green

Chrome +
- vanadium—yellow-green

a large influence on the resultant color.

When two or more coloring oxides are used in a glaze, the amount of each has to be reduced to avoid excessively dark colors. In general, a sparing use of coloring oxides gives the most pleasant glazes, unless deep, saturated colors are desired. Many glazes which seem attractive on a test tile, and which are in the middle range of value, look very dull in a larger amount, as seen when used on a pot. It seems that the most attractive pieces of pottery usually have either light glazes or very dark ones. There are, of course, many exceptions to this rule.

5. Use of Glaze Stains

In addition to the metallic oxides used to color glazes, there are available also a great variety of stains and colorants which are commercially prepared for use as underglaze colors or glaze stains. The composition and use of these stains is discussed in a later section. All of these stains can be added to the glaze batch in the same way the metallic oxides are added. Of course, these commercial stains are prepared from the metallic oxides but are calcined with other materials to bring out certain colors. Pink stains, for example, are made from combinations of chrome and tin oxide. Although the potter does not know exactly what oxides are contained in any particular commercial stain, since the manufacturers of such stains do not publish their formulas, he can use such stains effectively after finding out experimentally what colors they give in his particular base glazes. Actually, the use of commercial stains as glaze colorants has some advantages. Subtle tones of grey, pink, mauve, grey-green, or grey-blue can sometimes be arrived at more easily by using commercial stains than by adding very small amounts of chrome oxide, iron chromate, cobalt oxide, and the like to the glaze. The stains are also very useful as modifiers of other colors obtained from the oxides. Cobalt glazes, for instance, may be effectively toned down with commercial "grey" stain. Stains sold as "glaze stain" or as "underglaze stain" may be used. The former are somewhat cheaper.

6. Black Glazes

Black glazes may be produced by an over-charge of coloring oxides. Oxides of cobalt, iron, copper, and manganese are usually used. About 2 percent of any three of these will yield a black color in most base glazes. The difficulty is that when a rich black has been obtained, it may be found that the glaze, because of the addition of considerable flux in the form of metallic oxides, has become too fluid. The base glaze may then have to be adjusted by additions of clay; or if too much coloring oxide is added to make a black, the metallic oxides may crystallize out in the cooling glaze and produce a dry or even wrinkled surface. A mirror-like black can be made by additions of copper oxide and iron oxide. The most attractive black glazes are those which are slightly mat or crystalline in surface. Such glazes are quite elusive and are perhaps best made with some natural slip glaze, such as Albany slip, darkened by additions of iron or cobalt oxide.

7. Test Tiles for Glazes

Glazes are usually tried out on small test tiles. These may be pieces of clay about one and one-half inches square and about one-fourth of an inch thick. If the glazed surface is too small, it is difficult to get a good idea of the appearance of the glaze, and on the other hand, if the test tile is too large, an undue amount of space is taken up in the kiln. If a hole is drilled through the top of the test tile, groups of related tests may later be strung together on a wire. Some sort of impressed texture on the face of the tile will give valuable information as to how the glaze will behave on rough surfaces.

Some potters make glaze trials on little tags of clay shaped somewhat like tombstones. They can be made very rapidly from a ball of clay about the size of a large jawbreaker. These little pieces stand upright in the kiln and have the advantage of showing the flow of the glaze on a vertical surface, which, after all, is the typical surface as far as pottery making goes. To test for the flow of glaze, flat tiles are sometimes propped up in the kiln at an angle.

Test tiles may be made on the potter's wheel. A shape is thrown resembling a dog-dish. When it is leather-hard, the bottom is cut out to within one inch of the sides, and the sides are then sliced up into segments about one inch wide. These little segments, having a fragment of the bottom attached to them, will stand up in the kiln and make excellent testing pieces. They may have throwing marks on their surface, which is an advantage when testing glazes which are to be used on thrown pots.

8. Glazing and Marking Tests

It is advisable to bisque-fire test tiles before applying test glazes, especially if this procedure is used in the production for which the test is a rehearsal. There are several ways of applying glaze to test tiles. One way is to dip them. The glaze to be tested may be put into a small bowl or a receptacle like a watch-glass. The tile is then lowered into the glaze face down. If a tiny sample of glaze is to be tested, it may be applied to the tile with a brush, care being taken to get enough on.

One excellent way to get the glaze onto the tile is with a spatula. The broad blade of the knife is loaded with the fluid glaze which is spread onto the tile by laying the edge of the knife on the tile and drawing it across the tile as the glaze flows off the knife.

On each test it is wise to have several thicknesses of glaze represented. The whole appearance of a glaze may depend upon thickness or application, and each test should show this possible variation. This can easily be done by double or triple dipping or painting in making the test.

It is best to mark test tiles with an underglaze pencil on the back of the tile. If such a pencil is not available, marking fluid can be made by mixing a pinch or two of lead oxide or frit into a teaspoon of underglaze black stain, and mixing this with enough water to make it of brushing consistency. Marking should be bold and legible lest the results of hours or even days of work may be lost.

To make a series of color tests of some base glaze, the base glaze must first be carefully weighed out in sufficient quantity for the intended number of tests and then mixed thoroughly by dry grinding in the ball mill or by repeated sifting. The mixed dry glaze is then weighed out into packets of 30 or 50 grams each. It is better to use 50 grams for each test so that the intended additions are not so small as to make accurate weighing impossible. The small packets of dry glaze can be conveniently kept in sacks or sandwich bags until additions are made to them. Next, the colorants for each test are weighed out on a sensitive balance and added to the packet of base glaze in the sack, and the appropriate number is marked on the sack. Accurate weighing is important, since a small error in weighing—say one-half of a gram of some oxide—may result in a significant error in the test. In the case of very small amounts, such as less than one-half gram, it is best to weigh out one gram of material and then carefully divide the small pile of material into four or eight parts with the palette knife. Such mechanical divisions are more accurate than weighing, unless a very sensitive balance is used.

The test glazes are best mixed on a glass or marble slab, using a spatula or a palette knife with a broad blade. Water is conveniently added with a small syringe, with which one can squeeze out just the right amount of water to bring the mixture to the proper application consistency. After each test is made and marked, the glass is washed clean and the next test is mixed.

9. Recording Tests

The student of glazes will soon find himself swamped with paper work. Orderly and complete records of experiments are necessary if the results of the tests are not to be forgotten or lost. It is a good plan to keep a record in one ledger of all the base glazes which one has developed or used. These base glazes can be numbered or named for identification. In the ledger, along with the formulas and recipes of the base glazes, one can write the characteristics of each glaze, such as maturing temperature, surface, and application thickness. In another ledger, one can keep the record of all tests which are fired. It is a good idea to assign a number to each test and to mark that number on the test tile. It does not work out well to try to mark all the facts about the test on the tile. If each tile is marked with a number, a corresponding number can be entered in the ledger, and there all the necessary information about the test can be written, such as the clay body, the base glaze, what the additions to the glaze were, etc. It is time-consuming to write all this in the ledger, but it is a sure way of keeping track of what went into the tests.

Equally important with recording what went into the tests is the record of the results. After a firing, a notation should be made in the ledger of what happened to the tests.

10. The Necessity for Testing

It may be wondered why it is necessary to do the seemingly never-ending testing which characterizes work with glazes. Like any other activity, glaze testing can certainly be overdone, and in ceramics it is common to find persons who seem to work exclusively at testing and who never accomplish any finished results. However, a certain amount of testing is useful and necessary as a method of learning about the materials and processes of the craft. As in any other work, there is no substitute for experience, and making some actual glaze tests will be more instructive than reading such a treatise as this. Facts which come to light in the course of practice tend to take their place and remain fixed in the memory as part of one's working knowledge.

Aside from the educational value of testing, the practicing ceramist will need to develop new colors and textures from time to time, and testing for new effects tends to sharpen one's interest and to keep the work alive and creative. The real problem of pottery making, however, is the application and use of colors and textures rather than the development of new ones. Any orderly worker with a healthy curiosity about ceramics can, in a short time, develop literally hundreds of handsome glazes. The use of such glazes is another matter. It requires a creative imagination, together with well-rounded skill and judgment, to produce mature, personal, and truly valuable work. It is true that the vast majority of beautiful glazes which have been developed in laboratories are gathering dust in drawers, still waiting to be used creatively on pottery.

Chapter 23

Glaze Mixing and Application

1. Ball Milling

Glazes are prepared by mixing them with water to form a fluid slip. Intimate intermingling of the various materials of the glaze helps promote melting, and for this reason it is necessary that all the materials in the glaze be thoroughly mixed. Mixing and grinding can be accomplished on the ball mill, which is a rotating, closed jar filled about one-third full of rounded flint pebbles. The dry glaze and sufficient water are put in the jar and the cover is secured in place. The jar is then placed on the device which rotates it, and it is allowed to grind for about half an hour. In the ball mill the action of the pebbles falling over one another thoroughly mixes and grinds the glaze slip. A mill must go at the right speed for efficient grinding. If it revolves too fast, the pebbles are carried around by centrifugal force and do not tumble on each other. If, on the other hand, the mill goes too slowly, there is not enough tumbling action. If the glaze slip is too thick, grinding may not take place because the pebbles will stick together. Milling a batch of glaze in a ball mill will produce a smooth, uniform slip in which any additions of coloring oxides will be thoroughly dispersed. Continued milling in a ball mill will serve not only to mix a glaze but also to grind the individual particles to smaller size. The ball mill can also be used to grind and mix dry batches of glaze. However, if such dry batches have considerable clay in them, it may be found that the material cakes against the walls of the jar instead of mixing.

2. Mixing and Screening Glazes

Most glaze materials are now supplied already ground to pass a 200-mesh screen and do not require further grinding. The glaze maker's problem is more one of mixing the various ingredients together and dispersing the coloring oxides which have been added to the batch. Small batches of glaze can be satisfactorily prepared by mixing by hand in a mortar with pestle. Or, if no coarse material is used in the glaze, small batches may be mixed with a malted-milk mixer or kitchen mixer. For most work, screening is a very satisfactory method of mixing glaze. Dry glaze may be mixed by sifting it through a 30-mesh screen several times. Glaze slip can be mixed by screening it through a 60-mesh screen. If finer dispersion is required, or if there are some coarse particles to be screened out, a 100-mesh screen may be used. Glaze slip can be rapidly passed through the screen by bumping the side of the screen or by rubbing the surface of the screen with a paint brush as the glaze is going through.

3. The Proportion of Water in Glazes

The amount of water to add to a dry glaze batch will depend on several factors. For one thing, some kinds of glaze take much more water than others. High-fired glazes, which contain considerable clay or colemanite glazes, for example, will take much more water than fritted glazes. The consistency of the glaze is also controlled by how the glaze is to be used. Glaze which is to be applied to porous bisque needs to be quite thin, while glaze which is to be dipped onto non-porous bisque must be thick. For normal application on medium-porous bisque, the glaze should be about the consistency of thick cream. If, during mixing, too much water is added to the glaze, the glaze may be allowed to settle and the excess water may be poured or siphoned off the top.

For any one glaze it is a good idea always to add the same amount of water for mixing. The consistency of glaze batches may be checked by the comparative weight of a given volume of glaze slip or by the use of a wooden stick with a lead weight on the end of it which, when allowed to sink into the glaze slip, will float at a similar level for batches of similar consistency.

Glazes are best stored in glass, enamel, or wooden containers. If the containers are covered, no water evaporates from the glaze and it stays the same consistency. Galvanized iron containers, such as buckets, are not satisfactory because of the corrosive effect of many glazes on the zinc-coated surface. Glazes may, of course, be kept for an indefinite period provided no organic material such as gums have been added.

4. Floatatives, Gums, and Flocculents for Glazes

Many glazes have heavy ingredients in them which sink rapidly to the bottom of the glaze slip. To prevent this, a floatative is added. Raw clay in the glaze helps to keep all the ingredients from settling rapidly. If there is no raw clay in the glaze, an addition of 1 percent of bentonite usually corrects the difficulty without altering the fired glaze in any way. Some gums, such as sodium alginate, also help in keeping the glaze in suspension. All glazes settle to some extent, and it is very important while using a glaze to stir it frequently. Otherwise some of the heavier materials will sink to the bottom and some of the glaze used may not be of the correct composition.

Gums are often added to glazes to make them dry onto the ware in a tough coating which will not powder or mar when being set in the kiln. A small amount of gum will usually be sufficient. Gum arabic or gum tragacanth is usually used for this purpose. These gums come in a solid form and must first be dissolved in alcohol. About one cupful of gum can be dissolved in about one-half pint of de-natured alcohol. This solution is then added to about three quarts of water and is ready for use. For a gallon of glaze slip, about one-half cup of gum solution can be used. One disadvantage of using gums is that their presence in the glaze causes spoiling. This can be prevented or delayed by adding a few drops of formaldehyde to the glaze. Sometimes sugar or molasses is added to the glaze to toughen the coating on the ware. When the glaze dries, the sugar crystallizes on the surface and forms a slight crust. All organic gums and binders burn out in the fire and have no effect on the finished glaze. In general, it is wise to use as little gum in glazes as possible; and it will usually be found that in studio work, where reasonable care is taken in handling the glazed ware, no gum is necessary.

Japanese stoneware tea-jar. This beautiful little piece is very rough on the outside and is thinly coated with an olive colored glaze. The black glaze at the top has run down the sides of the jar during firing. The lid is of ivory. *Courtesy of The Smithsonian Institution, Freer Gallery of Art, Washington, D.C.*

(below)
Japanese pottery bowl, 1832, Musashi, Korakuyen. This low-fired earthenware piece is covered with a thick crackled lead glaze which reveals the reddish brown color of the clay beneath. The glaze has run to form a thick roll and droplets on the underside of the piece. *Courtesy of The Smithsonian Institution, Freer Gallery of Art, Washington, D.C.*

Japanese stoneware jar. Although utterly simple in shape, this piece has great dignity and beauty of surface. The glaze is thinly applied, revealing the grey and brown clay. The roughness results largely from unground particles in the glaze, probably feldspar. The inscription is applied with a quill in black slip-glaze. *Courtesy of The Smithsonian Institution, Freer Gallery of Art, Washington, D.C.*

(below)
Japanese tea bowl. This low-fired earthenware piece is covered with a black lead glaze. The leaf patterns are cut through the glaze before firing and accented with a bit of white glaze. *Courtesy of The Smithsonian Institution, Freer Gallery of Art, Washington, D.C.*

In glazing vitreous, non-porous ware it is necessary to use a heavy glaze slip which will adhere to the surface of the ware in sufficient thickness. Such heavy glazes may be prepared by flocculating the slip with an addition of about one-half of 1 percent of aluminum sulphate or magnesium sulphate (epsom salts). The salts must first be dissolved in a small amount of hot water, then added to the glaze, which is already milled with a normal amount of water. The addition of salts to the glaze has the effect of thickening it without making it lumpy. By adjusting the thickness of the glaze in this way, it can be made to adhere in any desired thickness to non-porous surfaces.

5. Glazing by Painting, Dipping, and Pouring

Glazes may be applied to pottery by painting, dipping, pouring, or spraying. For small-scale work, painting may be the best method. It is relatively easy to do and requires only a small amount of glaze. The glaze is applied with a soft brush in short, loaded strokes. It is usually necessary to go over a piece with two or three coats to be sure that all parts are evenly covered. Even though three coats are applied, the painted glaze often appears splotchy after firing, because of an uneven coat of glaze. Another difficulty is that when the second and third coats are applied, the brush tends to pick up patches of glaze, causing thin spots. The only way to ensure a completely uniform coat of glaze by painting is to add some gum to the glaze and perhaps to tint each successive coat with a different color vegetable dye.

Applying glaze by dipping and pouring has the advantage of rapidity and of producing a very even coat of glaze on the ware. It is quite easy to do but takes a relatively larger reserve of glaze, especially for bigger pieces. No glaze is wasted, however, since the only glaze which is used is that which actually goes on the ware.

The methods used in dipping and pouring glaze on pottery vary according to the shape of the piece and the amount of glaze available. Smaller pieces can be completely immersed in the glaze, and the finger marks where the piece was held can be touched up later. In commercial production, dipping tongs are used which hold the ware securely at three points. Some skill and practice is required for successful dipping. The piece is held with two or three fingers over the bucket. It is then rapidly immersed, shaken vigorously while under the surface, then drawn out, emptied, and shaken to remove excess glaze. The whole operation should take only a few seconds, for if the piece is held under the glaze a moment too long, too thick a glaze coat will be built up on it. The motions used in draining the piece of glaze should be studied to avoid drips and unevenness. In the case of very porous ware, it may be advisable to dampen the ware before glazing to reduce its absorbency.

The insides of pieces may be glazed by filling them with glaze and then quickly emptying them. This is, in fact, the only feasible way of glazing narrow-mouthed pieces. The outside of the piece may be glazed later by dipping, pouring, or spraying.

Pieces can be glazed on the outside by holding them or supporting them upside down over a pan and pouring a cascade of glaze over them. If the piece is turned rapidly while the glaze is being poured on, very even glazing is possible.

Sometimes, however, the variations in thickness which result from the different techniques of pouring glaze can be used decoratively to enhance the form of the piece. Such accents are bound to be somewhat accidental, and they can be meaningless unless a measure of control is exerted at the moment of glazing.

One useful method of glazing the outside of a piece is to place a pan on a banding wheel. Then, on some kind of prop, the piece to be glazed is supported upside down in the pan. While the wheel rotates, the glaze is poured over the pot, the excess glaze being caught by the pan.

When pieces are to be glazed by dipping and pouring, their bottoms may first be dipped in hot wax to prevent the glaze from adhering. Care must be taken not to splash wax on any part of the pot which is to be glazed. Ordinary paraffin is suitable. The bottom or foot of the pot must be free of glaze to prevent its sticking to the kiln shelf during firing, unless the piece is to be supported on spurs or pins.

6. Spraying Glazes

Glazes may be sprayed on the ware with a spray gun. Spray guns operate on compressed air and are similar to those used for spraying paint and other liquids. Glazes which are to be sprayed should be carefully ground or screened so that they will not clog up the spray gun. The ware which is to be glazed is usually rotated on a banding or decorating wheel while the stream of atomized glaze slip is directed toward it. The glaze lights on the piece in small droplets.

Spray glazing has the advantage of requiring very little reserve glaze. An average-size piece can be easily glazed with as little as one cupful of glaze. At the same time, spraying is wasteful of glaze unless the glaze which does not light on the pot is collected afterward from the spray booth. In small-scale work, where many different glazes are ordinarily used, it is seldom feasible to save the glaze scraped off the booth.

As a method of glaze application, spraying has some disadvantages relative to dipping and pouring. It is slow, and some find the noise of the necessary compressor and fan unpleasant. Also, it is difficult to build up an even coat of glaze with the spray gun. After the piece is covered, it is very hard to tell where the glaze is too thin, and some parts of a pot, such as places under the handle and around the bottom, may be almost entirely missed. Unless the glaze is checked by probing with a pin or knife, such thin places may not be detected until after firing. If the spray gun is held too far from the piece, the glaze coat may be excessively powdery because the glaze lights on the piece in small dusty granules.

If glazes are to be sprayed, an exhaust fan must be provided to carry off the dust. Unless such a fan is very efficient, it is also wise for the operator to wear a dust-mask to avoid the possibility of breathing glaze dust.

7. Thickness of the Glaze

It is difficult to specify how thickly glazes should be applied, since different glazes call for widely varying thickness. The average glaze is somewhat less than one thirty-second of an inch thick in the raw state. One-sixteenth of an inch is a heavy application. In some cases, such as transparent glazes applied on vitreous white wares, the glaze coating may be one sixty-fourth of an inch thick or even less. The raw glaze coating is always considerably thicker than the finished, fired glaze, because of the consolidation of materials which accompanies melting.

The thickness of the glaze has an important effect on its fired appearance. Some glazes, for instance, which are semi-opaque when thinly applied, may be completely opaque when they are put on more thickly. Transparent glazes, however, may have about the same appearance whether they are thick or thin, and for this reason they are easy to apply. The thickness of a glaze can be gaged by scratching the raw glaze with a pin or knife point.

Chapter 24

Firing Glazes

1. Setting Glazed Ware in the Kiln

Glazed ware must be handled very carefully to avoid marring the delicate raw-glaze coating. It is well to handle the ware as little as possible, but it usually must be picked up to remove any adhering bits of glaze from the bottom and to check for thickness. Also, one must be careful not to allow glaze from one piece to get on another, as this may result in unsightly smudges on the finished pieces. With experience, one gets used to handling glazed ware skillfully, so that no damage is done to the glazes.

Before setting glazed ware in the kiln, the inside of the kiln should be brushed off carefully, especially the crown and walls, to prevent loose crumbs of fire brick from falling on the glazed ware during firing. The kiln shelves and props should also be carefully dusted off. New kiln shelves are painted with a kiln-wash consisting of equal parts china clay and flint, mixed with water to the consistency of heavy paint. More kiln wash may need to be added to the shelves after a few firings to cover up bits of glaze which may have dripped onto them.

The ware to be set in the kiln is arranged on a work table according to size and intended position in the kiln. If the kiln fires unevenly, certain glazes may be used in the cool or hot spots to anticipate this. If pieces of similar height are grouped, it simplifies the job of deciding what height props to use for each shelf, and makes the setting easier. It is convenient to place the props first, three to the shelf, and then to nest the pots on the shelf, allowing about one-eighth of an inch space between pieces. When the shelf is filled, the next shelf can be lowered onto the three props. If the shelves have a tendency to wobble, a pad of plastic fireclay wadding between props and shelf may be used. The cone plaque is placed in a position easily visible through the spy-hole, the door is closed or bricked up, and the firing is begun.

2. Formation of the Glaze in the Fire

The first actual change in the glaze during firing is the volatilization of carbon and sulphur. Thus, at red heat, whiting, $CaCO_3$, becomes CaO. These changes cause no difficulties, and the heat of the kiln may be advanced quite rapidly during the early stages of firing, since there is no drying or dehydration to accomplish.

After red heat is reached, glazes begin to "sinter," that is, they become caked onto the ware in a tough coating. This sintering is due to the beginnings of fusion in some of the ingredients of the glaze.

Actual melting in most glazes begins several cones below the maturing temperature. Most cone 9 glazes begin to melt at about cone 4. In the early stages of melting the glaze becomes very rough and may crack like drying mud. As the melting proceeds and the glaze becomes more and more liquid, it settles down to a smooth layer on the ware.

Most glazes go through a boiling or bubbling stage during melting. Lead glazes, at a certain stage in melting, have large bubbles which can sometimes be observed through the spy-hole of the kiln, rising and breaking like bubblegum. Normally, when melting is complete, these bubbles disappear. The evolution of small bubbles in the melting glaze is thought to help in mixing the molten material and in bringing about complete fusion. If bubbling is still going on when the glaze begins to cool and to freeze, small pits or pinholes may mar the glaze.

When glazes are melted and are at or near their maturing temperature, they are viscous liquids, smoothly spread over the surface of the ware. One may reach in the spy-hole with an iron rod to touch the surface of the molten glaze on a pot, and it will be noted that the glaze is thick and sticky, much like honey or molasses. When the kiln is shut off and the temperature begins to fall, the glazes chill and gradually solidify.

3. Managing the Kiln and Gaging Temperature

The techniques used in firing will, of course, depend on the particular kind of kiln used. In the early stages of firing, an advance of 50 to 100° per hour is usual, although thicker wares may need to be fired more slowly. The degree of fusion in glazes is a matter of time and temperature, not of temperature alone; and if the firing is very rapid, more heat may be needed to mature the glazes. In the early stages of firing, before the cones have started to melt, it is helpful to have a pyrometer on the kiln to indicate the temperature. The use of a pyrometer can help in saving fuel, since it permits firing to proceed as rapidly as is consistent with good final results.

As the temperature of the kiln nears the maturing temperature of the glaze, the firing is slowed down to allow the glaze to smooth out and all volatiles to escape. When the cones begin to bend, at least twenty minutes—preferably more—should be allowed to elapse between the bending of each cone. After the final cone is down, it is usual to maintain constant temperature in the kiln for about a half-hour. This "soaking period" helps to ensure the complete melting and smoothing out of the glaze.

After the kiln is shut off and cooling begins, the kiln should be tightly shut and the damper closed to prevent too rapid cooling. After the temperature has dropped about 100°, the rate of cooling may be increased somewhat, since the glazes are, by then, stiffened. When the kiln is cooling from dull red heat to dark, there is danger of dunting or cracking the ware, and this stage must be passed slowly. The kiln may be safely opened at about 200°. In general, the period of cooling should be about the same as, or longer than, the period of heating. For most efficient firing, the whole firing cycle should be as fast as is consistent with the desired results in the finished ware.

Pyrometric cones should always be used in glaze firing, even if the kiln is equipped with a pyrometer. While the pyrometer may accurately tell the temperature of the kiln, the cones are a more reliable indication of the state of the glazes, since their melting and deformation indicate the effect of both heat and time on the ceramic materials in the kiln.

An experienced potter can estimate

the temperature of his kiln by its color. Being able to judge temperature by color is sometimes a help in noting unevenness in the kiln and in appraising the effects of burner adjustments on temperature. If one is used to firing always to the same temperature, the color at that temperature will be quite recognizable.

Draw trials are sometimes used as an aid in judging when a firing is complete. Small rings of clay may be set up in the kiln inside the spy-hole. These rings are made of the same clay and coated with the same glazes as the pots in the kiln. When the cones are bending, the rings are drawn out with an iron rod, dipped in water to cool, and examined for fusion and maturity of glaze. Sudden cooling prevents draw trials from giving much idea of what the final color of the glazes will be, but they do give a good indication of how far melting has proceeded. Before the invention of the pyrometric cone, draw trials were the chief means of judging when a firing was finished.

Unless the ware in the kiln is intended for reduction firing, the glaze firing should be kept oxidizing; that is, the fire should be clean and free from smoke and show no sign of flame at the spy-holes or damper. This is accomplished by adjusting the burners so they have sufficient air and by opening the damper enough so that there is a flow of gas through the kiln. If too much air is allowed to pass through the kiln with the fuel, however, either from the burners or from the ports around the burners, the temperature will not advance because of the cooling effect of the air. In the electric kiln, of course, this is no problem, since no fuel is being burned. The atmosphere in the electric kiln is always neutral or oxidizing.

Kilns burning gas, oil, or wood all have their own peculiarities, and experience is necessary to work out the proper settings for burners and dampers to get the best results. When any new kiln is put into operation, it may be assumed that the first few firings will be less than satisfactory, and that good results can only follow the establishment of a routine of firing based on experience with that particular kiln.

4. Uneven Temperatures

Uneven temperature inside the kiln is a problem which plagues most potters. Few kilns fire with perfectly even temperature throughout, and some are bad offenders, having a difference of several cones between top and bottom. In general, the down-draft type of kiln fires the most evenly. Often the tendency of a kiln to fire unevenly can be corrected by simple changes in the way the ware is set, the height of fire-walls, the size of the channels leading to the flue, the height of the chimney, the number and kind of burners, the rate of firing, or the adjustment of burners and dampers. But if the kiln fires unevenly after all possible corrections have been tried, the potter will simply have to learn to live with the uneven fire. Most glazes have a range of three cones—that is, they do not have a radically different look if fired one cone hotter or one cone cooler than normal. If the kiln does not fire evenly, glazes which are sensitive to slight over- or under-firing may have to be avoided. Effects which require exact temperatures may be placed in certain parts of the kiln where it is known that a particular temperature will be reached. Where the temperature variation in a kiln is large, different base glazes may be employed for the top and the bottom of the kiln, but this makes setting the kiln awkward.

5. Gas and Electric Firing Compared

Natural gas is probably the best fuel for firing pottery, although electricity is certainly the most convenient. Gas has the advantage of economy and also makes possible a variety of atmospheres in the kiln. However, gas kilns are bulky, need to be connected to chimneys, and require some skill and experience to manage. For these reasons many situations call for electric kilns. Electric kilns are simple to operate and are practically foolproof. They are clean, compact, and odorless; they require no chimney and add no fire hazard to rooms or buildings. The cost of operating an electric kiln, although usually considerably more than natural-gas firing, is still low enough to be entirely practical.

Pottery which is fired in an electric kiln is apt to be lacking in variety of surface, warmth of color, and texture, compared to pottery which is fired in a kiln burning gas, oil, or wood. This is no doubt due to the atmosphere in the electric kiln which is static and neutral. It is difficult to account for the actual differences which do occur between gas and electric firing. Glazes tend to be more shiny and glossy in electric firing, and some glazes which are opaque in gas firing will be more transparent in electric firing. It is always well to make tests before changing from electricity to gas, or vice versa, to determine how much difference there will be in the appearance of the glazes.

6. Firing with Bottled Gas, Oil, and Wood

Bottled gas (liquefied petroleum gas) gives results in pottery firing in every way identical with natural gas. It is more expensive and requires special equipment for storage and combustion. When bottled gas is burned rapidly, as in a kiln, large storage tanks are required to keep the gas from freezing in the tank because of rapid evaporation. Bottled gas and natural gas require slightly different types of burners.

Results from oil firing are comparable to those obtained from gas. Oil burners, however, are more complex, more expensive, and more subject to mechanical failure than gas burners. Oil burners are usually dependent on electrically driven blowers, which means that one must be constantly on the alert against power failures during firings. Oil firing is inconvenient relative to gas firing: oil pumps and oil lines may become clogged; there is an unavoidable odor; and outside storage tanks must be provided for and kept full. In spite of all these difficulties, if no gas is available, oil may be the best fuel, and certainly beautiful ware can be made in oil-fired kilns.

Wood or coal is seldom used today for firing kilns, since more convenient fuels are everywhere available. However, the masterpieces of pottery which have been made in the past in wood-burning kilns testify to the fact that wood as a fuel does not limit the kind or quality of ware which can be made. Actually, wood firing is not as troublesome, difficult, or expensive as one might think. The author has designed a wood-fired kiln of 20-cubic-foot capacity which fires to cone 9 in about fourteen hours, using about two cords of wood. In an area where wood from sawmill scrap or other sources is cheap, the cost of wood firing may be about the same or even less than firing with gas. In firing a kiln with wood, very careful management of the fires is necessary, and the more or less constant attention of the fireman is required during the whole firing.

7. Failures in Firing

Firing glazed ware is the most exciting part of pottery making. There is an element of suspense and waiting, and the feeling of having committed all of one's efforts to the fire, the results of which are at best somewhat uncertain. Once the pots are in the kiln, all that can be done is careful management of the fire. And there are quite a few things that can go wrong.

Most bad firing is due to inattention to detail, and the prevention or cure of these difficulties is obvious. For instance, shelves may not rest securely and may totter; pots may touch each other and stick; refractory crumbs may fall into glazed pieces; the cone plaque may blow up in the early stages of firing and not be noticed until red heat is reached; cones may rest on nearby pots as they bend; or too rapid cooling may cause pots to dunt or craze. The most common firing difficulty, however, is over-firing or under-firing. Sometimes this may be out of the control of the potter, but more often it is caused by bad judgment as to when to shut off the kiln or by lack of attention during firing. A kiln really requires careful watching, and firing should be considered an important part of the creative process of pottery making.

8. Once-Fired Ware

Glazes may be applied to either bisque or raw ware. Glazing raw ware and firing it only once has the advantage of eliminating the first firing, with the consequent saving of effort and expense. However, because of the increased hazards in glazing and the increased number of seconds and kiln wasters, once-firing seldom proves, in the long run, to be more efficient than twice-firing. In glazing raw ware, great care must be taken in handling to avoid breakage. The processes of dipping and pouring glaze are more difficult. Regardless of the glazing process, great care must be taken to prevent the water of the glaze from soaking into the clay and causing the pot to crack. Such cracks may not be detected until the ware comes from the glaze kiln. Setting the kiln with glazed raw ware is also difficult because of the fragility of the pieces.

Many glaze flaws occur with much more frequency in once-fired ware than in twice-fired ware, especially crawling and pinholing. These difficulties are described in a later section. When all the hazards of once-firing are taken into account, it will usually be decided that twice-firing is advisable. One exception to this is commercially-produced stoneware, which is usually once-fired. Such ware is heavy in cross-section, which minimizes some of the hazards in glazing. Also, the standards of acceptability for glaze finish are low in this type of ware.

Chapter 25

Glaze Flaws

The various flaws which develop in glazes are not easy to get under control, particularly in small-scale production where numerous glazes are used and there is not the opportunity for sustained experimentation and control work. Unfortunately, some of the most attractive glazes, aesthetically, are particularly subject to flaws, such as semi-opaque glazes and mat glazes. The "sure-fire" glaze is apt to be a smooth, glassy, and rather uninteresting glaze.

The reasons for most of the defects which develop in glazes are well known, and careful compounding, application, and firing can ensure good results. But the beginner should not underestimate the difficulties of producing perfect glazed pottery.

1. Crazing

Crazing is a common glaze flaw, but one which is rather easily corrected in most cases. Crazing is the development of a fine network of cracks in the finished glaze. These cracks may be present when the ware is first taken from the kiln, or they may develop days or months after the ware has been fired. Ware which is crazing when it comes from the kiln makes a tinkling sound each time a new crack appears. Crazed ware may be unsightly and unsanitary, and may permit leaking or seepage through ware which is used to contain liquids.

To understand the cause and cure for crazing, we must look for sources of tension between body and glaze. A glaze which crazes is actually under tension. It is too small for the area over which it is stretched, and it therefore breaks like a splitting seam in a too-small pair of trousers.

During firing, when glazes are molten and are spread over the still red-hot ware in the kiln, they all fit perfectly. It is during the cooling of the ware that the tension develops in the glaze. In the case of crazing, the difficulty arises from the fact that the clay body, when it cools, contracts less than the glaze coating. This contraction on cooling must not be confused with the firing shrinkage of clay bodies, all of which occurs during the heating of the ware. It is, rather, the contraction which occurs in any solid upon cooling. Most solids, notably metals, expand when they are hot and contract when they are cool. We are all familiar with the expansion joints which are provided on bridges to allow for this expansion on a hot day. Clay bodies and glazes are no exception to the general rule that things expand when hot, contract when cool.

Some materials expand more when heated, and therefore contract more when cooling, than do other materials. The value which expresses this relative tendency of solids to expand and contract when heated and cooled is called their coefficient of expansion. Fortunately, fired clay and glass have a coefficiency of expansion which is similar enough to make it possible for the glass to be melted onto the clay and to stick to it during cooling without undue strains developing between the glass and the clay. When such strains do occur, however, the glass cracks.

The cause of crazing, then, is always to be found in a high coefficient of expansion (and therefore contraction) in the glaze, relative to the expansion of the body. The following list gives the expansion coefficients for the oxides which commonly make up ceramic glazes:

SiO_2	0.05	$\times 10^{-7}$, per ^{0}C, linear
Al_2O_3	0.17	
B_2O_3	0.66	(for small amounts)
Na_2O	4.32	
K_2O	3.90	
PbO	1.06	
ZnO	.07	
CaO	1.63	
MgO	0.45	
BaO	1.73 *	

From this list it will be seen that the oxides vary widely in their heat expansion; silica expands less than one-eightieth as much as soda. Clay, being made up of alumina and silica, has a medium expansion, but some glazes, especially those high in soda, may have a high expansion, and therefore do not "fit" on the clay.

The mechanics of crazing are as follows. During the heating-up phase of firing, the clay body is matured and made more or less vitreous, and the glaze is melted into a liquid silicate spread over the clay. At this stage, although the glaze must be completed by cooling and solidifying, the clay body is quite finished and, except for a loss of heat, it does not change much during the cooling of the kiln. After the glaze has solidified, both the glaze and the clay body begin to contract from cooling. As long as this contraction is similar in degree, no strain is set up between the clay and the glaze; but if the glaze contracts more than the clay, it is put in tension and must crack or craze.

Crazing may be corrected by cutting down on the thermal expansion of the glaze and hence on its cooling contraction. This is accomplished by choosing oxides for the glaze which are lower in their coefficient of thermal expansion. Sometimes this is difficult to do without radically altering the maturing temperature or appearance of the glaze. In practice, the effective substitutions to correct crazing may include: (1) increasing the silica, (2) decreasing the feldspar, (3) decreasing any other material containing soda or potash, (4) increasing the boric oxide, (5) increasing the alumina, or (6) substituting lead for potash and soda. Reference to the list of expansion coefficients given above will show that all of these changes involve the decreasing of high-expansion oxides and the increasing of low-expansion oxides. Usually, a modest increase in silica in the glaze will stop crazing. However, if a glaze contains a good deal of soda or potash in the form of feldspars, frits, or raw alkalies, it may be impossible to correct crazing without completely altering the character of the glaze. If a highly alkaline glaze is desired for some particular color effect, crazing may have to be accepted as inevitable.

Crazing may also be prevented by adjusting the clay body. Sometimes it is more convenient to change the clay than it is to change glaze formulas. In this case, the obvious remedy is to increase

* English and Turner.

the high expansion materials in the clay so that when the clay cools it will contract more and keep the glaze in compression. In practice, this means adding more feldspar or fritted material which contains high expansion oxides such as soda or potash.

Another and more practical way of correcting crazing by adjustments in the clay body is to add more flint to the clay. This may seem contradictory, since silica added to the glaze is also a remedy. However, flint added to a clay body acts quite differently than flint added to a glaze. When it is added to a glaze, it is melted into a liquid and cools as part of an amorphous or non-crystalline solid—glass. When flint is added to a clay body, it remains a crystalline solid during the heating and cooling cycle. This is an important difference, since the crystalline silica in the body has quite different properties than the fused silica in the glaze. The property of the silica in the body which controls crazing is its inversion at 573° from alpha to beta quartz. This change in crystalline arrangement is accompanied by a slight increase in volume, which is reversible, that is, silica which has expanded when heated to more than 573° will, when cooled, contract to its original size. The crystalline changes in silica, although they produce minor changes in the size of the ware, are sufficient to affect the fit of glazes. When pottery is being cooled in the kiln and reaches the temperature of 573°, the slight contraction in the body throws the glaze into compression and prevents it from crazing. This accounts for the fact that additions of flint to a clay body tends to correct crazing. If the amount of flint in a clay body is excessive, however, ware may break or crack during cooling, even if the cooling is accomplished quite gradually. This is due to an excessive volume change. Bodies which contain less than about 10 percent of flint may be expected to be difficult to fit with glazes. Bodies which contain more than about 25 percent of flint may be hard to fire without dunting or cracking.

Over-firing may be a cause of crazing. If the firing has proceeded to a point where the free flint in the body has entered into glassy melts with the other materials, it does not go through any crystalline change upon cooling and so does not lose volume and put the glaze into compression.

Another type of crazing is the result of the usage of the ware or its exposure to the elements after firing. This is called moisture crazing. If a clay body is even slightly porous and moisture can enter it through exposed, unglazed surfaces, it will, in the course of time, take on what humidity is available. Over a long period of time, such moisture brings about a slight hydration of the fired clay, which is attended by a slight increase in volume. This may be sufficient to upset the fit of the glaze and to make it craze. To test for the likelihood of moisture crazing, ware may be subjected to steam pressure in an autoclave. This is the equivalent of extended time under normal conditions of humidity. If a sample can withstand 100 pounds steam pressure for a period of two hours without crazing, it is unlikely that it will ever craze in normal usage.

Crazing is induced by heat shock, and if ware is taken from the kiln when it is still too hot, it may craze even though crazing may never develop if the same ware is properly cooled. Similarly, rough usage in the oven or in top-of-the-stove cooking may cause pottery to craze.

The use of crazed glazes for decorative effects is discussed in a later section.

2. Shivering

Shivering is the reverse of crazing, and therefore the remedies are the opposite of the prescriptions for crazing. Shivering occurs when a glaze is under too great compression, which causes it to separate from the clay and peel or shiver. The effect might be compared to a sidewalk which buckles and rises from the ground in places as a result of expansion. Shivering is certainly a serious flaw, but it is easily corrected. The remedy is to increase the high expansion oxides in the glaze and thus make it contract more when it is cooling. This decreases the compression in the glaze which causes the trouble. In practice, the flint in the glaze is decreased and the feldspar or other alkali-bearing materials are increased. If the cure is to be effected in the body, a decrease in the flint content of the clay usually takes care of the difficulty.

Glazes should be under a slight amount of compression if they are to remain in an unbroken film on the ware and never craze. Fitting glazes which are under compression may sometimes break the ware, especially if the walls of the pot are very thin and the glaze is thick. This kind of breaking usually occurs, if it is to occur, during the last part of the cooling of the ware, or after the ware has been out of the kiln for a few hours. Breaking of this sort is most likely to occur if the glaze is very thick on the inside of the piece and is applied thinly, or not at all, on the outside.

3. Crawling

In crawling, the glaze parts during melting and leaves bare spots of clay exposed. The crawl may expose only a few tiny places, or it may leave a pattern of exposed areas resembling the cracks in dried mud. In extreme cases, the glaze may roll up into droplets or blobs, or it may crawl off most of the piece and be found in a melted puddle on the kiln shelf below the piece.

Crawling may result from glazes being applied over unclean bisque ware, or from any other condition which causes the glaze to adhere imperfectly to the ware in the raw state. If a piece of bisqued pottery has a greasy spot on it, the raw glaze coating may be, at this point, in poor contact with the clay surface. Such a condition may go unnoticed, since the glaze coat on the surface may appear to be well applied. During the early stages of firing, however, when the glaze is beginning to sinter, the area which is not in good contact with the surface will loosen, crack, and perhaps fold back, leaving a bare spot. If the bare spot is of any considerable size, it will not heal over by the subsequent melting and flow of the glaze. To prevent crawling, bisque ware should be handled as little as possible and should be stored in a dust-free place. If bisque ware has become dirty, it should be carefully washed with water before glazing.

When glaze is applied by spraying, an excessively wet sprayed coat put on over a previously applied layer may cause the glaze coating to loosen, with the possibility of subsequent crawling in the fire.

Sometimes glazes will crawl on the inside of a piece but not on the outside, or vice versa. This may be caused by first glazing the inside and then applying a wet coat of glaze on the outside. Water may seep through the walls of the pot from the outside and loosen the glaze on the inside.

A frequent cause of crawling is the

shrinkage and cracking of the raw glaze. Some glaze materials—notably clay, zinc oxide, light magnesium carbonate, white lead, and colemanite—have a considerable shrinkage. If cracks appear in the dried surface of the glaze, crawling may result. Any cracks in the raw glaze should be rubbed over until filled with dry glaze. Glazes which have a high raw shrinkage may be corrected by substitutions of raw materials. For example, calcined clay may be substituted for raw clay. Or gum may be added to the glaze slip to minimize cracking and to hold the glaze in closer contact with the clay during the early stages of heating in the kiln.

Certain types of glaze are much more subject to crawling than others. Fluid, transparent glazes seldom crawl, but the difficulty is common with very mat glazes, glazes which have a high viscosity when melted, and glazes which have a high clay or colemanite content. In the case of the more fluid glazes, the cracks or breaks in glaze surface which occur in the early stages of firing tend to heal over when the glaze melts and flows.

Another frequent and annoying type of crawling is that which occurs over underglaze painting. Underglaze color, if it is applied too heavily, may remain on the ware as a dusty and refractory coating under the glaze. The melted glaze may have difficulty spreading itself over such a surface, in much the same way that water will not spread evenly over a dusty road, but crawls up into little globules. The cure for this type of crawling is to apply the underglaze color more thinly. A small amount of gum or binder in the underglaze color may also help to prevent the glaze from crawling.

It must be admitted that even when all the possible causes of crawling are carefully avoided, crawls will sometimes still occur. If the trouble persists, it is better to change to another glaze, whatever the virtues of the offending glaze may be. At best, an occasional crawl will appear for no apparent reason.

4. Pitting and Pinholing

Pitting and pinholing are, by all odds, the most annoying and difficult glaze flaws to cure. The glaze may come from the kiln covered with minute pits or pinholes. These pinholes may be small, or they may be larger, resembling miniature volcano craters. Re-firing may only serve to make the pinholes larger or more frequent.

Several conditions may be suspected as the cause for this trouble. A simple and easily cured source of the difficulty is the presence of air pockets or small "blebs" in the surface of the ware. This sometimes occurs in cast ware when the slip is not stirred sufficiently and remains full of air when it is cast. These little pockets of air under the glaze may pop through the molten glaze during firing, leaving a small break in the surface of the glaze.

Unfortunately, not many cases of pinholing are caused by the condition of the clay body. The composition of the glaze and the firing cycle are more often to blame. All glazes contain some volatile materials and normally go through a certain amount of agitation and boiling as these volatiles are released. Most pinholes and pits are the frozen craters of such boiling activity. It is as if one could suddenly freeze a pan of simmering water and fix the form of the myriads of little bubbles which are rising and breaking on the surface. The worst offenders for pitting are mat glazes and other glazes which are actually under-fired and are used and valued for their under-fired appearance. In such glazes, the escape of volatiles may be very much in process when the kiln is shut off and the glaze begins to cool and to solidify. A longer firing cycle, which allows time for the volatiles to escape, will frequently cure the difficulty.

Glazes which are fluid when melted are much less apt to pinhole than are dry, mat, or under-fired glazes. When the more fluid glaze reaches its lowest viscosity at the height of firing, there is a much greater chance for the pits and pinholes to heal and for the glaze to settle down to a smooth unbroken surface.

Sometimes a glaze which is not prone to pinholing will, if over-fired by two or three cones, come from the kiln badly pitted. Such pits or blisters are caused by the boiling of the glaze as it nears the vapor phase. The boiling leaves craters, scars, or pits in the solidified glaze.

Even after the most careful adjustments in the firing cycle, some glazes will persist in pitting. It is, of course, difficult to fire a kiln exactly the same each time, and minor variations may cause a glaze which usually comes out well to be badly pitted. If pitting persists, it is wise to abandon the glaze rather than to attempt to follow an impossibly exact firing schedule.

Glazes which contain more than the normal amount of either zinc or rutile have a tendency to pinhole.

Heavy reduction firing, especially in the early stages of firing, may deposit considerable amounts of carbon in the pores of the clay. Subsequent oxidation of this carbon may cause pitting as the carbon dioxide passes through the glaze.

The following remedies should be tried to cure pinholing and pitting: (1) Lengthen the firing cycle. (2) Apply the glaze more thinly. (3) Add more flux to the glaze to make it more fluid. (4) Cut down on the content of zinc oxide and rutile in the glaze. (5) Increase the maturing temperature. (6) Fire with a less heavily reducing atmosphere in the early stages of firing. (7) Hold the temperature of the kiln at its highest heat for a soaking period. (8) Allow a longer time for cooling between the top temperature and the temperature at which the glazes solidify.

5. Blistering and Blebbing

Lead glazes, if accidentally subjected to reducing atmospheres in the kiln, are apt to blister. The glaze is greyed and blackened and the surface may be covered with large blisters and craters. Lead oxide is sensitive to atmosphere and is easily reduced. Care must be taken, therefore, when firing lead-glazed ware, to protect it from direct impingement of the flames from burners. Glazes which contain lead in fritted form only are less subject to blistering from reduction than are glazes which contain raw lead compounds.

If glazes are too thickly applied, blisters may result. This is frequently seen on the inside of bowls where the glaze has pooled into the bottom, or where the glaze coating has been too thickly applied. In such cases, large blisters may be seen in the glaze, and those at the surface may be easily broken into. The cure for this difficulty is a thinner application of glaze.

Blebs are raised bumps which appear on the surface of glazed ware. They are caused by air pockets which lie just below the surface of the clay. These air pockets at the height of firing may swell like small balloons, leaving a raised place or bump on the finished ware. Carefully made pieces having no entrapped air will not be subject to this difficulty.

6. Under-firing and Over-firing

Perhaps the most common of all glaze flaws are over- or under-firing. Under-fired pieces have a rough, scratchy, and sometimes unpleasantly harsh surface. Over-fired ware, on the other hand, is shiny, and the glaze may run too thin on the upper parts of the ware, gather around the foot, or run off onto the kiln shelf. Either under-fired or over-fired glazes may have colors which are quite different from the color developed by normal firing.

Under-fired ware may frequently be salvaged by a second glaze firing in which the glaze matures as desired. Over-fired ware, if the flaws developed are serious, is lost. However, over-firing may develop very beautiful qualities in the ware, even if they are not planned for, while under-fired pots are almost always unsatisfactory.

Usable glazes have a range of two or three cones, which greatly lessens the chance of losses from over- and under-firing.

7. Application Flaws

Poor application is a very frequent cause of glaze flaws. Glazes which are too thin may be rough and not the intended color. Glazes which are too thick may run, blister, crawl, or cause lids to be stuck to pots or pots to the kiln shelves. Glazes which are unevenly applied may cause unsightly and unwanted streaks or splotches. Glazing is one of the critical processes in pottery making and, until it is brought under control, satisfactory finished results cannot be expected.

8. Kiln Accidents

In spite of the most skillful compounding, application, and firing of glazes, accidents in the kiln may ruin otherwise good pottery. Shelves may break and fall on pieces. Pieces may lean and stick to each other. Bits of brick or mortar may fall from the crown of the kiln onto glazed surface. Volatile color, especially chrome, may migrate from one piece to another, staining the glazes. Glaze may drip off of one piece and down onto another. These are the accidents that try the soul of the potter, and the craft demands more than the usual amount of patience and the ability to take disappointments and to continue working in the sure knowledge that some of one's best efforts will be lost.

To prevent kiln mishaps, extreme care must be taken in setting the kiln. In handling shelves and ware, care must be taken not to allow crumbs of fire clay or brick to fall on the glazes. All shelves must be firmly supported, and those which are badly cracked should be discarded.

Chapter 26

Engobes

1. Engobe Composition

An engobe, or a slip, is a layer of colored clay applied to the surface of a piece of pottery to change its color or to add some decorative accent. There are many ways of coloring and applying engobes, and an important part of the art of pottery decoration is concerned with the compounding, application, and glazing over of slips or engobes.

Engobe compositions must be so designed that the engobes will (1) cover the ware with a suitably dense coating of the desired color, (2) cling to the ware during the shrinkage which accompanies drying and firing, (3) vitrify or harden at a temperature similar to, or somewhat lower than, the maturing temperature of the clay on which they are to be used, and (4) survive under the glaze coating without being dissolved into the glaze and without checking or peeling. Actually, all of the conditions are rather easy to satisfy, and engobes usually have very wide tolerances in composition, application, and firing range.

Very useful engobes may be made by adding coloring oxides to the particular clay which is being used for the ware. For instance, if one has a good throwing clay, a darker colored engobe can be made of it simply by adding some iron oxide and manganese, perhaps 2 percent of each. Such an engobe may be painted, dipped, trailed, or sprayed onto a pot, and it will stick well, provided the piece is still damp and has not begun to shrink.

The difficulty with such an engobe is that it must be applied to rather wet clay; otherwise, if the engobe is applied when the clay is leather-hard, since the pot has already undergone part of its shrinkage, the engobe may loosen and peel off when it shrinks. Another difficulty with such engobes is that the only colors possible are those which are darker than the clay body, since it is impossible to alter any clay mixture toward lighter values without radically changing the kinds and proportion of clays in the mixture.

To get around these difficulties, engobe compositions are designed to have less shrinkage than the clay upon which they are to be applied and to be made up of light-burning materials so as to be essentially white, unless colored with added coloring oxides. To insure whiteness and opacity, tin oxide or zirconium oxide are frequently added.

The materials which go into engobes may be conveniently divided into groups consisting of (1) clays, (2) fluxes, (3) fillers, (4) hardeners, (5) opacifiers, and (6) colorants.

The clays used in engobes are chosen for whiteness and for their relative shrinkage. Combinations of kaolin and ball clay usually fill the requirements of an engobe. If more shrinkage is needed, the ball clay can be increased relative

Covered jar in stoneware, by the author. The side of this piece is unglazed and is covered with a rough whitish engobe on which the decoration has been brushed with black slip. The top and bottom parts of the piece are glazed black.

Footed stoneware jar, by the author. This piece, which is made from a reddish brown clay, is glazed with a high-clay mat glaze. The glaze has been dipped on; and where two layers of glaze overlap, a lighter color results. The dark speckles in the glaze result from impurities in the clay.

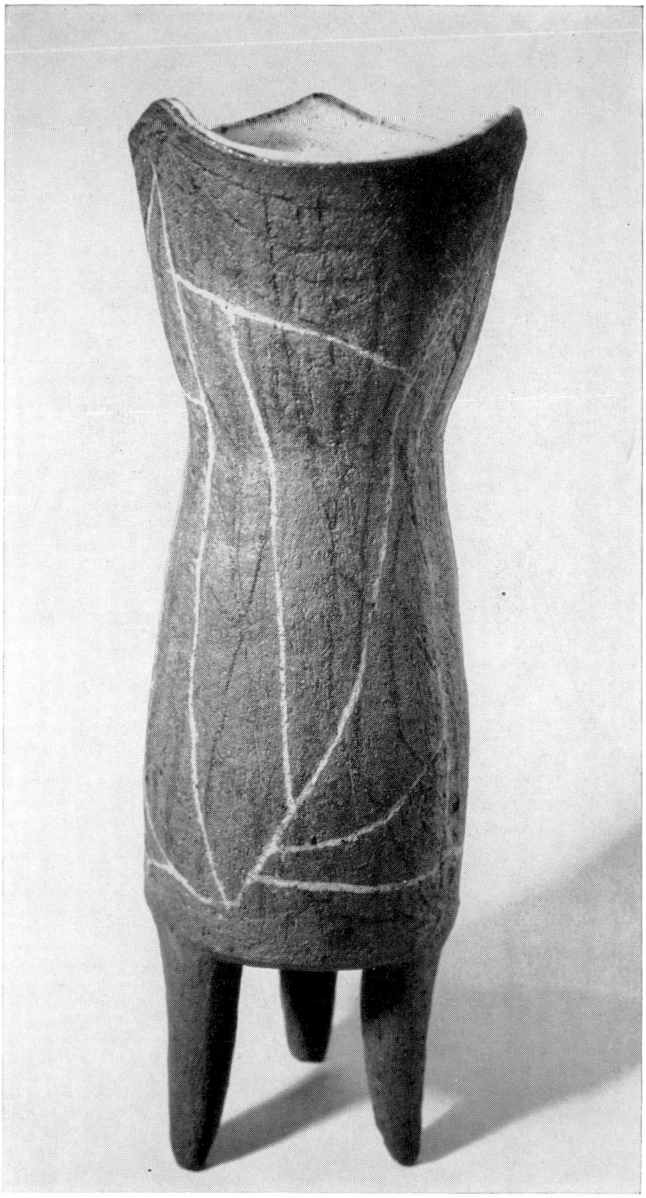

Stoneware jar, by the author. The outside of the piece is unglazed and is reddish brown in color. The lines are inlaid in light and dark slips. The inside of the piece is glazed with a grey magnesia glaze.

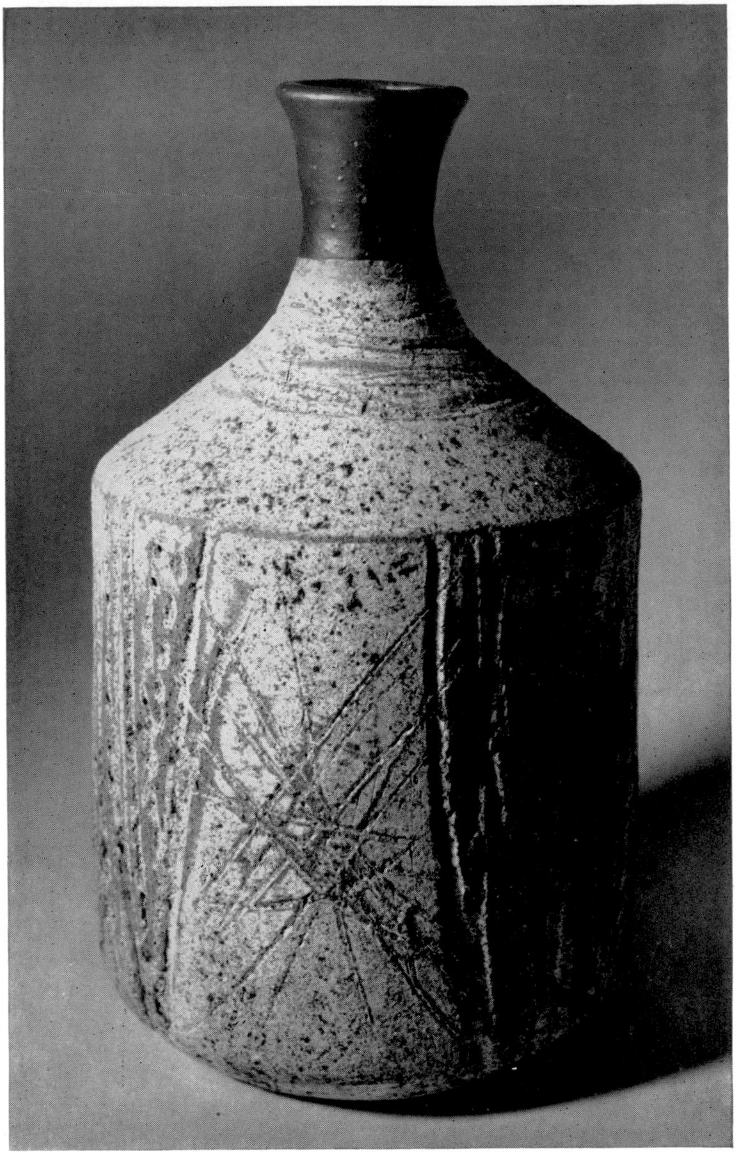

Stoneware bottle, by the author. The outside, which is deeply scratched, is coated with a rough specked slip and is unglazed. The inside and the lip are glazed with a brown slip-glaze.

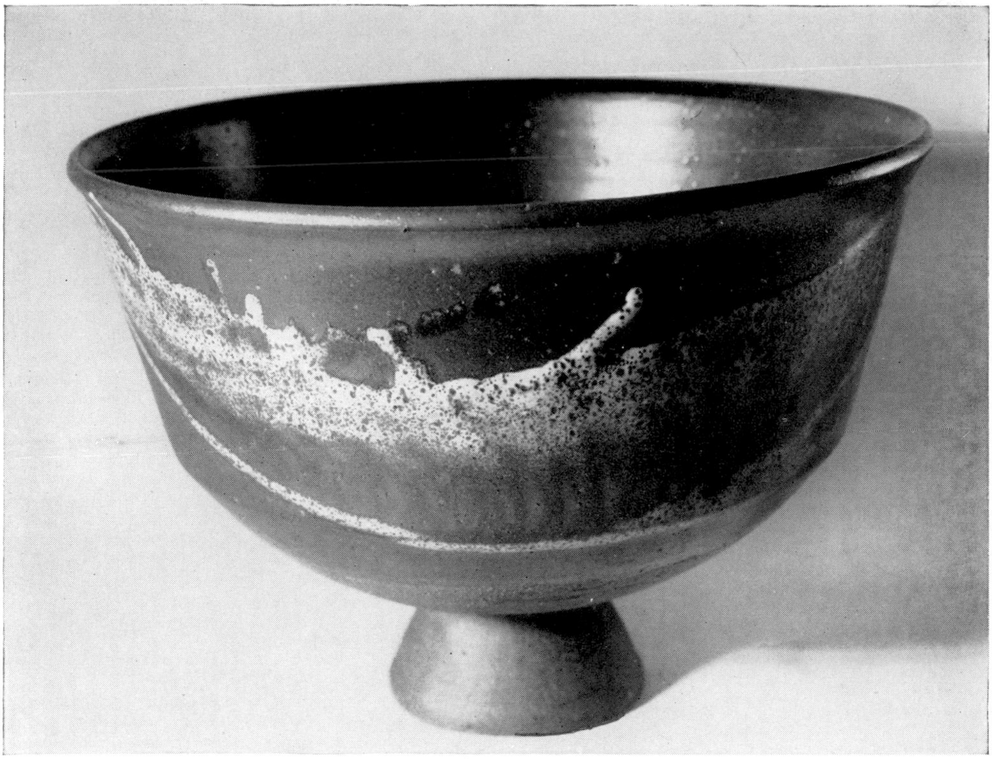

Stoneware bowl, by the author. The piece is glazed with a reddish brown slip-glaze. The light markings result from a freely applied splash of opaque glaze.

Stoneware bowl, by the author. The piece is thinly glazed with a very mat grey glaze. The specks and spotting result from impurities in the body which bleed through into the glaze. The inside of the piece is glazed black, and the foot is an orange-brown.

Stoneware jar, by the author. The surface of this piece was incised and scratched with a pointed tool and saw blade. This texture is emphasized by a mat glaze which tends to run off the high spots and gather in the depressions. The color is a cool grey. The inside of the jar is black.

Stoneware bottle, by the author. The clay is textured heavily and covered with a magnesia glaze. An added dip of glaze at the top gives a lighter color.

to the kaolin, and if less shrinkage is needed, the kaolin can be increased. In most engobes the amount of these two clays together will total between 40 and 70 percent.

The fluxes used in engobes will vary with the maturing temperature. For higher temperatures, cone 1 to cone 14, feldspar is the best choice. For the lower ranges of temperature some leadless frit, perhaps used in combination with talc, is used. Small amounts of whiting may be added as an auxiliary flux.

For a filler, flint is used. Engobes usually contain a generous amount of flint. It lessens the shrinkage and lends the desirable property of hardness to the engobe, and it also increases the likelihood of glaze fit. Fifteen to 30 percent of flint is usual in engobe compositions. Pyrophyllite, a nonplastic aluminum silicate, may be used as a filler. It functions in engobes and clay bodies like a calcined clay.

For hardening, a little borax added to engobes has been found to be useful. Borax, being soluble, tends to re-crystallize in the engobe when it dries on the ware, and this forms a tougher, harder coating which is less subject to damage in handling. Organic binders, such as sugar or gums, may be used for this purpose, but they have the disadvantage of spoiling with age.

For opacity, zirconium oxide may be added to the engobe. For the darker colors, this is not really necessary. But if an opaque and very white engobe is needed, the opacifier helps to ensure whiteness and enables the engobe to be applied more thinly without loss of opacity. Tin oxide works equally as well as zirconium oxide, but it is more expensive.

The accompanying chart shows some typical engobe compositions. In engobes,

ENGOBE COMPOSITIONS

Temperature Range →	*Cone* 08–1			*Cone* 1–6			*Cone* 6–11		
State of ware to which engobe → is applied	damp	dry	bisque	damp	dry	bisque	damp	dry	bisque
Kaolin	25	15	5	25	15	5	25	15	5
Ball clay	25	15	15	25	15	15	25	15	15
Calcined kaolin		20	20		20	20		20	20
Leadless frit	15	15	15			5			5
Nepheline syenite				15	15	20			5
Feldspar							20	20	20
Talc	5	5	15	5	5	5			
Flint	20	20	20	20	20	20	20	20	20
Zircopax	5	5	5	5	5	5	5	5	5
Borax	5	5	5	5	5	5	5	5	5

as compared to glazes, there is a rather broad tolerance for differences in composition. Sometimes a material in an engobe may be increased or decreased by 10 percent or so without making any noticeable difference in the fired result. What is required of an engobe is that it stick onto the ware during the drying process without cracking, peeling, or breaking loose at the edges, and that, in firing, it does not come loose from the surface of the ware, dissolve in the glaze, or upset the fit of the glazes. Although engobe tests may be rather hard to evaluate, adjustments in the raw shrinkage of the engobe and in its flux can easily bring about a working combination of materials.

2. Coloring Oxides in Engobes

Engobes may be colored with any of the coloring oxides which are used in glazes. The colors resulting from such additions, when seen under the fired, transparent glaze, are very similar to the colors produced by the direct addition of the coloring oxide to the glaze. A higher percentage of coloring oxide must be added to engobes than to glazes to obtain a similar hue. Coloring oxides may be used in a great variety of combinations to obtain many colors. As would be expected, cobalt added to an engobe gives a blue color, copper gives green, and so on. These colors reach full saturation only when the engobe is covered with the glaze.

Since engobes are essentially clay coatings on the ware, the colors which seem most suitable are those in the earthy range, such as black, brown, tan, light grey, and grey-blue. Strong greens, yellows, or blues had perhaps best be achieved with glazes rather than with engobes. Highly textured or spotty colors can easily be obtained from engobes by adding granular materials such as granular manganese, ground red brick or shale, or granular ilmenite.

The following list gives the typical amount of coloring oxides which are added to engobes, and the probable resulting color:

2%	Iron oxide	— Light tan
4%	Iron oxide	— Brown
6%	Iron oxide	— Dark brown
1%	Iron chromate	— Light grey
2%	Iron chromate	— Medium grey
1%	Cobalt oxide	— Medium blue
1%	Cobalt oxide	— Grey-blue
2%	Iron oxide	
3%	Copper oxide	— Medium green
10%	Vanadium stain	— Yellow
6%	Manganese dioxide	— Purple-brown
3%	Granular manganese	— Speckled brown
6%	Rutile	— Creamy tan
3%	Iron oxide	— Black
2%	Cobalt oxide	
2%	Manganese dioxide	

The glaze used over engobes has an important influence on the color and the quality of the engobe. Alkaline glazes, for example, will have their peculiar brilliance of color when used over colored engobes. Clear glazes which are high in lead, and which are used thinly over engobes, give the effect of merely wetting the engobes and revealing every detail of texture or brushwork. Lead glazes have a tendency to dissolve the engobe, and if a high lead glaze is to be used, the engobe composition should include an ample amount of flint and opacifier.

Semi-opaque glazes over engobes may give very beautiful, partially veiled effects. Subtle gradations of color and texture may result from the glaze partially concealing and partially revealing the engobes. If an engobe is used which is heavily loaded with iron oxide, manganese oxide, or other dark coloring oxides, it will bleed through semi-opaque or opaque glazes and give mottled, rich textural results, especially if the thickness of the glaze is varied.

3. Vitreous Engobes

An engobe which has a very low shrinkage because of the small amount of plastic clay in it, and which matures to a dense opaque coating over the ware, may be called a vitreous engobe. Vitreous engobes may be applied on either dry or bisque ware with safety, since they have little shrinkage and can accommodate themselves to the already shrunken ware. If bisque ware is decorated with vitreous engobes, the glaze may be applied directly over the engobe without the necessity of firing on the engobe. This process has the advantage of not requiring the careful timing which is necessary in slip decoration over damp ware. Bisque ware may be stored and given an engobe decoration at any time. Another advantage of decoration with vitreous engobes over bisqued ware is that the decoration, if it is not satisfactory, may be washed off and another one may be applied in its place. Vitreous engobes have the disadvantage of not giving the freedom of technique which is possible on damp ware. It is not advisable to use slip trailing, as this is apt to peel off, and other techniques, such as sgrafitto, which depend on a damp and soft base of clay for their effect, are not at their best with vitreous engobes.

Vitreous engobes are compounded with a minimum amount of clay, just enough to give good adhesion. About 10 to 20 percent is usual. The filler, usually flint, may be present in a higher quantity than in the case of normal engobes for application to damp ware. Usually the flux is also increased. Vitreous engobes are more like glazes in their composition and may be thought of as under-fired, very opaque glazes which are put on under the regular glaze to influence color and to achieve pattern. Since vitreous engobes are glazed over when they are still raw, some gum or hardener in the composition is almost necessary. When vitreous engobes are used on ware, the glazing techniques are somewhat limited because of the danger of disturbing the engobe coat. Spraying the glaze may be quite satisfactory, but dipping and pouring may loosen the engobe and cause checking, peeling, or cracking.

4. Techniques of Applying Engobes

A great variety of engobe application techniques are possible. Engobes may be applied by painting, dipping, brushing, trailing from a syringe or slip trailer, or by spraying. Resist patterns may be made with wax, liquid latex, or cut paper attached to the ware by dampening with water. Linear patterns may be scratched through the engobe into the damp clay beneath—the familiar sgraffito technique.

Engobe decoration has the virtue of plasticity, ease of application, and a close relationship to the clay which makes it, perhaps, more homogeneous with the pot than most kinds of decoration which are carried out in the glaze. Slip or engobe decoration is, of course, associated with the earthy, natural, and frequently very beautiful wares of the Pennsylvania Dutch, the English earthenwares of the pre-industrial era, and the peasant wares of central Europe. The warm, earthy colors of these wares, their spontaneous, rapidly-done, and unaffected patterns, and their sturdy functional shapes make them still a standard of excellence for slip-decorated pottery.

Chapter 27

Underglaze Colors and Decoration

1. Pigments Used in Underglaze Painting

One of the fascinations of pottery glazes is that colors and changes of color and texture may appear at different levels in the glaze coating, either on the surface or below the surface, and may be seen through a layer of glass. This makes for depth and variety of color and for a luminosity, which is quite unlike color in paint. Underglaze colors are seen beneath the coating of glaze, which may reveal them distinctly or may partially veil them with some other color. Underglaze colors may be applied by brushing or spraying over the body of the ware or over an engobe. The colors are then covered by a transparent glaze.

The pigments or colors used in underglaze painting are designed to (1) give the desired color when they are covered over with a transparent glaze, (2) resist the blurring, fusion, or running which is apt to occur when a glaze melts and flows over them, and (3) brush on easily, which requires that they be finely ground. The underglaze colors which are sold commercially are made to meet the exacting standards of the dinnerware manufacturers, and are compounded, calcined, and ground under carefully controlled conditions to ensure uniformity.

The coloring oxides—such as iron oxide, cobalt oxide, or copper oxide—may be used in underglaze painting, but they have the disadvantage of relatively coarse particle size, limited range of colors, and the tendency to run or smear under the glaze, as compared to underglaze colors which have been prepared especially for this purpose.

In order to get the full range of possible colors in underglaze pigments, combinations of oxides are used, such as chrome and tin, which gives various shades of pink and red, or chrome and zinc, which gives brown. All sorts of greens and blues are made by combinations of copper, cobalt, and chrome. Naples yellow is made by combining antimony and lead. In making underglaze colors, the metallic oxides are combined with enough flux to make them sinter and enough refractory material, such as flint, to keep them from running or blurring in use under the glaze. The combined materials are calcined until they sinter into a hard but unmelted mass. The material is then ground in a ball mill to a very fine particle size. While it is possible for the studio potter to make underglaze colors in this manner, it is better to buy the prepared colors, which have the advantage of uniformity. Manufacturers of ceramic colors and stains do not, of course, publish the formulas which are used for their products, but the general proportioning of oxides used to get the various colors is well known. The following recipes will indicate the typical ingredients in some underglaze stains:

Naples Yellow	
Antimony oxide	24
Red lead	48
Tin oxide	16
Niter	2
Brown	
Iron oxide	30
Green chrome oxide	28.5
Zinc oxide	72
Black	
Red iron oxide	10
Chrome oxide	76
Black cobalt oxide	20
Manganese dioxide	12
Blue	
Black cobalt oxide	26
Zinc oxide	104
Flint	70
Pink	
Tin oxide	100
Whiting	40
Flint	40
Fluorspar	15
Lead chromate	6

There are hundreds of different underglaze colors offered to the trade by various manufacturers. In spite of the confusing variety of names for these colors, there are a limited number of types of colors, and the potter will usually settle on a few colors which work well with his particular glazes and processes. Although underglaze pigments are expensive compared to the coloring oxides, their great tinting strength makes them economical to use.

2. Application of Underglaze Pigments

The application of underglaze colors to the ware is simple. They are applied either directly on the raw or bisqued ware, or on the surface of the engobe. The color is mixed with water and sometimes with other additional media to improve the brushing consistency or to produce a tougher dry film of pigment. For better brushing, glycerine may be added, a few drops to each tablespoon of color and water. A small quantity of dextrine or gum arabic helps to keep the color from dusting or smearing after it is on the ware. In some cases, if the glaze has a tendency to crawl over the color, a small amount of flux, in the form of a low-melting frit, is added. The right amount of flux to add may be determined by testing, but it is usually added on the palette, more or less by eye rather than by weight.

The colors are applied very much in the manner of water-colors. In fact, a combination of underglaze color and gum arabic is essentially the same in working properties as the colors sold for water-color painting. The most beautiful underglaze painting is usually made up of separate brush strokes which are not gone over or retouched. To paint in this manner requires, of course, great skill and confidence with the brush. Colors may overlap, but the resulting color in the fired product may not be what one would expect from ordinary pigments. The colors are strong and should be applied thinly. If they are applied too thickly, the glaze will crawl off the color. If an underglaze decoration is not satisfactory, it is difficult to remove entirely from the bisque ware because, even though the ware is carefully washed, some of the color is likely to cling to it.

Underglaze color, thinned with considerable water, may also be sprayed on the ware with an air-brush. Solid colors may be laid on, or patterns developed by the use of stencils or sgraffito techniques.

Underglaze colors may be used for coloring the glaze itself in the same way that the coloring oxides are used. Coloring glazes in this way, however, may add excessively to their cost.

The kind of glaze which is used over underglaze pigments has an important influence on their color. Glazes containing zinc oxide, for example, will prevent the development of pink colors, and, in general, zinc should be avoided in any glaze intended for use over underglaze color. Lead glazes bring out a different range of color than alkaline glazes. The firing temperature also influences the color, and the higher glaze firing temperatures will dull the color of some underglaze colors or make them disappear altogether. Some colors, however, such as the blues resulting from cobalt oxide, are stable at all temperatures. Reducing atmospheres in the kiln also change many colors and prevent the development of others.

3. Underglaze Prints

Underglaze prints are made from designs which are first engraved on copper or steel rolls. These designs are then printed (on a printing press) onto thin transfer paper. The medium used for printing is a mixture of underglaze color and a suitable oil, such as fat oil of turpentine. The transfer paper, with the fresh printing on it, is then placed face down on the ware and rubbed, which transfers the design to the surface of the ware. A similar transfer of the color to the ware may be made by decalcomania, or by printing directly on the ware with rubber stamps or silk screen printing. Recent developments have even made possible the transfer of designs to pottery by photographic processes. In all types of underglaze printing, the regular ceramic underglaze colors are used, mixed with media which are designed for the particular process employed. Most of the mechanical processes of printing on pottery require the use of an oily medium, and it is frequently necessary to run the ware through a hardening-on fire which burns off the oil and makes glazing over the colors possible.

Chapter 28

Overglaze Decoration

1. Majolica

Overglaze processes may be divided into two different kinds. One type is decoration carried out in colored glazes on the raw glaze surface. The other type is decoration applied to the already fired glazed surface of the ware and fused on in a low-temperature firing.

Decoration on the raw glaze surface, usually called majolica, is actually a kind of glaze-on-glaze painting. The ware is first covered over with a background glaze which is to form the base or background for the decoration. This glaze is usually white, or light in color, and is ordinarily opaque or nearly so. Over this glaze coating the decoration is applied with colored glazes. When fired, the decoration melts into and fuses with the background glaze. Majolica decorations are colorful in appearance and have rather soft and blurry edges as a result of the tendency of the glazes to run together slightly.

A suitable background glaze for majolica is one which is quite opaque and which does not run or flow much in the fire. The colored glazes to be used in decorations may be made from the same base glaze as the background. Or they may be made up from some other base glaze which has been tested and found not to crawl when applied over the background glaze. The colored glazes are made up by the addition of coloring oxides to give the desired shades of color. If the colored glazes are to be applied thinly, they may be made with a rather high concentration of coloring oxide, so as to have a high tinting strength, even though thin. If the colored glazes are to be applied thickly, by trailing with the bulb or by heavily applied brush strokes, a smaller amount of coloring oxide may be more satisfactory.

The difficult thing about majolica decoration is that the raw background glaze is extremely dry, absorbent, and perhaps powdery, and it is difficult to do brushwork over it. To correct this, the background glaze may be made with additions of sugar or molasses, which, during drying, forms a slight crust on the surface of the glaze, giving a better surface to work on. Or a thin spray of gum arabic solution over the surface of the raw background glaze may serve the same purpose. Another technique is to apply the glaze, suitably flocculated, over bisque which is made non-absorbent by soaking it in water, and then to paint the decoration on the still damp surface of the glaze. Because of the difficulty of glazing damp ware, this technique is rather awkward. The astonishingly detailed masterpieces of Renaissance majolica painting were probably done on glaze surfaces which had been partially fired, or sintered into a background surface resembling water-color paper in working properties.

A recent development is the use of an emulsion in the background glaze which causes it to dry onto the ware like wall paint. Such a surface makes an ideal background for painting, and the colors can be brushed over it with great freedom. The type of emulsion used in water-based wall paints has been found to be suitable. This gives a glaze coating so tough that even overglaze decals may be applied to it.

In majolica decorating, glazes can be freely applied one over the other or overlapping. Colors may be brushed, stippled, scumbled, trailed, spattered, sprayed through stencils, dusted, or rubbed on. Many variations of application technique will occur to the inventive decorator. Different colored glazes which are applied one over the other by spraying or dipping may give interesting mottled or streaked textures in the finished glaze.

Underglaze colors also may be applied over the raw glaze. The regular commercial underglaze pigment can be thinned with water and painted directly on the glaze. In the fire the color fuses into the glaze, giving a somewhat blurred edge rather than the sharply defined edge characteristic of underglaze decoration.

A variation of majolica decoration is the technique of scratching through the glaze with a pin. When fired, such scratches become thin lines of body color in the glaze. Beautiful patterns can be done with such lines, combined, perhaps, with touches of color. A glaze must be selected which does not run enough to heal over the scratched lines.

Majolica ware must be carefully fired to prevent the glazes from running too much and thus making the decoration too blurred. Crawling, running, and separating of the colors are the common difficulties. They can be overcome by the selection of glazes and by careful control over their application and their firing.

2. Overglaze Enamels

Overglaze enamels are applied to the finished glazed ware and fired on in a separate firing. The enamels used are actually low-fired, colored glazes which, in fusing, attach themselves to the surface of the glaze on the ware. They are usually fired at about cone 014 to 012. This low-firing range permits a varied palette of brilliant color. The enamel colors may be prepared with lead or alkaline frits. They are reasonably permanent after firing, although the use of strong detergents and mechanical dishwashing may gradually remove them from the ware.

Overglaze enamels are usually purchased as prepared colors from a color manufacturer rather than made up in the studio. They can, however, be compounded by grinding together a suitable frit, a small amount of clay, and about 8 percent of tin oxide, plus coloring oxides to give the desired colors.

Overglaze enamels are ordinarily applied with an oily medium, such as fat oil of turpentine, linseed oil, or other drying oils. The technique of applying the color is similar to that used in oil painting, and some "china painting" looks quite similar to thin painting in oil. In general it is best not to mix colors indiscriminately or to put one color over another unless the effect has been tested. Firing may proceed on a rapid schedule, since the ware itself has already been through the glaze fire and does not undergo any change. It is a matter of melting the overglaze colors and getting them to adhere by fusion to the glaze of the ware. Overglaze decorations may be done on commercial white glazed plates or tiles; or glazed earthenware or stoneware pieces can be decorated, or elements added to their decoration, by enamel fused on in a third firing.

3. Overglaze Prints

Overglaze prints are ordinarily applied as decalcomanias. In this process, the overglaze enamels are printed, usually by lithography, in a design on paper which is faced with a gelatinous coating. To transfer this design to the ware, the surface of the ware is first coated with a varnish. Then the printed face of the decal paper is placed against the tacky varnish on the ware and rubbed from the back until good contact is achieved. The paper back of the decal is then washed off in water, which does not affect the print, which is now firmly stuck to the ware with the varnish. After the print is transferred to the ware, the ware is put through a decorating fire which burns off the varnish and fuses the enamels to the surface of the glaze.

Overglaze enamels may also be printed directly onto the ware by the silk screen process. This is not extensively done in industry because of the difficulty of printing on curved surfaces and the lack of fine detail in silk screen printing relative to decal. Decals have the advantage of the numerous colors which can be applied to the ware in one operation.

It must be admitted that overglaze decorations seldom seem to have a very integral relation to the ware upon which they appear, but seem rather to be afterthoughts or unnecessary embellishments. This is not so much due to any flaw in the process itself as to the manner in which it is traditionally used. The difficulty may arise partly from the fact that overglaze decorations appear on the surface rather than in or under the glaze, and for that reason tend to give the appearance of "applied art" rather than an inseparable part of the ware.

Chapter 29

Reduction Firing and Reduction Glazes

1. Theory of Reduction Firing

Reduction firing and reduction glazes have come to be widely favored by the studio potter. Reduction firing is impractical for industrial production since it is difficult to control sufficiently for the exact reproduction of colors. Perhaps partly for this reason it finds favor among those potters who place a value on the unique qualities of each piece they make.

Whatever its limitations may be, there is no doubt that a reducing fire produces some of the richest and most satisfying glazes both as to color and tactile qualities. Moreover, the classic achievement of the ancient Chinese in ceramics consists almost entirely of pottery made by reduction firing. This gives the technique a prestige sanctioned by the best work of the past.

The theory of reduction firing is simple. When a fuel such as gas, oil, or wood is burned, the carbon contained in the fuel combines with the oxygen in the air to produce the chemical reaction of burning, and the products of this reaction are heat and carbon dioxide. The chemical equation for combustion is

$$C + 2\,O \underset{\text{(heat)}}{\rightarrow} CO_2$$

If not enough oxygen is present during combustion, some free carbon is liberated (the familiar black smoke coming from the chimney), as well as carbon monoxide, CO. At the elevated temperatures in the kiln, such free carbon and carbon monoxide are chemically active and will seize oxygen from any available source, including some of the oxides in ceramic materials. The carbon may be thought of as being hungry for oxygen. When ceramic materials are deprived of some oxygen, they are said to be reduced. This reduction in the amount of oxygen in the material may affect its color.

Reduction is easily accomplished in kilns which burn fuel. The air supply is cut down and the draft in the kiln is diminished by closing the primary air ports and dampers. This causes the unburned fuel to remain in the kiln, and a smoky, dense atmosphere inside the kiln develops. Some smoke may be observed coming from the chimney or from the spy-holes. The degree of reduction can be controlled by varying the amount of air which is allowed to mix with the fuel in the burners.

When kilns were more primitive in construction, and when potters relied entirely on wood or other solid fuels, reduction was a natural, if not an inevitable, occurrence, hard to prevent rather than hard to achieve. No doubt the Chinese developed their magnificent reduction effects because these effects were the natural result of the way they fired their kilns. Reduction should not be thought of as a difficult process resulting from some involved technique, but rather from a smoky fire, as contrasted with the clean-burning oxidizing fire which is normal in an efficiently operating kiln.

2. Effect of Reduction on Clay Bodies

Not many ceramic materials are much effected by reduction firing, and most of the effects characteristic of reduced ware are the result of the changes brought about in a few materials.

The main constituents of clay, alumina, and silica are not appreciably affected by reduction. These oxides are exceptionally stable and may be reduced only by the special techniques of metallurgy. However, the appearance of a clay body can be drastically affected by the atmosphere of the kiln. One result in the appearance of a clay which is caused by reduction is the grey or black color which results from carbon which is deposited in the pores of the ware during firing and which may remain there in the finished product. In porcelain, for example, if the firing is excessively reducing, the color may be a greyed or dirty white rather than pure white.

The major effect of reduction on clay bodies is the change which is brought about in the iron contained in the clay. In reduction, the iron oxide which is present to some extent in all clays turns from brown or tan to grey or black. Iron oxide exists in several different combinations, and each proportion of iron to oxygen has a characteristic color as follows:

Fe_2O_3	— Ferric iron	— red
Fe_3O_4	— Ferrous-ferric	— yellow
FeO	— Ferrous iron	— black
Fe	— Metallic iron	

The stable form of iron oxide is ferric iron, or red iron oxide, and most iron compounds in nature are in this form. In reduction fire, the iron oxide tends toward the ferrous state, or black iron oxide, and this accounts for the characteristic black or grey color of clays which have been fired in reduction.

If a sample of clay which contains some iron is fired in reduction, it may come from the kiln a warm tan or brown on the surface, but inside, if the piece is broken open, the color of the body will be seen to be grey or black. This grey or black is the result of iron in the ferrous state. The tan or brown on the surface is caused by the re-oxidation of the iron back to ferric iron oxide. This re-oxidation usually occurs during the cooling of the kiln. Often the surface of the clay will be reddish or orange in color. For reasons as yet not understood, this red or orange color of clay is warmer than the clay colors which are obtained from oxidation firing, although the color results from the oxidation of the extreme outer surface of the clay. In fact, one of the beauties of some reduced pottery is this exceptionally warm clay color, which is known to connoisseurs of old Chinese pottery as the "iron foot" effect. To obtain the richest tones of rust and brown in clay color, the ware must be fired in quite a reducing atmosphere, including some reduction in the early stages of firing before the clay becomes vitrified.

In porcelain or whitewares, which contain only small amounts of iron oxide, the only noticeable effect of reduction is to change the character of the white to a blue-white as distinguished from the warm whites which result from oxidizing atmospheres. The cool white of reduced porcelain is produced by the presence of a small amount of ferrous iron in the clay.

When reduced stoneware is covered by a clear glaze, the body under the glaze shows as a cool grey. The glaze protects the iron in the body from re-oxidizing, whereas the unglazed portions of the clay may be brown or rust.

Stoneware bodies intended for reduction firing may contain some iron or red clay, if a dark color is desired. However, if more than about 2 percent of iron is present in a clay, either in the form of a red clay or as added iron oxide, the fired ware may be very brittle and may crack during the volume adjustments of cooling. About 1 percent of iron in a body for reduction firing will give warm rust to brown color.

In white bodies which are exceptionally iron-free, the blue-grey cast which results from the reduction of the small amount of iron has an effect similar to that of bluing in the wash; it makes the clay seem even whiter than it is.

3. Reaction of Base Glazes to Reduction

The reaction of colored glazes to reduction involves several "transmutation" effects; that is, colors result which are the opposite of or are different from those obtained in an oxidizing fire. Before considering these, a word should be said about the effect of reduction upon the base glaze itself. Theoretically, a leadless glaze, or glass, is not much affected by reducing atmospheres. The oxides in glazes—such as alumina, silica, calcium, barium, and potassium—are stable oxides, not easily reduced to their metallic states, and no chemical change is made in them by reduction that does not occur in oxidation. Yet reduced glazes do seem to have a surface quality different from that of oxidized glazes, particularly in the case of mat glazes. In reduction, mat glazes seem to be smoother, more "buttery," more lustrous. Perhaps this quality is due to the longer firing cycle which is common in reduction firing, or perhaps it is due to longer soaking at top temperatures. In any case, the dense, smooth, opaque, satiny quality of some reduction glazes is irresistibly attractive and was prized by the ancient Chinese for its resemblance to jade. Such effects are difficult or impossible to achieve in an oxidizing fire.

4. The Color Range of Reduction Glazes

Although the range of color in reduction glazes is less than that of oxidation glazes, there are still a great variety of colors possible. Among the colors which are not possible are green, turquoise, and aqua colors from copper, but these can be approximated by combinations of chrome and cobalt, although the hues are not quite the same. Yellow is not possible in reduction, since uranium turns black and vanadium does not give any color. Grape-purple is not possible either, since manganese in reduction will yield only brown. Cobalt, however, can be made to give a blue-violet, and red-violet can result from reduced copper.

The colors which are not possible in reduction are more than compensated for by rich and subtle greys and by the unusual colors which result from iron oxide and copper oxide.

5. Colors from Iron Oxide in Reduction Glazes

In contrast to oxidation, iron oxide in reduction glazes gives cool colors of grey, grey-green, blue-green, or olive green. Iron oxide is fairly easily reduced, and in glazes it changes from ferric iron, Fe_2O_3, to ferrous iron, FeO, which is characteristically black, grey, or green. The color produced by adding a small amount of iron oxide to a glaze fired in reduction is called celadon. It is a subtle, slightly greyed, cool green and can be quite readily distinguished from the greens produced in oxidation glazes by additions of copper oxide or chrome oxide. Celadon glazes were a favorite of the ancient Chinese potters. A favorite technique was to use a celadon glaze over a pattern lightly incised in the clay. The pattern is beautifully shaded by the slightly pooled green glaze. The color has depth, character, and a changeability which is reminiscent of the color of a large body of water.

Celadons are typically clear glazes and are most colorful when used over a light body or engobe. Used over darker stoneware, celadon glaze will produce a dark greyed green.

The base glaze for celadon color should be high in feldspar and consequently fairly high in sodium or potassium. At least .4 equivalents of calcium should be present, and as much as .7 calcium may be used. Very simple celadon glazes can be made which contain only feldspar, whiting, and a small amount of clay. If too much feldspar is present, the glaze will craze over most bodies, but the celadon color will develop satisfactorily. A typical celadon base glaze might be as follows, for firing at cone 10:

KNaO	.25				
CaO	.45	Al_2O_3	.3	SiO_2	3.5
BaO	.2				
ZnO	.1				

In practice there is a considerable latitude in the formulation of celadon glazes, and the above composition is only typical of many possible formulas. Some barium oxide in the composition definitely favors a cool green color. If too much barium oxide, magnesia, or alumina is used, an opaque glaze will result and the color will be grey rather than green. A clear, fairly fluid glaze is the best for the development of the color. It is probable that the old Chinese celadons were made up of feldspar, limestone, ash, and some red clay which furnished the iron oxide for the color. Combinations of these simple materials will give very beautiful glazes if the firing is properly managed.

Only a small amount of iron oxide is required in a glaze to produce celadon color. One-half of 1 percent will give a light green. One percent gives a medium tint, and 2 percent will give a dark or "northern type" celadon. Amounts above 2 percent give a very dark and rather murky olive green, tending toward brown. Celadon glazes must be thoroughly ground in a ball mill to prevent mottled color or iron spots in the finished glaze.

Celadons require a fairly heavy reducing fire. Care must be taken to keep all burners on the kiln reducing, otherwise tan flashes may be noted on the ware where oxidation has occurred. Considerable variation in the color is usual from various firings, even though careful attention has been paid to keeping the firing conditions uniform.

Opaque celadons are difficult to produce. If tin oxide or zirconium oxide is added, the color usually turns to a grey or grey-green rather than the cool green of the best celadon. Celadons can be made opaque by inducing opalescence. An opalescent glaze or glass is one which is clouded by the presence of innumerable small entrapped bubbles. Phosphorus added to a feldspathic glaze will produce this effect. About 4 to 8 percent of bone ash (calcium phosphate) is sufficient to opacify a glaze, and if the glaze also contains a small amount of iron oxide—1 percent or less—and is fired in a heavily reducing atmosphere, a bluish, opalescent color will result. The "Chun blue" glaze of Sung Dynasty stoneware is a glaze of this type. In the best examples, the glaze is a deep, lavenderish blue, thick and unctuous. Chemical analyses of fragments of glaze from old Chun pots reveal the presence of phosphorus together with soda, potash, lime, alumina, and silica in proportions which would indicate a very simple glaze recipe made up of feldspar, limestone, clay, and quartz. The phosphorus no doubt came from additions of ash to the glaze. Undoubtedly the manner of firing had a great deal to do with the successful production of this beautiful glaze, because when a mixture is tried which has the same chemical make-up as the old glazes, and is fired in a gas kiln, it more often than not fails to yield the same color. The natural cycle of wood firing, with its frequent alternation between oxidizing and reducing conditions, may have been an important factor in producing the color. The Chun blue glaze is one of the few ancient Chinese glaze effects which cannot easily be reproduced, and for that reason it is a rather intriguing problem.

Some of the old Chinese Chun pots have copper red markings which appear as spots, splotches, or areas on the blue glaze. Many authorities have assumed that the whole piece was glazed with a copper bearing glaze which turned red only at certain points where the reducing flame licked it. The discovery of old saggers with holes cut in them, apparently to let in flame, has been pointed to as evidence in support of this theory. However, chemical analysis of the blue areas of glaze proves that no copper is present in the blue glaze, which must, therefore, get its color from iron oxide. The red markings are no doubt caused by washes of copper slip under, or on, the glaze, or by the additions of a copper red glaze under or over the opalescent celadon glaze. The fact that some of the copper red markings are in obviously planned areas or patterns seems to indicate that their placement was deliberate rather than accidental.

When the iron oxide content of reduced glazes is 6 percent or more, a saturated iron effect results. In saturated iron glazes, the iron, instead of yielding cool tones of grey or green, gives rich browns or red. This color results from the re-oxidation of the iron on the surface of the glaze during cooling. When the iron oxide content of a glaze is high, the iron oxide has difficulty staying in the glassy solution during cooling. Some of the iron crystallizes out on the surface of the glaze. These crystals are subject to oxidation, especially if air is allowed to enter the cooling kiln, and they turn to a brown or red color. The mass of the glaze under the surface remains black in color.

Base glazes for saturated iron color should be fluid, fairly high in alkali, and should not contain a high amount of alumina, which inhibits the re-crystallization which is necessary to the effect. A typical formula for an iron-red cone 9 reduction glaze might be:

KNaO	.25				
CaO	.55	Al_2O_3	.28	SiO_2	3.5
ZnO	.1				
MgO	.1				

Ten percent of iron oxide is added to this formula, and the glaze is applied rather thinly. Base glazes for celadon and for saturated iron are similar. If too much magnesia is present, the color will be mottled with opaque greenish patches. If the glaze is too refractory, because of too much alumina, barium, magnesia, or silica, rather dry, dirty browns will result instead of the brilliant crystalline red which is characteristic of the glaze at its best. When thickly applied, iron-red glazes may go black, and if the glaze pools into throwing marks and runs thin on high spots, spectacular combinations of red-brown and black may result on the same piece.

Saturated iron glazes require rather heavy reduction for the best color, and if the fire is too oxidizing, the glaze is apt to come out dull brown or black. For some unknown reason, crystalline iron reds do not develop in feldspathic glazes which are fired in oxidation.

When smaller amounts of iron are used in the glaze—up to about 7 percent —a khaki color may result. This glaze, which is a favorite of the Japanese potters, may be smooth, rich, and a rather autumnal, reddish brown in color.

6. Colors from Copper Oxide in Reduced Glazes

Copper oxide in reduction glazes produces that unique color known as copper red, ox-blood, peach bloom, or flambé. Like celadon, this glaze color was made famous by the old Chinese potters.

Copper oxide, like iron oxide, is easily reduced. In a reducing fire, it tends to change from CuO, cupric oxide, to Cu_2O, cuprous oxide, and to Cu, metallic copper, which is red in color. Dissolved in glaze, reduced copper oxide gives a variety of reddish tones, ranging from brownish red, to bright blood red, to orange or light peach colors, to purplish red. Since these red colors from copper are the complementary color of green, the color resulting from copper oxide in oxidation, the reduced glaze has been called a "transmutation" glaze.

Successful production of copper red glazes depends on the right kind of fire and on a suitable base glaze composition. The type of glaze composition which favors copper red colors is a rather highly alkaline glaze, fairly fluid at top temperature, and containing, in addition to the alkaline fluxes, some boron. Magnesia, barium, and alumina should be held to fairly low amounts, but calcium oxide may be present in a fairly large quantity, provided it does not stiffen the glaze. A typical base for a cone 10 copper red glaze might be as follows:

ZnO	.1				
CaO	.5	Al_2O_3	.35	SiO_2	4.0
MgO	.05	B_2O_3	.15		
KNaO	.35				

About 3 percent tin oxide added to the base helps to develop the color and to keep the glaze from becoming transparent over the clay. Also stannous oxide, SnO, is a good reagent for the formation of the red color.

For red colors, copper is added in small amounts, from one-half to one and one-half percent. Either copper carbonate or black copper oxide may be used. Cuprous oxide (red copper oxide), Cu_2O, is perhaps better yet, since it is already reduced.

Most stoneware glazes containing a small amount of copper will, when given a reducing fire, show some red color. However, the more mat and opaque types of glazes, such as those high in magnesia or clay, will develop only a rather muddy brownish red. Some glazes which are rather opaque will, if used for copper red, show a mottling of red, brown, and grey. For the full development of the color, the glaze must be fluid and must contain considerable alkaline flux.

Analysis of fired copper red glazes have revealed that the red color results from cuprous oxide, with perhaps an influence also of some copper crystals of colloidal fineness. The presence of sub-oxides of copper produces muddy tones of brown or black.

Copper red glazes are very sensitive to the fire, and they are hard to duplicate exactly. A fairly moderate amount of reduction seems most favorable to the color; if the reduction is too heavy, the glaze tends to become dark and murky in color. Fair copper reds can be produced by firing the kiln to maturity with an oxidizing atmosphere, then cooling it with a gas flame entering the kiln, which maintains a reducing atmosphere, down to dull red heat. Much work could yet be done in determining the amount of reduction which most favors the color and the timing of the reduction in the kiln cycle which would be the most effective. In general, if a neutral fire is maintained all during the heating cycle, followed by a brief period of heavy reduction at maturity, and normal cooling, brilliant copper reds may result.

The addition of a small amount of iron oxide to the glaze—one-half of 1 percent or less—may make the red more brilliant in hue. Or the glaze may be applied over a very thin wash of iron oxide which is put on the ware before glazing. Sometimes a clear glaze is put on over the glaze containing the copper to prevent re-oxidation of the glaze during cooling. It is noticeable that when a copper red glaze has re-oxidized to a green color during cooling, the glaze under the surface may still be red.

One problem encountered in firing copper red glazes at cone 10 or higher is that copper is quite volatile at that temperature, and if the firing is unduly prolonged for any reason, the copper may largely volatilize out of the glaze.

The variety of copper reds, which have quite a range from rich deep red-purple to the faintest blush of pink, is due to different glaze composition, various firing schedules, and various amounts of copper in the glaze. It must be admitted that the production of uniform color from firing to firing is very difficult. This waywardness of the color has made copper red an intriguing problem for the potter, and work has been done on this type of glaze all out of proportion to the inherent charms of the color.

7. Other Colors Obtained in Reduction Firing

Aside from the rather spectacular results obtained with iron and copper oxides, the color of reduced ware tends to be rather grey and not marked with brilliant hues. In selecting glazes for reduction firing, it is well to avoid too many colors of a middle-value grey or brown, and to seek variety in whites, blacks, blues, and greens, in addition to those colors derived from iron and copper. The beauty of reduction glazes is their warm, soft, subtle and quiet colors —colors which suggest earthiness and the mellowing effect of high heat. These qualities, when over-done, may be just plain dull.

One of the most attractive types of high-fired, reduction glazes is the high-magnesia glaze, which has already been described under the section on porcelain and stoneware glazes in Chapter 10. In reduction, the high-magnesia glaze takes on a dense, smooth, opaque, and almost lustrous surface which is exceptionally attractive in its tactile appeal. A typical cone 9 base glaze of this type might be:

KNaO	.25				
CaO	.35	Al_2O_3	.38	SiO_2	3.5
MgO	.35	B_2O_3	.15		
ZnO	.05				

Magnesia glazes, if applied over dark stoneware clay, will take up some iron from the clay and fire to a soft grey color. If the clay contains granular impurities or has been colored with ilmenite or black iron oxide, the glaze will be flecked with black or reddish spots.

Magnesia glazes can give beautiful hues of blue, blue-grey, and blue-green. Cobalt oxide, being very little affected by reduction, gives a strong blue-violet color. The blue from cobalt oxide may be modified by small additions of chrome oxide, iron oxide, rutile, ilmenite, manganese, nickel oxide, or iron chromate. In reduction firing, the greyed blues made in this manner can be subtle and full of depth and variety of color and texture. Combinations of chrome oxide and cobalt oxide in high-fired reduction glazes which are high in magnesia, give brilliant hues of turquoise and blue-green. About one-half percent or less of both chrome oxide and cobalt oxide are sufficient to give strong colors.

In reduction glazes, manganese oxide gives brownish colors, and in combination with iron, rutile, or ilmenite, it may yield rich, warm, and rather stony effects. Yellow glazes are not possible in reduction, but if rutile is washed onto the surface of a magnesia glaze in a thin coating, a creamy gold color can be produced.

Black glazes are especially beautiful in reduction. Good blacks may be made by the addition of about 10 percent of dark coloring oxides—such as combinations of cobalt, iron, and manganese—to a fairly stiff magnesia base glaze. At their best, black colors in reduction can be soft, mat, and satiny in feel. The difficulty usually encountered with black is that if an excess of coloring oxides are added, the glaze either becomes too fluid because of the additional flux, or the metallic oxides devitrify too much on cooling, giving a harsh, dry, and sometimes wrinkled surface. Fine blacks can be made from natural slip glazes, such as Albany slip, by adding up to 5 percent of cobalt, manganese, or iron oxides.

A beautiful range of greyed, pastel colors can be obtained in reduction firing by adding small amounts of underglaze or glaze stains to the base glaze. Commercial stains made to produce grey, brown, black, or blue colors often yield tones when used as glaze colorants which are difficult to obtain with the coloring oxides. For example, one-half of 1 percent of a commercial black underglaze stain added to a stoneware glaze may give a dusty blue-green. Or 1 or 2 percent of a grey underglaze stain may give a deep grey-green.

8. Kiln Practice in Reduction Firing

Although a great deal of research needs to be done on reduction firing to make it more reliable and to find out the exact procedures necessary for certain effects, the rule-of-thumb methods now in use can be relied upon to produce good work.

The classic examples of reduced pottery are, of course, the stonewares and porcelains of the ancient Chinese. Since great quantities of pottery of high quality ware produced in what were, actually, the first large factories in history, the firing obviously must have been under good control. The question arises as to why the Chinese, over 1000 years ago, were able to control reduction firing quite well, while we, with all our controls and technique, have difficulty. The answer is that in firing kilns to elevated temperatures with wood or other solid fuels, a neutral or slightly reducing atmosphere is normal rather than exceptional. In wood-firing, the fuel is thrown into the fire-boxes intermittently. With each stoking of wood, reducing conditions result in the kiln; that is, the wood, in the early stages of burning, gives off more or less smoke or carbon monoxide. As burning proceeds and air can combine with the fuel more completely, the smoke subsides, and essentially oxidizing conditions prevail in the kiln. Actually, in wood-firing, if the most efficient advance of temperature is achieved, the atmospheric conditions in the kiln will be near to ideal for producing reduction glaze effects. Normal stoking, followed by complete burning, gives alternating reduction and oxidation in cycles of five to fifteen minutes. If more reduction is required at the end of the firing, the fireman need only put on a little more fuel and close the damper slightly, and if less reduction is required, he need only use smaller pieces of fuel and see to it that the draft is lively. In short, if wood is used as a fuel, the control and stabilization of the reduction fire is a relatively simple matter.

With gas or oil kilns, the reduction is accomplished by starving the burners of air and cutting down on the draft through the kiln by partially closing off the damper in the flue. Any open-fired kiln which burns either gas or oil is easily reduced, and the question is, actually, when and how much to reduce. The amount of reduction can be gaged in several ways. If the appearance of the inside of the kiln is somewhat murky or cloudy, rather than clear, reduction is taking place. Another indication is the presence of flame at the damper, which is usually at the bottom of the chimney. Flame here indicates that unburned fuel has traveled clear through the ware. Another sign of reduction is the appearance of flame at the spy-holes. Or if a sliver of dry pine wood refuses to burn in the spy-hole, the kiln is reducing. Usually when the kiln is reducing, there is quite a strong back-pressure; that is, the damper is closed sufficiently to force some of the hot gas out of spy-holes or any other openings in the kiln.

A neutral fire is indicated by a moderate back-pressure at the spy-hole, accompanied by a slight greenish flame and a small amount of flame visible at the damper. A moderate reduction is indicated by strong back-pressure, yellow flame at the spy-holes, and heavy flame at the damper. A heavy reduction is indicated by black smoke coming from the flue and spy-holes.

Since all kilns have their peculiar and individual characteristics, it is difficult to generalize on schedules for reduction firing. So much depends on the kiln, the kind of ware being fired, the glazes, and the effects which are aimed at. The following points are intended as a general guide which will be helpful in working out a schedule to suit particular needs:

(1) The early part of the firing up to at least 800° may be strictly oxidizing. Reduction before this point is unnecessary and may cause trouble by not allowing the carbon con-

tained in the ware to burn out and by causing later bloating or blebbing, resulting from too much carbon in the pores of the ware.

(2) For the development of good reduced color in the clay, some reduction should begin at around 800°. This permits the reduction of some of the iron in the clay while the clay body is still open enough to admit the carbonaceous vapors which affect the reduction. If the clay is vitrified when reduction begins, it will have, when firing is complete, the appearance of oxidized ware, no matter how heavy the reduction in later stages is.

(3) A neutral or very slightly reducing atmosphere is usually sufficient from around 800° up to the highest temperature. Heavy reduction during this period serves no purpose and may injure the ware by causing bloating and by increasing the possibility of pitting and pinholing.

(4) It is important that the firing schedule not be too fast. Slow firing, especially toward the end of the cycle, permits the best development of glaze colors and surface quality.

(5) Some increase in reduction is usual toward the end of the fire, when the last cones are bending. Celadon glazes may need a fairly heavy reduction at this point. In general, very heavy reduction, accompanied by clouds of smoke, serves no purpose at this period of the firing, and most effects can be secured by keeping the atmosphere only slightly smoky.

(6) After the cones are down and the glazes are fully melted and matured, a final period of oxidation may favor the development of iron reds and may prevent brownish color in copper red. More important, however, than oxidizing at this point is a long soaking period during which the temperature does not fluctuate. At least one-half hour, and preferably longer, should be allowed between the bending of the last two cones.

(7) The kiln should be well sealed during cooling.

The difficult thing about reduction firing is that it is hard to tell exactly how much the kiln is reducing. However, if, over a number of different fires, the potter carefully observes the condition of damper, burner, spy-hole, flue, and the appearance of the interior of the kiln, he should develop a feel for the proper conditions needed for his particular kiln and glazes. Meters are now available to determine and to record the amount of carbon monoxide in the kiln or flue. These meters are too expensive and complex to come into general use in studio potteries, but further research with an exact indicator of this sort may answer some of the unsolved problems of reduction firing.

Since many potters must use electric kilns only, the idea of achieving reduction in the electric kiln is a tempting one. This can be accomplished by introducing solid fuel of some sort into the kiln during firing. Various fuels have been tried, including charcoal, moth balls, oil soaked bandages, twigs, and the like. The kind of fuel used is not critical as long as carbon is released. The quantity of fuel added must be determined by experiment for any particular kiln. Since the atmosphere in the electric kiln is static and inert, not very much carbonaceous matter need be added to achieve reducing conditions. The main disadvantage in reduction firing in electric kilns is that the reduction seems to be hard on the elements and makes more frequent replacement necessary.

Reduction colors have been approximated in an oxidizing fire by the addition of a local reducing agent to the glaze itself. Silicon carbide is usually used for this purpose. The silicon carbide must be very finely ground; otherwise the glaze will boil violently and craters will be left in the finished glaze. So-called "volcanic glazes" are made by adding the coarser ground silicon carbide to the glaze. For reduction effects, the silicon carbide should be minus 300-mesh or smaller. One to 4 percent of silicon carbide in a glaze is sufficient to bring about local reduction, and if an alkaline base glaze is used with about 1 percent of copper added, fairly good copper reds can be made. They are rather erratic, however, and for depth, brilliance, and beauty of glaze, there is no substitute for reduction firing in producing copper red. A small amount of silicon carbide is sometimes added to copper red reduction glazes to make the development of the color more certain.

Reduction firing is usually done in the higher ranges of temperature, cone 8 to cone 14. One reason for this is that reduction glazes at their best are either of the highly feldspathic or magnesia types, and these glazes do not mature at lower temperatures. Some of the typical reduction glaze colors—such as copper red and celadon—can be made at lower temperatures by employing glazes fluxed with boron. Firing procedures and colorants for glazes are, in general, the same for the lower temperature. One difficulty, however, is that below cone 4, pyrometric cones cannot be used in reduction firing because, when reduced, the iron bearing cones of the lower temperature series do not give accurate indications of temperature. This difficulty can be partially overcome by the use of a pyrometer and draw trials. Since reduction firing at temperatures below cone 8 has no advantage other than a saving in fuel, it usually seems advisable to hold to the higher temperatures.

Chapter 30

Special Glazes and Glaze Effects

1. Luster

Luster is a form of overglaze decoration in which a thin metallic film is developed on the surface of the glaze. There are two types: in one type the luster is achieved in an oxidizing fire with the aid of reducing agents; and in the other type a reduction fire is used.

Lusters produced in oxidation are applied to the glaze in the form of metallic salts combined with resinates, plus an oily medium. Sodium resinate is prepared by boiling lye and rosin together. This material is then combined with metallic salt, either in the form of chlorides or nitrates. Oil of lavender is usually used as a medium. The luster is painted or sprayed onto the glazed surface and fired to red heat. The carbon formed by the resinate and oil reduces the metal, which is deposited in a very thin film on the glaze. The gold or silver banding and striping commonly used on tableware is fired on in an oxidizing decorating fire along with the other overglaze decoration in enamels. Prepared lusters of this type can be purchased ready for use from color manufacturers and are satisfactory in every way.

The other type of luster, which is developed in a reducing fire, was perfected by the Persian potters. In this process, the metallic salts are applied to the ware without any local reducing agent, and the metallic luster film is formed by strong reduction in the decorating fire. Copper sulphate, silver nitrate, gold chloride, and bismuth sub-nitrate are used as sources of the metals. Copper carbonate and silver carbonate may be used instead of the soluble salts. In luster, copper gives red, salmon, or gold color; gold gives reddish purple; silver produces yellowish or ivory lusters; and bismuth lends a colorful iridescence to the surface.

Some vehicle must be used to apply these metallic salts or carbonates to the surface of the ware. The ochres, which are non-plastic, iron-bearing clays, are the traditional vehicles, combined with some starch or gum to secure the luster film to the ware before firing. About three parts of ochre to one part of the metallic salt or carbonate by weight has been found to be a workable proportion. The ochre and color, plus the starch or gum, are ground to a smooth brushing consistency and are applied to the ware in a very thin film. The firing should reach the temperature at which the glaze just starts to melt and become tacky so the luster film will attach itself firmly.

Luster films of the Persian type may be fired in an oxidizing fire during the heating cycle. When the top temperature is attained, the kiln is heavily reduced for about one-half hour. Strongly reducing conditions are maintained during the cooling cycle until the kiln darkens. Reduction during cooling may be accomplished by keeping a small flame burning in the kiln, with the damper kept almost shut. The reduction during cooling may result in the ware being somewhat blackened by smoke when it is taken from the kiln, and the lusters may need to be polished or burnished with a mild abrasive. The luster may be applied over almost any type of fired glaze surface, although if too much lead is present in the glaze, some darkening or greying may result from the reduction. Many of the most colorful of the old Persian pieces have a luster employed as a final touch over a transparent alkaline glaze which may appear over an engobe which has been both carved in sgraffito and touched with underglaze color. The combination of color under and in the glaze, plus the iridescence of the luster on the surface, results in color effects of great brilliance and depth.

Over-all luster effects, or "flash lusters," are made by adding the metallic salt or carbonate directly to the glaze, which is fired in the usual way during the heating cycle but is reduced during cooling, which causes a thin metallic film to develop on the surface of the glaze. Either lead glazes or leadless glazes may be used. Lead glazes may favor the development of color from silver. Usually a low-fired glaze is used, but lusters have also been made successfully with high-fired glazes.

Glazes of the following type have been found to be successful for the development of luster in the temperature range of cone 06 to cone 04.

PbO	.5				
K_2O	.2	Al_2O_3	.18	SiO_2	1.5
CaO	.3				

K_2O	.1				
Na_2O	.6	Al_2O_3	.3	SiO_2	2.5
CaO	.2	B_2O_3	.25		
ZnO	.1				

To the base glaze mill batch is added 1 to 2 percent of silver nitrate, or 3 to 4 percent of bismuth sub-nitrate, or 1 to 2 percent of copper sulphate. Different amounts of metal will, of course, yield different concentration and character of color.

During the cooling cycle, reduction is begun at about 900° to 800°. About one-half hour of fairly heavy reduction, followed by reducing conditions maintained with a flame or by the introduction of carbon fuel into the kiln during the cooling until the kiln darkens, will be sufficient to develop the luster.

Luster glazes of the overall type may be used over fired glazed surfaces in majolica-like technique. This results in the lustered part of the decoration standing out somewhat from the surface of the ware in the manner of an overglaze enamel.

Luster was used with magnificent effect by the Persian potters of the Middle Ages. The technique was the perfect ceramic vehicle for a culture which had developed a strong, rich, decorative tradition. Good modern examples of luster are seldom seen, perhaps because the complexity and variety of color in the surface are not easily adapted to the modern idiom.

2. Salt Glazing

Salt glazing has the attractive feature of being accomplished entirely in the firing process. The ware is put in the kiln raw and taken out glazed. Bisque firing and glaze application are eliminated. Salt glazing was widely used in the nineteenth century for the production of utilitarian wares such as crocks, jugs, and churns, which were usually made in small potteries whose main equipment consisted of a mule-driven pug mill, a kick wheel, and a salt kiln. The process of salt glazing was discovered by German potters in the fifteenth century, and from that time on, German potteries have continued to make salt glazed ware of high technical quality. The German drinking stein is a familiar example of salt glazed ware.

In salt glazing, the ware is placed raw in the kiln, and the temperature is advanced until the maturing temperature of the clay is reached. For successful salt glazing, the body of the ware must be mature. When a clay body reaches maturity, some of the silica in the body is in the vitreous state and is therefore much more reactive. When the maturing temperature of the body is reached, salt is thrown into the fire-boxes of the kiln. The salt rapidly dissociates into a vapor, and the sodium in the salt combines with the silica of the ware to form a thin glaze. Water enters importantly into this reaction, as is illustrated by the equation below, which is a hypothesis for the chemical reaction involved in the salt-glazing process:

$$2NaCl + H_2O \rightarrow 2HCl + Na_2O$$
$$Na_2O + X\,SiO_2 \rightarrow Na_2O \cdot X\,SiO_2$$

The water which provides the oxygen to form sodium oxide from salt is furnished by the moisture in the fuel, the atmosphere, or in the moisture which is added to the salt before it is put in the kiln. Hydrochloric acid escapes from the kiln as a fog. Repeated salting builds up the glaze coating to the desired thickness.

For successful salt glazing, a down-draft open-fired kiln is preferable. There should be ample space near the burners for combustion and for the salt to volatilize. The salt may be thrown in around the burner or through an opening above the burner. The kiln should fire with a reasonably even distribution of heat and should be vented into a chimney to prevent the fumes from escaping inside the building. Kiln furniture, such as shelves and props, should be coated with a paste of aluminum hydrate, which prevents the glaze from forming on it. After repeated firings, the kiln becomes glazed over on the inside, and the results are therefore better and less salt is required than when the kiln is new. Either gas or oil is a suitable fuel. Wood was formerly used, and undoubtedly some of the rich color and texture of the old salt glazed pieces is due to the effect of ash flying through the kiln together with the salt vapors. Wood firing alone results in a kind of vapor glazing, although ordinarily only the parts of the ware exposed to the draft of the kiln will be glazed.

The temperature used in salt glazing depends on the maturing temperature of the clay bodies used. Salt firing can be successfully done as low as cone 04, providing the clay used hardens and approaches maturity at that point. Stoneware temperatures of cone 6 to cone 10 are more usual, and the characteristic warm greys or grey-browns of salt glaze ware are more likely with stoneware clays fired to the higher temperatures. A temperature should be used which brings the clay to a hard, dense, impervious condition.

Most ordinary clays will salt glaze successfully. Some free flint in the body seems to favor a thicker coat of glaze. Clays which contain considerable iron oxide will salt glaze a dark, rather heavy brown color, such as is seen on salt glazed drain tile. To obtain light greys, or for light amber or tan effects, a clay body having very little iron in it must be used. A smooth, fairly grog-free body is usually preferred, since the thin salt glaze does not cover up the roughness or gritty surfaces caused by grog.

Color in salt glazed ware is obtained by the use of engobes. Most engobe compositions work well, especially those containing considerable free flint. Since partially reducing conditions usually prevail during salt glazing, the color range is somewhat limited compared to the range of oxidized glazes. Cobalt oxide is used for blue, and iron oxide for various shades of tan, brown, or brownish black. Rutile in the engobe may result in beautiful ochre colors. Instead of using an engobe, coloring oxides may be brushed thinly directly on the ware. Or the color may be brushed onto the ware in the form of soluble salts such as iron chloride or cobalt sulphate.

Salt glaze is perhaps at its best over impressed textures in the clay or over sprigged designs. Texture may be beautifully revealed by the pooling of the glaze in the hollows and depressions of the design. The texture of salt glaze itself may have a very rich texture or slight roughness. The "orange peel" surface is caused by the glaze gathering on the surface into slight beads or droplets.

The pots are placed in the kiln with some space between them to allow for the circulation of the vapor. It used to be the practice to make pots which could be piled one on top of another in bungs, thus eliminating the need for shelves and props. Jars were made so they could be placed one on another, lids were made so they would stack up, and smaller crocks were placed on larger ones.

One difficulty with salt glazing is that the salt vapors will not go down inside of pots; so the insides have to be covered with a glaze, which is applied in the usual manner. Albany slip was commonly used for this because it was cheap, reliable, and easily applied. However, unless it is protected from the salt vapor by being enclosed, Albany slip may not melt smoothly. Lead glazes may be used for the insides of pieces, and although such glazes may be overly bright, they do not seem to be adversely affected by the salting.

When the kiln is being set, a series of draw trials are placed in front of the spy-hole. Draw trials are a necessity in salt glazing because they indicate the progress of the salting and the thickness of glaze coat. Cones are of little use to indicate the end point of the firing because they are affected by the salt vapors and subside before their normal deformation temperature is reached. Cones do help, however, in indicating the temperature at which the body is nearing maturity and at which salting should begin. Salt may be thrown into the fires by the use of a small shovel or scoop, or it may be moistened and packed into paper cups which are thrown into the fire. Sometimes a salt brine is used, which is dripped in front of the burner, since some moisture and steam is essential to the glazing reaction. In salting a kiln of about 12 cubic feet capacity, about one pound of salt may be thrown in at a time. When the vapor inside the kiln begins to clear up, another batch is added. A total of about five to seven pounds of salt may be needed. The salt vaporizes quite rapidly, and dense clouds of vapor roll through the kiln. While salting, it is necessary to close the damper somewhat to retain the vapors in the kiln until they can react with the ware.

After several saltings, a red-hot draw trial is hooked out of the spy-hole, cooled in water, and examined. If it is insufficiently glazed, the firing is continued and more salt is thrown in. When a draw trial shows a substantial coating of glaze, the firing is stopped and the ware cooled in the usual way.

Because of the necessity of firing part of the time with the damper closed, and because of the necessity of using an open-fired kiln, salt glazed ware is frequently flashed by the flame. This gives it an uneven color, sometimes darker on one side than on the other. For certain kinds of pottery, such accidental flashings may be very pleasant and appropriate. In salt glazing, exact color is hard to control. Ware may vary considerably from one firing to another because of slightly differing atmospheric conditions.

3. Slip Glazes

Slip glazes are glazes which are made wholly or largely from clays of low fusion point. Many common clays, when fired to cone 8 or higher, will fuse and become fluid enough to spread over the surface of pottery as a dark-colored glaze. Since a good deal of heat is required to melt any clay—even a clay loaded with iron and other fluxes—slip glazes are possible only in the stoneware range of firing and are commonly used over stoneware bodies. Since all clays which have a low melting point contain iron and other mineral impurities, slip glazes have a color range limited to tan, browns, and black.

The best-known clay for slip glazing is Albany slip. This clay, which is mined near Albany, N. Y., contains considerable iron and other impurities and melts by itself at about cone 8. At cone 11 it is a bright, smooth brown or tan glaze. In reduction firing, Albany slip tends to become a reddish brown. Albany slip was widely used as a glaze on the utilitarian wares of the nineteenth century. It is the familiar brown or black which appears on the inside of salt glazed pieces, or on bean pots, crocks, and jugs. It has also been used extensively as a glaze on porcelain insulators.

Although albany slip is perhaps the most widely used clay for slip glazing, many local clays will make interesting glazes for stoneware. As a test, a small amount of clay can be put on a bit of broken brick or kiln shelf and run through a glaze fire. If it melts completely and flattens itself out into a smooth puddle or glass, it may be usable as a glaze without further additions. Sometimes the clay is too refractory and needs the addition of some flux to make it melt satisfactorily as a glaze. Feldspar, nepheline syenite, or frit may be added for this purpose. Small additions of whiting and zinc may alter the color or texture of the glaze, and if darker colors of brown or black are desired, iron or iron and cobalt may be added.

Slip glazes are usually applied over raw ware. Since the glaze is largely made up of clay, it has a high shrinkage, and this may cause difficulties in application. If the ware is glazed while it is still leather-hard, the ware and the glaze shrink together, and the tendency of the glaze to crack may be avoided. Another possibility is to calcine the slip glaze lightly at red heat, which completes its shrinkage, and then to grind the material and apply it to bisqued ware in the usual way. One good thing about slip glazes is that they have a long firing range and may be good over a range of several cones difference in heat. In general, they are free from the usual glaze flaws and do not craze or pit. Crawling may occur, however, because of the tendency of the glaze coat to crack during drying.

Some of the most famous and admired old Chinese glazes are slip glazes, such as the "Temmoku" glaze, or "Hare's fur" glaze, the "oil spot" glaze, "mirror black," "partridge feather," and other dark iron glazes. All of these effects were secured by the use of natural slip clays of various kinds, with perhaps the addition of wood-ash or other flux. These glazes are difficult to reproduce exactly because particular clays give certain colors and textures which are hard to match exactly with some other clay. The temmoku or hare's fur glaze is characterized by streaks of brown or black which run down the sides of the piece in a pattern suggestive of fur. The glaze is a fairly fluid one and tends to puddle in the center of bowls and to run and form a roll or heavy drop on the outside where the glaze ends near the foot. The glaze may run very thin at the edge of the piece. In the best examples of hare's fur from Sung Dynasty wares, the glaze has a warm lustrous brown color, streaked with a rich black, and gathers in a fat roll at the base of the pot. This glaze was greatly admired by early Japanese connoisseurs, who gave it the name *temmoku.*

The so-called partridge feather glaze is marked by brown spots or mottling on a black field. The spots may be richly variegated and suggestive of the markings on feathers. This glaze can be made from a slip clay which goes through a boiling phase during its melting. The brown spots or marks are the remains of craters or bubbles which formed, broke, and with the advancing heat settled down to a smooth surface with only a change of color marking their position. The oil-spot glazes result from the same phenomenon. Oil spot glazes are usually dark brown or black in general color, and are marked by small. rather evenly spaced spots, which may be lighter brown or silver colored. These spots are the remains of healed-over blisters which occurred during firing. To secure the mottled effects of hare's fur or oil spot glazes, a slip clay should be used which is high in iron and contains some sulfur, which induces boiling during firing. Some lime in the form of whiting or dolomite may be added. Firing should be oxidizing, and the higher temperatures of cone 10 to cone 12 give the best results. If the glaze is over-fired, the spots or mottling will disappear, and for this reason, close firing control is necessary. Some surface clays from along the Hudson River in New York have been found to produce perfect hare's fur glazes without the addition of any other material. The following combinations using Albany slip may produce mottled glazes or oil spots when fired to cone 11:

Albany slip	80	Albany slip	75
Ochre	10	Iron oxide	5
Spodumene	10	Burnt sienna	10
		Feldspar	10

Slip glazes are perhaps of more interest to the potter than they are to the average collector or user of pottery. The almost uniformly brown or black color of such glazes must be used with great sensitivity if dull results are to be avoided, and the best slip glazed ware is very subtle in character. Slip glazes do have a fascination which comes from the directness of the process and from the fact that they are found on some of the best pottery of the past.

4. Ash Glazes

Wood or vegetable ashes have been used as glaze materials since antiquity, and they may lend a quality to glazes which is difficult to obtain with other materials. The discovery of ash as a glaze material undoubtedly came about when the early Chinese potters noted that the ware in their open-fired, wood-burning kilns was being partially glazed by the ashes which were carried through the kiln by the draft. Some of the old pre-Han Dynasty stoneware pots show a partial glaze on one side or on the shoulder where a film of ash from the fire landed on the ware and formed a thin coating of glaze. Some of the earliest glazes made in China were probably combinations of ash from the fires of the kilns together with some red clay, and very practical high-temperature glazes can be made from ash, feldspar, limestone, and clay.

The chemical analysis of wood and vegetable ashes shows that they contain 10 to 15 percent alumina, 30 to 70 percent silica, up to 15 percent of potash, up to 30 percent of lime, together with some iron oxide, phosphorus, magnesia, and other elements. These oxides are all useful in glazes, and potash is a valuable flux. Most ashes will melt to a fluid glass at around cone 10. When ash is used alone as a glaze, it will usually result in a rather thin watery-looking glaze. Ashes vary rather widely in composition, and even the ash of a given variety of tree will vary, depending on the soil in which it grew. The use of ash in glazes depends, therefore, on testing and experimentation with the material at hand. It may be difficult to locate a reliable source of ash which will be uniform in composition, but some potters have successfully used the ashes from the burning of waste in sawmills or furniture factories. The ashes from burned corncobs, rice hulls, or other agricultural wastes such as fruit pits offer possible sources.

To prepare ashes for use in glazes, they must be first mixed with a quantity of water and the resulting thin slurry passed through an 80-mesh screen. The material which does not pass the screen is discarded. The ash and water mixture is then allowed to settle, and the water is decanted off. The water will contain some of the soluble alkalies from the ash, and it may be advisable to give the ash a second washing and decanting to remove more of the soluble material. Too much washing, however, may remove too much of the potash and diminish the effectiveness of the ash as a flux. After decanting, the ash is allowed to dry and is then ready for use.

As a start in working out ash glazes, a simple combination of two parts of ash, two parts of feldspar, and one part of clay may be tried. If the glaze resulting from such a proportion is too fluid, more clay may be added, and if the glaze is too stiff, more ash or some other flux such as whiting may be added. Ash glazes will need high firing to fuse, and cone 8 to cone 11 is the usual temperature range. The following gives the probable limits of the various materials usual to ash glazes:

Ash	20 to 70%
Feldspar	20 to 70%
Whiting	5 to 20%
Flint	15 to 25%
Clay	5 to 20%

Other materials such as colemanite, talc, dolomite, red clay, slip clay, or nepheline syenite may be used to make up the glaze. One way to incorporate ash into a glaze composition is to take any stiff stoneware glaze and to add progressively larger amounts of ash to it until it shows the marked influence of the added material.

Ash glazes, particularly those which

are fired in reduction, have a peculiarly broken surface texture which may be very attractive. High-fired reduction glazes which have some ash in their composition, together with rutile and a small amount of coloring oxide, can yield very soft, beautifully mottled and colored surfaces.

5. Crystalline Glazes

Ordinarily, when the glaze cools, it remains an amorphous, non-crystalline substance. Under special circumstances, however, the glaze can be made to crystallize partially as it cools, and the various forms of crystalline glazes are the result. In ordinary glazes the presence of alumina prevents the glaze from crystallizing as it cools. Alumina also serves the valuable purpose of increasing viscosity, which prevents the glaze from running excessively. To make crystalline glazes, the amount of alumina in the composition must be drastically reduced, usually to less than 0.1 molecular equivalents, which in a high-fired glaze is one-third of normal. Many crystalline glaze compositions have no alumina at all. The absence of alumina usually makes the glaze very fluid, and in producing ware with crystalline glazes, some provision must be made for the flow of glaze. Usually the pots are set in the kiln on a soft china clay cookie, which is easily ground from the bottom of the piece, along with the glaze which has run down over it.

A high content of zinc oxide in the glaze favors the development of crystals. In crystalline glazes, about 0.3 equivalents of zinc are usual. The presence of some rutile or titania also favors crystalline development. The base glaze may contain lead as a flux, or it may be fluxed with alkalies or boron. Alkaline glazes are usually used.

Because of the presence of large amounts of zinc and rutile, crystalline glazes are typically somewhat opaque, and the absence of alumina makes them fluid and bright in surface. The crystals in the finished glaze may be either small and appear in clusters or groups, or the crystals may be large and spectacular in appearance. The presence of coloring oxides such as iron, copper, or cobalt may color the glaze and may also tint the crystals in an interesting fashion.

The firing cycle is a critical factor in producing crystals in glazes. The heating phase may be carried out at the usual speed, but cooling must be slowed down at the point where the materials in the glaze tend to crystallize. This is usually at a temperature somewhat below the top temperature, but above the point where the glaze solidifies. The point of temperature at which crystallization occurs must be determined experimentally. Slow cooling through the right range of temperature will, if the glaze composition is right, produce large crystals.

Because of their abnormal composition and unusual firing cycle, crystalline glazes are rather hard to produce and perhaps should be classified as oddities among glazes. The presence of spectacular crystals on the sides of a pot, interesting though such crystals may be in themselves, has, in most cases, contributed as little to the aesthetic significance of the piece as it has to the function.

Aventurine glazes are crystalline glazes made with a considerable amount of iron oxide in the glaze. In this type of glaze the alumina must be absent or present in very small quantity. The flux may be either lead, soda, or potash, but very high-lead glazes are usually favored.

The iron oxide is usually present in amounts of from 5 to 9 percent of the glaze batch. The iron, which is taken into solution during melting, crystallizes out during the cooling cycle, which results in a surface marked by brilliant reddish or gold-colored crystals. Cooling must be slow to bring out the most brilliant crystals. Aventurine glazes are sometimes startlingly colorful, but as in the case of other types of crystalline glazes, they seem to be more useful in arousing curiosity than in contributing to sound expression.

6. Crackle and Pooled Glazes

Crackle glazes may be defined as glazes whose tendency to craze is used for decorative effect. The causes for crazing have already been discussed in a previous chapter. If a glaze is to be deliberately made to craze, alkalies or other high expansion oxides are added to it. In practice, this means, in the case of high-fired glazes, the adding of feldspar, and in the lower-fired glazes, the adding of some alkali, such as potash or soda, preferably in the form of a frit. It is an easy matter to adjust any glaze to make it craze.

The more serious the crazing, the closer together the network of cracks will be. In some badly crazed low-fired glazes the cracks are so close together that it is rather hard to detect them. For a wide crackle, the glaze should be adjusted so as to be poised between fitting and crazing. Some of the old Chinese stoneware, such as the Ko ware of the Sung Dynasty, has craze lines which form beautiful large square patterns.

Craze lines may be emphasized by rubbing ink or other coloring matter into them after firing. One color may be rubbed in immediately after firing and another color may be applied after a few days, when another network of cracks will have developed, thus giving the appearance of a double network of craze lines. Another technique is to rub some coloring oxide, such as iron oxide, into the craze lines and then fire the piece again. The original craze lines will then appear as somewhat fuzzy lines of color, and the new craze lines, developed in the second firing, will be in a different position.

Pooled glazes are made by melting pools of glass into depressions in the clay or into the insides of bowls or trays. Glaze, frit, or bits of broken glass are piled thickly on the part of the ware which is to have the pool, and the firing is then carried to a sufficiently high temperature to melt the glass. Glass which is melted into a thick mass in this manner, especially if the material is somewhat alkaline, will have a tendency to craze, and the fired result may resemble cracked ice. These effects are sometimes erroneously called crystalline. Some low melting-point frit is a convenient material to use. Such a frit may be colored by adding coloring oxides or stains. Broken glass of various colors may also be used. The technique, since it is restricted to flat surfaces, is of limited usefulness.

7. Egyptian Paste

Egyptian paste is an interesting technique because it is actually the earliest form of glaze and was developed prior to 5000 B.C. In Egyptian paste, the glaze materials are added to the body in soluble form. When the clay dries, the glaze-forming materials migrate to the surface of the ware and are deposited there. When fired, a thin layer of glaze develops on the surface.

In formulating Egyptian paste, the clay content must be kept low to allow for sufficient glass-forming material to be present and to give an open, porous structure which will permit the migration of soluble ingredients to the surface. The material will contain about 60 percent of non-plastic ingredients, such as flint, sand, and feldspar. Clay may be added in amounts up to about 20 percent. At least 10 percent of some soluble soda compound is necessary. Soda may be added as soda ash, bicarbonate of soda, borax, or combinations of these. Coloring oxides are added directly to the batch. Copper oxide, which gives a beautiful turquoise color, is the favorite coloring oxide. About 3 percent will give strong blue. Cobalt oxide, manganese oxide, or yellow glaze stains may also be used. Coloring oxides may also be added as soluble sulphates or chlorides. Following is a typical formula:

Feldspar	40
Flint	20
Kaolin	15
Ball clay	5
Sodium bicarbonate	6
Soda ash	6
Whiting	5
Fine white sand	8

At best, Egyptian paste is relatively non-plastic, and the forms made with it are, of necessity, simple. Bentonite or dextrine added to the material will partially overcome this difficulty. Objects made from Egyptian paste are fired to about cone 08. Jewelry or small sculptures made in this way may be very beautiful in surface and color.

8. Red Glazes

Red glazes are a rather difficult problem. Listed below are all the possible sources of the color, some of which have already been described.

(1) Chrome red. This color is achieved by adding about 2 percent of chrome oxide or soluble salts of chromium to a very high lead glaze which is low in alumina and fires to a temperature not above cone 08. Little or no soda should be present in the glaze. The color is a brilliant orange-red. A typical cone 010 chrome red glaze might be:

White lead	68
Flint	20
Kaolin	10
Soda ash	2
Potassium bi-chromate	5

(2) Uranium red. Uranium oxide may be used in the same type of base glaze as that described above for chrome red. The color is a brilliant orange-red, possibly mottled with black.

(3) Aventurines. This effect is produced by adding about 7 percent of iron to a low-alumina base, as described above in the section on crystalline glazes. The color tends toward brown or reddish gold.

(4) Cadmium-selenium glazes. Cadmium sulphide and selenium are fritted together to form a red glaze stain. This stain, when added to a low-melting point frit containing some alkalies, will produce a brilliant opaque red color. The glaze must be cooled rapidly, as the color is fugitive. Manufacturers of cadmium-selenium stains will recommend a suitable frit composition for use with the stain to develop the best color.

(5) Chrome-tin pinks. Chrome and tin together, in a zinc-free glaze, produce various shades of pink or mauve. A true dark red is not possible with this combination, but

beautiful and subtle colors may result. Chrome must be present in small quantities—less than 1 percent of the batch.

(6) Saturated iron reds. These colors are best done in a reducing fire. The color tends toward brown.
(7) Copper red from reduction firing.
(8) Lustered surfaces. Copper and gold used in over-glaze lusters may give strong red and purple-red colors.

Of all of these types of red glazes, only those glazes colored with cadmium-selenium will be bright, spectrum red, or "fire-engine red."

9. Terra Sigillata

Terra sigillata is actually a type of engobe rather than a glaze. It is familiar as the burnished surface seen on the classical wares of the Greeks and the Romans and on the pottery of many primitive peoples. It may have a dense, rather waxy surface, usually red, brown, or ochre in color.

Terra sigillata is made by separating off the finer fractions of a common iron-bearing plastic clay. The slip so obtained is spread on the ware in a thin coat and fired to a low temperature.

To prepare terra sigillata, red clay and water are mixed until the resultant slip is quite thin, having a specific gravity of 1.2 or less. Some deflocculent may be added to the slip to aid in keeping the particles floating. About 0.3 percent of sodium hydroxide to the weight of the dry clay has been found to be a satisfactory deflocculent for most clays. Milling, while not indispensable, may help to separate and float the particles of clay. The slip, after thorough mixing, is allowed to settle for a few days. The water from the surface is then decanted off, and about the top one-third or less of the clay slip in the vessel is skimmed off for use; the rest is discarded.

Terra sigillata may be applied by dipping, painting, or spraying on damp or dry ware. It should be applied very thinly; otherwise the layer of slip may crack during shrinkage. The surface may be burnished before firing by rubbing with a hard smooth instrument like the back of a spoon. Most terra sigillatas are at their best when fired to temperatures below cone 08. At this heat, red, orange, and ochre colors are possible, and the waxy shine of the material will survive the fire. If the temperature of firing is too great, the terra sigillata loses its smooth, waxy surface and looks much like any other unglazed engobe. Some clays can be burnished before firing and will have a fired surface similar to terra sigillata, although they are not coated with any slip.

The color range of terra sigillata is about the same as that of iron-bearing clays. In making the material, clays should be selected which are already very fine in grain structure. Different clays can be blended for color effects.

Although terra sigillata may make a piece of pottery somewhat impervious to moisture, it does not seal off the surface of the clay positively as does a glaze.

10. Raku Ware

Raku is actually a procedure for making pottery rather than a special color or glaze effect, and raku pots can be made in a variety of bodies and glazes. In making raku, the pottery is bisqued in the usual way, but in the glaze fire, it is placed, after glazing, directly in the red-hot kiln, then withdrawn and rapidly cooled as soon as the glaze has melted. The technique was developed and used by the Japanese potters for making tea ceremony wares, and the Japanese connoisseurs greatly admired the somewhat irregular surfaces and colors which are characteristic of this kind of pottery.

Clay bodies for raku are designed to resist the thermal shock of being placed in a red-hot kiln without the usual warming up period. Stoneware bodies with plenty of grog in them work well. The body should contain at least 50 percent of stoneware clay or fire clay, and about 20 percent of grog. The amount of flint should be kept below 10 percent to avoid dunting. The following composition is typical:

Stoneware clay	30
Fire clay	25
Ball clay	15
Feldspar	5
Flint	5
Grog	20

The pots are bisqued at about cone 04 to cone 01. If the bisque fire is too high in temperature, the pottery may be too mature to withstand the heat shock of the glaze fire. The ware should be quite open and porous after bisquing. Engobe decorations may be put on the ware before the first fire.

Glazing is usually done at around cone 08 or lower, and the kiln is heated empty to about this temperature. A top-loading kiln, or one with a wide hinged door, is best for raku, and a pyrometer is useful in keeping the temperature at the right point while the glazing is proceeding.

The best glazes for raku are very high lead glazes which melt rapidly and smoothly. A typical base glaze formula might be:

White lead	55
Flint	25
Feldspar	10
Clay	5
Whiting	5

Softer glazes, with the lead content as high as 70 percent, have been used. High lead frits may be used rather than raw lead, and these have the advantage of less shrinkage in the raw glaze coat and less boiling in the fire. The glaze may be made clear, opaque, or colored in the usual way. Glazes are applied rather thickly, and the pots are then carefully dried before being placed in the glaze kiln.

In firing, one or two pots are placed in the hot kiln with a long pair of tongs. The kiln usually cools somewhat as a result of the door being opened, and a few minutes elapse before the glazes begin to melt. The pots are observed through a spy-hole, and when the glaze is smooth and shiny, the pots are drawn out with the tongs and placed on a fire brick to cool. The glaze firing usually takes about 10 minutes.

The exciting thing about making raku is that the ware is finished in only a few minutes, and the glaze firing takes on a drama which is quite different from the usual long wait to get into a cooling kiln. Raku has perhaps more usefulness as a means of demonstrating pottery making than as a means of producing ware, since the finished raku pot is in no way different than an ordinary pot except that it is under-fired, soft, and bears the scar of the tongs, which mar the glaze when the piece is taken from the kiln.

11. Choices in the Use of Ceramic Materials

The selection and use of ceramic bodies, slips, glazes, colors, and textures present problems which ultimately involve aesthetic rather than practical considerations. Any discussion of ceramic techniques which fails to recognize such problems is less than complete.

Ceramics as a medium for artistic expression actually suffers from a plethora of means. There are too many colors, too many textural and tactile possibilities to choose from. Our present day technical skill has placed any known ceramic color or texture within fairly easy reach of anyone who wants to avail himself of the means. While the achievement of any desired color or texture may involve some testing and work, success is assured.

The real problem, then, is not a technical one of how to obtain any given effect, but of how to use it. The choices of colors, textures, and designs which the potter makes when he plans and executes his ware are, of course, a reflection of the true purposes and meanings of his work. In former times, the potter had only a limited number of effects which were available to him to use, and his expression was contrived in terms of these means. The means themselves had been contrived out of the practical and spiritual needs of many people. The problem of choice was, then, more or less solved for the individual potter.

In some ways the potter today is more fortunate, but in other ways he works under a handicap. He looks with nostalgia, perhaps, to the great achievements of the past in pottery, and to times which produced a truly healthy craft—vigorous, unself-conscious, and reflecting the real needs of people. The potter today is unfortunate in that he must work in comparative isolation, detached from any coherent and continuing tradition. He is also unfortunate in that his product tends to fall into the hands of indifferent and insensitive consumers, who are perhaps unaware of the values he has tried to put into his work.

But, on the other hand, the potter is fortunate in his knowledge of the craft, which far exceeds that of previous times, in his opportunity to draw from the great traditions of the past, in the freedom from back-breaking labor which the machine has given him, and in the ultimate satisfaction—if he is lucky enough to achieve it—of a truly personal, expressive art which is largely of his own making. And if such an art is solidly of himself, it will also be of solid value to others.

The following generalizations about making worthwhile pottery are risked in the full realization that tomorrow they may be shown to be false by good works done in contradiction to them: (1) Pottery bodies should be chosen to express the nature of the material or, more accurately, to express our conception of the nature of the material. The ceramic medium is, of course, capable of a bewildering number of effects. From these, one chooses colors, textures, and surfaces which seem related to their parent minerals, to the colors one responds to in nature, and to the qualities of the landscape and the earth which seem meaningful. This does not necessarily mean the choice of rough or earthy-colored materials only, but an aesthetic point of view which excluded such colors would be excessively limiting.

(2) Bodies, glazes, and colors should be chosen in relation to the intended use or function of the ware. A delicate rose-colored glaze which might be perfect for a stem vase is out of place on a bean pot. On the other hand, a piece exhibiting a violent excrescence of color or texture might triumphantly deny any function at all and yet end up by being the

most meaningful object in someone's collection.

(3) The decorative means employed should be in keeping with the form and with the spirit behind the form. This criterion would rule out silly, extraneous, frivolous, or unfeelingly applied patterns and designs on functional ware. One might say, of course, that if the function of a piece is dubious and its form nondescript, it would be suitably decorated with a trivial, inept design. But applied designs, unless they can become an inseparable and integral part of the thing they are applied to, had best be left off. Decorative treatment, unless it is conceived as a wholeness with the form, is always in danger of being extraneous and out of place.

(4) The means employed in pottery making should be selected in a positive spirit and carried out with sureness and conviction. This is the opposite of the unfortunately more common lack of conviction, which results in dimly conceived work that fails to express a clarified function, feeling, or idea. Strong conviction in pottery, as in any other art, can make the simplest means yield surprisingly convincing results.

APPENDIX

Glossary

Aeolian Wind-borne.

Air-floated Sorted as to particle size by air separation.

Amorphous Without crystalline structure.

Amphoteric Chemically neutral; neither acid nor base.

Bag wall A fire wall in a kiln which channels the course of the flame.

Bat A slab of plaster or fired clay used for drying out clay or as a platform for work in clay.

Bisque Ware which has had one firing unglazed.

Blow-hole An opening at the top of a kiln to let out heat and facilitate cooling, or to let out steam during the early part of firing.

Blunge To mix a slip.

B.T.U. British thermal unit. The amount of heat necessary to raise one pound of water one degree Fahrenheit.

Bung A stack of saggers or pots in the kiln.

Calcine To heat to red heat or more.

Calorie Metric unit of heat. The amount of heat necessary to raise one gram of water one degree centigrade.

Catalyst An agent which promotes chemical change.

Clam To mud-in the door of a kiln.

Coil To make clay objects by building with ropes or coils of clay.

Colloidal Jelly-like, without grain structure.

Crackle Decorative craze lines in the glaze.

Crazing The formation of a network of cracks in a glaze.

Damper A device for adjusting or for closing the opening from the kiln to the chimney.

De-air To remove the air from clay, as in a de-airing pug mill, which removes the air from the clay by passing it through a vacuum chamber.

Decant To remove the water which has collected at the top when a material settles in a liquid.

Deflocculate To disperse the particles in a slip so that less water is required for fluidity.

Dehydration The loss of water from a clay during firing.

Devitrify To re-crystallize on cooling.

Disc grinder A grinder composed of two discs, one stationary and one moving, which grind the material between them.

Dissociation point The degree of temperature at which a substance breaks down into its constituent parts.

Draw To remove fired ware from the kiln.

Draw trial A piece drawn from the firing kiln to gage the progress of the firing.

Dry pan A mixer for dry materials in which a pan revolves under heavy wheels or mullers.

Dunt To break from strains in cooling.

Effervesce To give off gas, as in the form of bubbles rising in liquid.

Effloresce To dry or crystallize into white powder.

Electrolyte An agent which causes deflocculation. A substance in solution, conducting electricity.

Engobe A layer of slip applied to ware to change the color of the body.

Eutectic 1. The lowest-melting mixture of two or more substances. 2. (adj.) Describing the temperature of lowest melting.

Extrusion The process of making shapes such as drain tile by forcing the clay through dies.

Faience Glazed earthenware. Originally, the tin-glazed earthenware made at Faenza, Italy.

Fat clay Highly plastic clay.

Filler A material of little or no plasticity which helps to promote drying and control shrinkage in clay bodies or engobes.

Filter-press A device which removes the excess water from clay slip to make it into plastic clay.

Fit The adjustment of a glaze to a clay.

Flocculate To thicken.

Flux A substance which causes or promotes melting.

Frit A material used in glazes and enamels which consists of a glass which has been melted, cooled, then ground to a powder for use.

Fuse To melt.

Gel To turn to a thick jelly-like consistency.

Glassification Turning to glass; melting into a glass.

Green ware Unfired pottery.

Grog Clay which has been fired and then ground into granules of more or less fineness.

Heat A physical form of energy generated by combustion, chemical action, or friction, and measured by calories or B.T.U.'s.

Igneous Formed by cooling from a molten state.

Jaw crusher A machine for crushing which is composed of one stationary and one movable jaw.

Kaolinization The formation in nature of kaolin from feldspar.

Lagging The material used for insulating the outside of kilns, such as asbestos.

Lawn To pass through a screen.

Leather-hard Clay which is dried sufficiently to be stiff, but which is still damp enough to be joined to other pieces with slip.

Levigation Refining clay by water floatation.

Luting Joining leather-hard clay by slip.

Mature Fired to a tight, hard, serviceable structure.

Mealy Crumbly, non-plastic.

Muffle The inner lining of a kiln which protects the ware from the direct impingement of the flame.

Neutral atmosphere An atmosphere in a kiln between reducing and oxidizing.

Open To make a clay more open or porous in structure by adding fillers or grog.

Open firing Firing in which the flame may impinge on the ware.

Oxide Any element combined with oxygen.

Paste A white clay body.

pH The relative alkalinity or acidity of a solution.

Pins Refractory, triangular supports used in placing ware in racks or saggers.

Pitchers Fired pottery ground to a powder.

Plasticity The property of a material enabling it to be shaped and to hold its shape.

Pug To mix.

Pyrometer A mechanical device for measuring the temperature in the kiln.

Pyrometric cone A device for measuring heat treatment in the kiln.

Raw glaze A glaze which contains no fritted material.

Reduction Firing with reduced oxygen in the kiln.

Refractory Resistant to heat.

Roll crusher A machine for crushing, composed of two rollers which break the material to be crushed as it passes through.

Sagger A fireclay box which protects ware from the flame during firing.

Salt glaze Glazing by the vapors from salt in the kiln.

Sedimentary Formed in layers or strata by sedimentation.

Sgraffito The decorative process which employs a scratched line through a layer of slip to expose the clay body beneath.

Shards Bits of broken pottery.

Short Non-plastic, poor in working properties.

Siccative A medium which promotes the drying of oils used in underglaze or overglaze colors.
Sinter To fire to the point where cohesion of the materials begins.
Slake To moisten clay with water.
Slip A fluid suspension of clay or other materials and water.
Slip glaze A glaze made mostly from clay.
Slurry A mixture of plastic clay and water.
Soak To hold the kiln at one temperature for a time.
Soluble Capable of being dissolved in water.
Spare The scrap clay which is trimmed off during casting pottery.
Spurs Triangular refractory supports which are placed under glazed ware in the fire to prevent sticking to the kiln shelves.
Stack To set a kiln with pottery.
Stilliards Ware racks for pottery.
Strata Layers, as of rock formations or clays in nature.
Strip mining Mining from open pits from which the over-burden of unwanted material has been stripped away.
Temperature The intensity of heat as measured in degrees Fahrenheit or degrees Centigrade.
Throw To make pottery by hand on a wheel.
Tooth Roughness in a clay, coarse grain structure.
Viscosity The relative resistance of a liquid to stirring or movement.
Vitrify To fire to the point of glassification.
Wad Bits of clay used to level shelves or sagger lids in the kiln.
Water glass Sodium silicate.
Water-smoking The early stage of firing during which water is being driven from the clay by the advancing heat.
Wedge To knead or mix plastic clay by cutting or rolling.
Wet pan A mixer for damp materials in which wheels or mullers revolve in a pan.
Wicket The door of a kiln.
Win To dig or mine clay.

Laboratory Tests on Clay

1. Test for the Water of Plasticity

This test determines the amount of water which is required to make a clay plastic and workable. The more water a clay requires to become plastic, the finer its grain structure is apt to be, and therefore the more it is apt to shrink on drying.

1. Thoroughly dry the clay sample and pulverize it so it will pass a 30-mesh screen.
2. Weigh out 500 grams of the clay onto a glass slab.
3. Fill a 500-c.c. graduate with water and add the water to the clay a little at a time, mixing well after each addition.
4. Knead the clay, adding more water from the graduate if necessary, until it is a smooth mass of about the right consistency for modeling.
5. Note the amount of water which has been added to the clay.
6. Calculate the amount of water of plasticity by the following formula:

$$\text{Percent water of plasticity} = \frac{\text{Weight of water}}{\text{Weight of dry clay}} \times 100$$

2. Test for Drying Shrinkage

The amount of shrinkage is a highly important characteristic of any clay. In this test the linear shrinkage is determined.

1. From a well-kneaded mass of clay of average modeling consistency, make a number of bars of the following dimension: 14 cm's long, 4 cm's wide, and about 1 cm thick.
2. On the face of each bar, make a sharp scratch exactly 10 cm long.
3. Allow the tiles to dry, turning frequently to avoid warping.
4. Determine drying shrinkage by the following calculation:

$$\text{Percent linear shrinkage} = \frac{\text{Plastic length—Dry length}}{\text{Plastic length}} \times 100$$

3. Test for Firing Shrinkage

Firing shrinkage is usually determined on samples which are fired to several different temperatures. This gives an idea of the progressive tightening of the clay with advancing temperature.

1. Fire the dried bars as made in the previous test.
2. Measure the length of the scratch on the fired bar.
3. Calculate the firing shrinkage by the following formula:

$$\text{Percent linear shrinkage} = \frac{\text{Dry length—Fired length}}{\text{Dry length}} \times 100$$

4. Total shrinkage may be calculated as follows:

$$\text{Percent linear shrinkage} = \frac{\text{Plastic length—Fired length}}{\text{Plastic length}} \times 100$$

4. Test for Water Absorption of Fired Clay

The degree of water absorption is a measure of the maturity of a fired clay body. As a clay body approaches vitrification, its absorbency nears zero.

1. Make bars of the clay about 5 x 5 x 10 cms. At least three bars should be made for each temperature at which the clay is to be fired and tested.
2. Fire the bars.
3. Carefully weigh the fired pieces to the nearest centigram.
4. Boil the fired pieces in water for two hours.
5. Dry the surface of the bars with a towel and weigh them again.
6. Calculate the absorption, using the following formula:

$$\text{Percent absorption} = \frac{\text{Saturated weight—Dry weight}}{\text{Dry weight}} \times 100$$

TYPICAL HEATING SCHEDULES FOR VARIOUS POTTERY FIRINGS

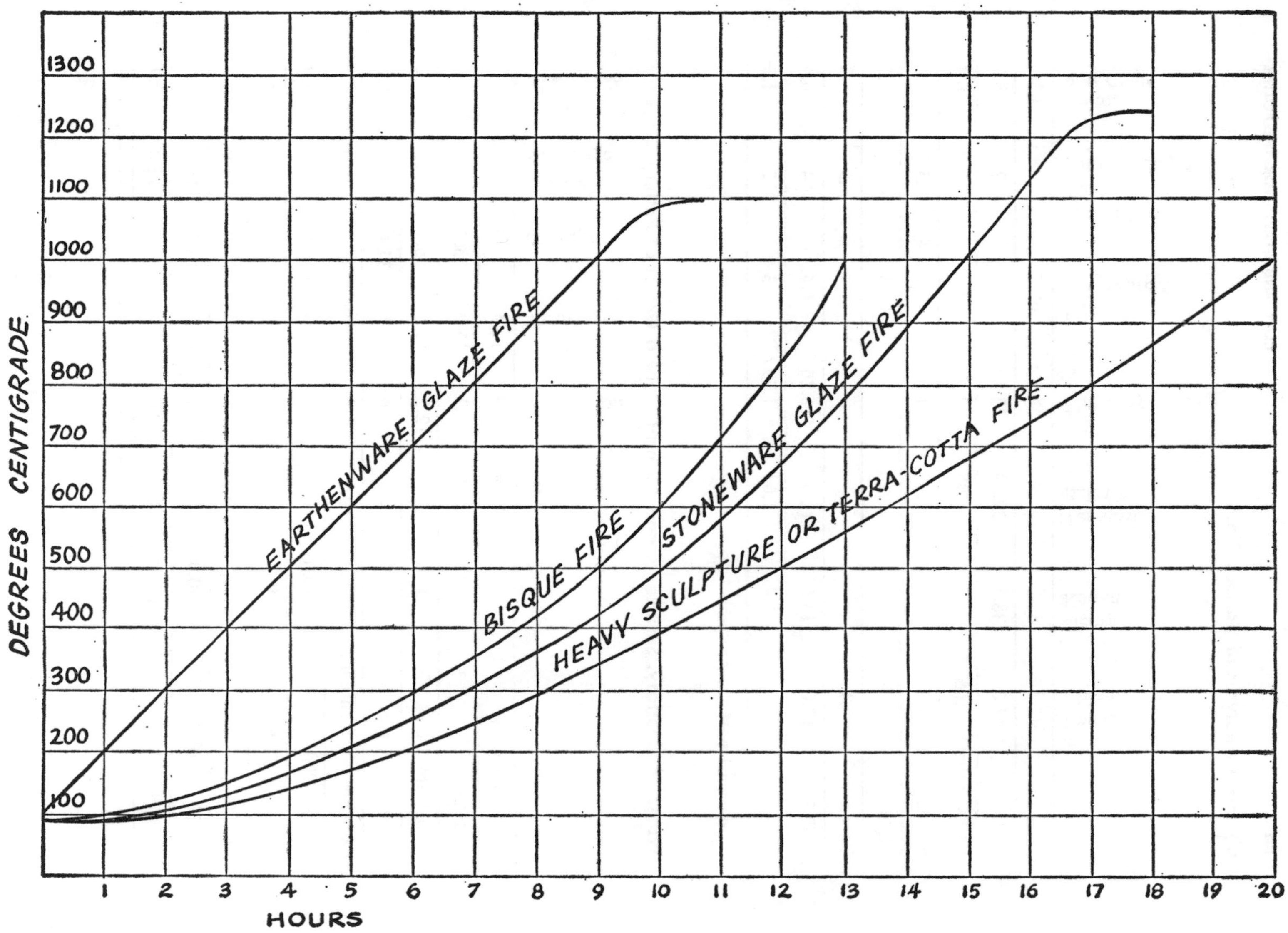

CHART 4

Chemical Analyses of Various Clays

	English China Clay	Georgia Kaolin	Tennessee Ball Clay	Fire Clay	Jordan Stoneware *	Barnard Black-burning Clay *	Dalton Red Clay*
SiO_2	48.3	45.8	53.9	58.1	69.4	41.4	63.2
Al_2O_3	37.6	38.5	29.3	23.1	17.7	6.7	18.3
$Fe_2O_3 + FeO$	.05	.7	.98	2.41	1.6	29.9	6.4
KNaO	1.6		.4	1.56	2.89	1.5	2.8
MgO			.3		.5	.6	.5
CaO	.1				.1	.5	.3
H_2O	12.0	13.6	12.8	13.26	6.4	8.4	6.4
TiO_2		1.4	1.64	1.79	1.3	.2	1.3

* United Clay Mines Analysis.

Water of Plasticity, Shrinkage, and Absorption of a Group of Pottery Clays

	Water of Plasticity	Fired to Cone 04 % Shrinkage	Fired to Cone 04 % Absorption	Fired to Cone 4 % Shrinkage	Fired to Cone 4 % Absorption	Fired to Cone 9 % Shrinkage	Fired to Cone 9 % Absorption
Ohio Red Clay	30.4	11.5	3.9	12.5	0	Bloated	
Red Clay	30.5	11.0	9.7	15.0	3.4	15.0	0
Stoneware Clay	30.0	9.0	12.2	10.5	8.4	12.0	3.2
Stoneware Clay	33.0	6.5	16.8	8.5	11.6	10.5	5.3
Common Surface Clay	26.0	10.0	1.5	Bloated		Fused	
Sagger Clay	40.0	10.0	9.5	13.0	16.0	16.0	5.0
English Ball Clay	42.6	14.0	16.0	18.0	15.0	18.0	2.0
Fire Clay	18.0	8.0	11.7	10.0	8.9	11.0	6.3
Florida Kaolin	40.0	12.5	25.2	16.5	12.7	18.5	6.5
Georgia Kaolin	35.0	8.0	29.6	9.0	26.9	12.0	22.9

Atomic and molecular weights of the elements and oxides commonly used in ceramics:

Element or Oxide	*Symbol*	*Weight*
Aluminum	Al	26.9
Antimony	Sb	121.7
Barium	Ba	137.3
Bismuth	Bi	209.
Boron	B	10.8
Cadmium	Cd	112.4
Calcium	Ca	40.
Carbon	C	12.
Chromium	Cr	52.
Cobalt	Co	58.9
Copper	Cu	63.5
Hydrogen	H	1.
Iron	Fe	55.8
Lead	PbO	207.
Lithium	Li	6.9
Magnesium	Mg	24.3
Nickel	Ni	58.6
Oxygen	O	16.
Phosphorus	P	31.
Potassium	K	39.
Selenium	Se	79.2
Silicon	Si	28.
Silver	Ag	107.8
Sodium	Na	22.9
Strontium	Sr	87.6
Tin	Sn	118.7
Titanium	Ti	48.1
Uranium	U	238.1
Vanadium	V	50.9
Zinc	Zn	65.3
Zirconium	Zr	91.
Aluminum Oxide	Al_2O_3	101.9
Antimony Oxide	Sb_2O_3	291.
Barium Oxide	BaO	153.4
Boric Oxide	B_2O_3	69.6
Calcium Oxide	CaO	56.1
Chromium Oxide	Cr_2O_3	152.
Cobalt Oxide	Co_2O_3	165.9
Copper Oxide	CuO	79.6
Iron Oxide	Fe_2O_3	159.7
Silicon Dioxide	SiO_2	60.
Lead Oxide	PbO	223.2
Lithium Oxide	Li_2O	29.8
Magnesium Oxide	MgO	40.3
Manganese Dioxide	MnO_2	86.9
Nickel Oxide	NiO	74.7
Potassium Oxide	K_2O	94.2
Sodium Oxide	Na_2O	62.
Strontium Oxide	SrO	103.6
Tin Oxide	SnO	150.7
Zinc Oxide	ZnO	81.4
Zirconium Oxide	ZrO_2	123.

Raw Materials Added to Glazes for Color and Texture

Material	*Formula*	*Mol. Weight*	*Equiv. Wt.*	*Fired Formula*	*Fired Wt.*
Antimony	Sb_2O_3	288	288	Sb_2O_3	288
Chromium Oxide	Cr_2O_3	152	152	Cr_2O_3	152
Cobalt Oxide, Black	Co_3O_4	241	80	CoO	75
Cobalt Carbonate	$CoCO_3$	119	119	CoO	75
Copper Oxide	CuO	80	80	CuO	80
Copper Carbonate	$CuCO_3$	124	124	CuO	80
Manganese Carbonate	$MnCO_3$	115	115	MnO	71
Manganese Dioxide	MnO_2	87	87	MnO	71
Nickel Oxide	NiO_2	75	75	NiO_2	75
Potassium Bichromate	$K_2Cr_2O_7$	294	294	$K_2O \cdot Cr_2O_3$	294
Iron Oxide	Fe_2O_3	160	160	Fe_2O_3	160
Tin Oxide	SnO_2	151	151	SnO_2	151
Zircon (Zircopax)	$ZrSiO_4$	183	183	$ZrO \cdot SiO_2$	183
Zirconium Oxide	ZrO_2	123	123	ZrO_2	123

End Points of Pyrometric Cones When Heated at 20° Centrigrade per Hour

Cone Number	*End Point*	*Cone Number*	*End Point*
012	840°C.	1	1125
011	875	2	1135
010	890	3	1145
09	930	4	1165
08	945	5	1180
07	975	6	1190
06	1005	7	1210
05	1030	8	1225
04	1050	9	1250
03	1080	10	1260
02	1095	11	1285
01	1110	12	1310
		13	1350
		14	1390

Weights and Measures

The metric system of weights and measures

Weight

1000	grams	= 1	kilogram	(kg.)
100	grams	= 1	hektogram	(hg.)
10	grams	= 1	dekagram	(dg.)
1	gram	= 1	gram	(gm.)
0.1	gram	= 1	decigram	(dg.)
0.01	gram	= 1	centigram	(cg.)
0.001	gram	= 1	milligram	(mg.)

Length

1000	meters	= 1	kilometer	(km.)
100	meters	= 1	hektometer	(hm.)
10	meters	= 1	dekameter	(dm.)
1	meter	= 1	meter	(m.)
0.1	meter	= 1	decimeter	(dm.)
0.01	meter	= 1	centimeter	(cm.)
0.001	meter	= 1	millimeter	(mm.)

Capacity or Liquid Measure

1000	liters	= 1	kiloliter	(kl.)
100	liters	= 1	hektoliter	(hl.)
10	liters	= 1	dekaliter	(dl.)
1	liter	= 1	liter	(l.)
0.1	liter	= 1	deciliter	(dl.)
0.01	liter	= 1	centiliter	(cl.)
0.001	liter	= 1	cubic centimeter	(cc.)

Comparisons of Metric and U.S. Systems of Weights and Measures

1 gram = .35274 ounce
1 kilogram = 2.2046 pounds
1 ounce = 28.3495 grams
1 pound = 453.5924 grams
1 millimeter = 0.03937 inches
1 centimeter = 0.3937 inches
1 meter = 39.37 inches
1 inch = 2.54 centimeters
1 foot = 30.480 centimeters

Temperature Conversion Chart
(after Albert Sauveur)

Any Centigrade temperature, in column °C., is expressed by the number of degrees Fahrenheit, read from the center column, same line. Similarly, any Fahrenheit temperature, under column °F., is expressed in Centigrade degrees by the adjacent number at the left in the center column. The center column can be used as meaning, originally, either Centigrade or Fahrenheit; and its equivalent in Fahrenheit or Centigrade, respectively, will be found by the number at the right or left.

°C.		°F.
−18	0	32
− 7	20	68
+ 4	40	104
16	60	140
27	80	176
38	100	212
49	120	248
60	140	284
71	160	320
82	180	356
93	200	392
104	220	428
116	240	464
127	260	500
138	280	536
149	300	572
160	320	608
171	340	644
182	360	680
193	380	716
204	400	752

°C.		°F.
216	420	788
227	440	824
238	460	860
249	480	896
260	500	932
271	520	968
282	540	1004
293	560	1040
304	580	1076
316	600	1112
327	620	1148
338	640	1184
349	660	1220
360	680	1256
371	700	1292
383	720	1328
393	740	1364
404	760	1400
416	780	1436
427	800	1472
438	820	1508
449	840	1544
460	860	1580
471	880	1616
482	900	1652
493	920	1688
504	940	1724
516	960	1760
527	980	1796
538	1000	1832
549	1020	1868
560	1040	1904
571	1060	1940
582	1080	1976
593	1100	2012
604	1120	2048
616	1140	2084

°C.		°F.	°C.		°F.
627	1160	2120	960	1760	3200
638	1180	2156	971	1780	3236
649	1200	2192	982	1800	3272
660	1220	2228	993	1820	3308
671	1240	2264	1005	1840	3344
682	1260	2300	1016	1860	3380
693	1280	2336	1027	1880	3416
704	1300	2372	1038	1900	3452
716	1320	2408	1049	1920	3488
727	1340	2444	1060	1940	3524
738	1360	2480	1071	1960	3560
749	1380	2516	1082	1980	3596
760	1400	2552	1093	2000	3632
771	1420	2588	1104	2020	3668
782	1440	2624	1116	2040	3704
793	1460	2660	1127	2060	3740
804	1480	2696	1138	2080	3776
816	1500	2732	1149	2100	3812
827	1520	2768	1160	2120	3848
838	1540	2804	1171	2160	3884
849	1560	2840	1182	2160	3920
860	1580	2876	1193	2180	3956
871	1600	2912	1204	2200	3992
882	1620	2948	1216	2220	4028
893	1640	2984	1227	2240	4064
904	1660	3020	1238	2260	4100
916	1680	3056	1249	2280	4136
927	1700	3092	1260	2300	4172
938	1720	3128	1271	2320	4208
949	1740	3164	1282	2340	4244

Suggested Additions of Coloring Oxides to Oxidation Glazes

Cobalt carbonate	½%	medium blue
Cobalt carbonate	1%	strong blue
Copper carbonate	2%	light green
Copper carbonate	4%	strong green
Iron oxide	2%	tan
Iron oxide	4%	medium brown
Iron oxide	6%	dark brown
Manganese carbonate	4%	medium purple
Manganese carbonate	6%	dark purple
Chrome oxide	2%	green
Rutile	5%	tan
Nickel oxide	2%	grey or brown
Iron chromate	2%	grey
Vanadium stain	6%	medium yellow

Cobalt carbonate	½%	grey-blue
Iron oxide	2%	
Cobalt carbonate	½%	purple-blue
Manganese carbonate	5%	
Cobalt carbonate	½%	blue-green
Copper carbonate	2%	
Copper carbonate	2%	warm green
Iron oxide	2%	
Copper carbonate	3%	yellow-green
Vanadium stain	3%	
Copper carbonate	3%	warm green
Rutile	3%	
Cobalt carbonate	½%	warm blue
Rutile	3%	
Vanadium stain	5%	warm ochre
Rutile	4%	

Suggested Additions of Coloring Oxides to Reduction Glazes

Cobalt carbonate	½%	medium blue
Cobalt carbonate	¼%	light blue
Cobalt carbonate	½%	turquoise
Chrome oxide	1%	
Cobalt carbonate	½%	warm textured blue
Rutile	3%	
Cobalt carbonate	½%	grey-blue
Nickel oxide	1%	
Nickel oxide	1%	grey or grey-brown
Manganese carbonate	4%	brown
Manganese carbonate	4%	textured brown
Rutile	4%	
Ilmenite	3%	spotty brown
Ilmenite	2%	textured yellow-brown
Rutile	2%	
Iron	1%	celedon
Iron	2%	dark olive celedon
Iron	4%	mottled green or brown
Iron	10%	saturated iron red
Copper	½%	copper red
Copper	1%	deep copper red
Copper	3%	red to black
Cobalt	1%	black
Iron	8%	
Manganese	3%	

Glaze Formulas

Glaze formulas are given for four temperatures: cone 08, cone 04, cone 4, and cone 9. All the formulas given are for colorless base glazes. In the case of clear or transparent bases, tin oxide or zirconium oxide may be added for opacity. All the base glazes may be colored by the addition of suitable coloring oxides.

Each glaze given represents a type of glaze, and the different types have differing responses to the various colorants.

Fritted glazes are not included because they require a particular frit composition, which may not be available. The low-temperature glazes can easily be recalculated to make use of lead frit or lead silicate instead of raw lead.

Low-temperature alkaline glazes are not given because, to be practical, they should employ soda and potash in the form of a frit. It is suggested that for alkaline glazes in the range of cone 08 to 04 the following proportion be tried:

Alkaline Frit	85
Whiting	5
China Clay	10

If the resulting glaze is too fluid, some clay should be added; and if the glaze is too stiff, the amount of clay can be cut down.

Glaze formulas may need to be altered and adjusted to work well with particular firing conditions and particular clay bodies. The appearance of the glaze may be different, depending on application, firing temperature, clay body, atmosphere in the kiln, and purity of the raw materials.

1 Cone 08 — Clear Lead

PbO .7			
CaO .15	Al_2O_3 .12	SiO_2 1.75	
ZnO .05			
KNaO .1			

White lead	60.2
Oxford spar	23.4
Zinc oxide	1.3
Whiting	5.0
Clay	.9
Flint	18.6

A smooth, clear glaze. Should be applied thinly. It becomes somewhat cloudy when thick. Five percent tin oxide added gives an opaque white.

2. Cone 08 — Lead

PbO .8		
KNaO .1	Al_2O_3 .15	SiO_2 2.00
CaO .1		

White lead	57.0
Whiting	2.7
Oxford spar	19.4
Clay	2.8
Flint	18.0

A zinc-free lead glaze. Somewhat opaque when thick.

3. Cone 08 — Lead-Colemanite

PbO .6		
KNaO .1	Al_2O_3 .15	SiO_2 2.00
CaO .2	B_2O_3 .15	

White lead	54.9
Oxford spar	17.9
Whiting	2.5
Colemanite	5.2
Clay	2.5
Flint	16.5

A clear, bright glaze.

4. Cone 08 — Colemanite-Barium Mat

KNaO .2		
CaO .4	Al_2O_3 .2	SiO_2 2.5
BaO .2	B_2O_3 .6	
ZnO .2		

Oxford spar	38.6
Barium carbonate	10.7
Zinc oxide	4.4
Colemanite	33.0
Flint	13.4

A soft, smooth, mat glaze.

5. Cone 04 — Clear Lead

PbO .6			
CaO .2	Al_2O_3 .2	SiO_2 2.00	
KNaO .15			
MgO .05			

White lead	45.9
Oxford spar	31.3
China clay	3.0
Talc	1.8
Flint	11.9
Whiting	6.0

A clear lead glaze which is excellent for use over slip decoration.

6. Cone 04 — Barium Mat

PbO .6		
BaO .2	Al_2O_3 .25	SiO_2 2.00
KNaO .2		

White lead	43.2
Barium carbonate	11.0
Oxford spar	39.2
China clay	2.1
Flint	4.4

A very stiff, dry, mat glaze. Should be applied thinly.

7. Cone 04 — Lead-Colemanite

PbO .4		
CaO .4	Al_2O_3 .25	SiO_2 2.5
KNaO .15	B_2O_3 .2	
ZnO .05		

White lead	29.8
Colemanite	6.0
Whiting	7.8
Zinc oxide	1.0
Oxford spar	30.4
China clay	6.5
Flint	18.4

A smooth, semi-opaque glaze.

8. Cone 04 — Colemanite-Barium Mat

KNaO .2		
CaO .5	Al_2O_3 .24	SiO_2 2.2
BaO .2	B_2O_3 .25	
ZnO .1		

Oxford spar	46.8
Flint	10.0
Colemanite	11.0
Whiting	13.0
Barium carbonate	13.0
Zinc oxide	4.0

A smooth, frosty, semi-opaque mat glaze.

9. Cone 04 — Transparent Lead

PbO .7		
KNaO .1	Al_2O_3 .15	SiO_2 2.00
CaO .2		

White lead	52.1
Oxford spar	20.3
Flint	18.7
China clay	3.0
Whiting	5.8

A smooth, clear glaze, excellent for use over slips or under-glaze colors. Five percent tin oxide added makes an opaque white.

10. Cone 04 — Semi-opaque Lead

PbO .5		
BaO .25	Al_2O_3 .15	SiO_2 1.75
CaO .15		
KNaO .1		

Oxford spar	21.7
China clay	3.2
Flint	15.4
White lead	40.0
Whiting	4.6
Barium carbonate	15.2

Smooth, bright, semi-opaque.

11. Cone 04 — High-alumina Lead

CaO .2	Al_2O_3 .3	SiO_2 2.00
PbO .6		
KNaO .2		

White lead	44.8
Oxford spar	40.7
Flint	2.8
China clay	6.0
Whiting	5.8

Semi-mat and semi-opaque.

12. Cone 04 High-Lime, semi-opaque

PbO	.5		
CaO	.25	Al_2O_3 .28	SiO_2 2.00
KNaO	.2		
MgO	.05		

White lead	38.8
Oxford spar	42.3
Flint	5.4
China clay	4.6
Whiting	7.5
Magnesium carbonate	1.3

When thickly applied, this glaze is opaque. When thin, it will reveal slips or under-glaze color. It is somewhat dull in surface.

13. Cone 4 Colemanite

CaO	.55		
KNaO	.2	Al_2O_3 .25	SiO_2 2.75
ZnO	.15	B_2O_3 .3	
MgO	.1		

Oxford spar	46.8
Flint	20.0
China clay	2.5
Whiting	8.3
Colemanite	13.7
Zinc oxide	4.0
Dolomite	6.0

An opaque, smooth, bright glaze. Excellent for effects characteristic of opaque colemanite glazes.

14. Cone 4 Transparent Colemanite

KNaO	.2		
CaO	.5	Al_2O_3 .25	SiO_2 2.2
BaO	.3	B_2O_3 .4	

Oxford spar	44.0
Colemanite	17.4
Barium carbonate	18.5
Whiting	7.2
China clay	2.4
Flint	10.5

A clear, rather fluid glaze.

15. Cone 4 Lead-Colemanite

KNaO	.25		
ZnO	.1	Al_2O_3 .28	SiO_2 2.5
CaO	.3	B_2O_3 .3	
MgO	.1		
PbO	.25		

Flint	7.2
Oxford spar	52.9
White lead	19.4
Dolomite	5.5
Colemanite	12.4
Zinc oxide	2.4

At cone 4, this glaze is very fluid and should be thinly applied. Five percent tin added makes a white, bright glaze that runs off the high points to reveal texture or edges in the clay.

16. Cone 4 Milky Colemanite

CaO	.46		
BaO	.13	Al_2O_3 .29	SiO_2 2.8
KNaO	.25	B_2O_3 .6	
ZnO	.16		

Oxford spar	43.9
Flint	24.7
Clay	1.0
Colemanite	20.6
Whiting	1.5
Zinc oxide	3.2
Barium carbonate	6.4

A smooth, bright glaze, opaque when thickly applied. It tends to show a bluish color when applied on red clay.

17. Cone 4 Transparent Lead

PbO	.3		
KNaO	.15	Al_2O_3 .2	SiO_2 2.4
ZnO	.2		
CaO	.3		
MgO	.05		

White lead	26.0
Zinc oxide	5.4
Dolomite	3.0
Whiting	8.3
Oxford spar	35.2
Flint	21.4
China clay	3.0

A clear, bright glaze which is excellent over engobes or when opacified with tin oxide.

18. Cone 4 — Transparent Colemanite

KNaO	.25				
BaO	.15	Al_2O_3	.35	SiO_2	2.5
MgO	.1	B_2O_3	.6		
CaO	.4				
ZnO	.1				

Oxford spar	47.5
Barium carbonate	7.9
Colemanite	22.3
Talc	2.9
Zinc oxide	2.2
Clay	5.1
Flint	11.8

A smooth, clear, fairly fluid glaze.

19. Cone 4 — Mat

PbO	.5				
BaO	.25	Al_2O_3	.27	SiO_2	3.0
CaO	.1				
MgO	.1				
KNaO	.05				

White lead	27.5
Dolomite	3.9
Barium carbonate	12.6
Oxford spar	7.4
China clay	11.5
Flint	36.9

A rough, stony glaze similar in texture to some high-fire glazes. When applied thinly, it will reveal dark slips beneath.

20. Cone 9–10 — Cornwall Stone Glaze

Cornwall stone	85
Whiting	15

When thickly applied, this glaze gives an opaque, smooth surface. It crazes over most clays, giving an effect similar to some old Chinese glazes.

21. Cone 9–10 — Ash

Mixed hard wood ash	35
Oxford spar	35
China clay	15
Talc	15

A beautiful opaque, stony mat.

22. Cone 9–10 — Ash

Mixed hardwood ash	20
Dolomite	15
Flint	20
Oxford spar	35
China clay	10

A soft, satin mat.

23. Cone 9–10 — Slip Glaze

Albany slip	60
Cornwall stone	25
Iron oxide	5
Whiting	10

In reduction firing, this glaze is a beautiful dark iron-red. When thickly applied, it tends toward green and black.

24. Cone 9–10 — Slip Glaze

Albany slip	65
Nepheline syenite	35

A smooth khaki-colored glaze. In reduction firing, it tends toward an iron-red color.

25. Cone 9–10 — Clear

KNaO	.2				
CaO	.7	Al_2O_3	.4	SiO_2	2.5
BaO	.1	B_2O_3	.19		

Oxford spar	42.6
Flint	8.7
China clay	8.0
Calcined clay	9.0
Barium carbonate	5.9
Colemanite	8.2
Whiting	17.3

A clear glaze. Because of its low silica content, it will craze over most clays. In reduction firing, it gives excellent grey and celedon colors when a small amount of iron is added.

26. Cone 9–10 Cornwall Stone Glaze

Na_2O .085			
K_2O .09	Al_2O_3 .35	SiO_2 3.00	
CaO .65			
MgO .10			
ZnO .075			

Cornwall stone	40.6
China clay	15.7
Flint	26.7
Dolomite	4.5
Whiting	10.9
Zinc oxide	1.5

A smooth, bright glaze. Excellent for celedon and iron-red colors in reduction.

27. Cone 9–10 Nepheline Syenite Glaze

KNaO .6		
ZnO .1	Al_2O_3 .7	SiO_2 3.5
MgO .1		
CaO .2		

Nepheline syenite	74.5
Zinc oxide	2.2
Dolomite	4.9
Whiting	2.7
China clay	6.9
Flint	8.7

A soft, satin mat, smooth and opaque.

28. Cone 9–10 Dry Mat

KNaO .2		
CaO .4	Al_2O_3 .44	SiO_2 2.2
MgO .2		
ZnO .2		

Nepheline syenite	33.6
Dolomite	13.4
Whiting	7.3
Zinc oxide	5.9
China clay	22.5
Flint	17.4

A very dry, stony glaze. It is unusually high in alumina and low in silica.

29. Cone 10–12 Porcelain Glaze

CaO .65		
KNaO .25	Al_2O_3 .32	SiO_2 4.00
MgO .05		
ZnO .05		

Oxford spar	50.4
China clay	3.7
Flint	24.9
Dolomite	2.6
Zinc oxide	1.1
Whiting	17.2

A smooth, clear glaze for high-fired stonewares or porcelains. On white porcelain it should be applied thinly.

30. Cone 9–10 Opaque Feldspathic

KNaO .3		
CaA .4	Al_2O_3 .35	SiO_2 4.00
ZnO .2		
MgO .1		

Oxford spar	47.4
Flint	29.1
China clay	1.7
Dolomite	6.2
Zinc oxide	5.8
Whiting	10.1

This glaze has a smooth buttery texture and is nearly opaque. Its high zinc content makes it unsuitable for some colors but favors others.

31. Cone 9–10 Colemanite

KNaO .2		
CaO .54	Al_2O_3 .3	SiO_2 3.4
MgO .1	B_2O_3 .18	
BaO .16		

Oxford spar	39.0
Flint	26.3
Clay	4.3
Magnesium carbonate	3.2
Barium carbonate	8.7
Colemanite	6.8
Whiting	11.6

A semi-opaque glaze which tends to show broken or streaked texture.

32. Cone 9–10 High Alumina Mat

KNaO .2			
MgO .35	Al_2O_3 .5	SiO_2 2.34	
CaO .45			

Oxford spar	48.9
China clay	25.1
Dolomite	22.4
Whiting	3.5

A stony, smooth mat, very opaque.

Books on Pottery and Ceramics

1. Andrews, A. I.: *Ceramics Tests and Calculations,* New York, J. Wiley & Sons, Inc., 1928.
2. Binns, C. F.: *The Potter's Craft,* 3rd Edition, New York, D. Van Nostrand Co.
3. Binns, C. F.: *Lectures,* Alfred, N. Y., Box of Books.
4. D'Amico, Victor: *How to Make Pottery and Ceramic Sculpture,* Scranton, Pa., International Text Book Co.
5. Dougherty, J. W.: *Pottery Made Easy,* New York, The Bruce Publishing Co., 1939.
6. Hetherington, A. L.: *Chinese Ceramic Glazes,* Cambridge, Cambridge University Press, 1937.
7. Home, R. M.: *Ceramics for the Potter,* Peoria, Ill., Bennett, 1942.
8. Honey, W. B.: *The Art of the Potter,* London, Faber and Faber, 1946.
9. Kenny, J. B.: *The Complete Book of Pottery Making,* New York, Greenberg, 1952.
10. Koenig and Earhart: *Literature and Abstracts on Glazes,* Revised Edition, Philadelphia, College Offset Press, 1951.
11. Leach, B.: *A Potter's Book,* London, Faber and Faber, 1946.
12. Leach, B.: *A Potter's Portfolio,* London, Lund, 1951.
13. Norton, F. H.: *Ceramics for the Artist Potter,* Cambridge, Addison Wesley, 1956.
14. Norton, F. H.: *Elements of Ceramics,* Cambridge, Addison Wesley, 1952.
15. Parmelee, C. W.: *Ceramic Glazes,* Chicago, Industrial Publishing Co., 1948.
16. Rosenthal, E.: *Pottery and Ceramics,* Hammondsworth, Penguin Books, 1949.
17. Sanders, H.: *Sunset Ceramics Book,* Menlo Park, Calif., Lane, 1953.
18. Wilson, H.: *Ceramics; Clay Technology,* New York, McGraw-Hill Book Co., Inc., 1927.

Index